PRINTING AND THE MIND OF MAN

CATALOGUE OF

AN EXHIBITION AT EARLS COURT

CATALOGUE OF A
DISPLAY OF
PRINTING MECHANISMS AND
PRINTED MATERIALS

ARRANGED TO ILLUSTRATE

THE HISTORY
OF
WESTERN CIVILIZATION

AND THE MEANS OF

THE MULTIPLICATION
OF
LITERARY TEXTS

SINCE THE XV CENTURY

ORGANIZED IN CONNEXION WITH THE
ELEVENTH INTERNATIONAL PRINTING MACHINERY
AND ALLIED TRADES EXHIBITION

UNDER THE TITLE OF

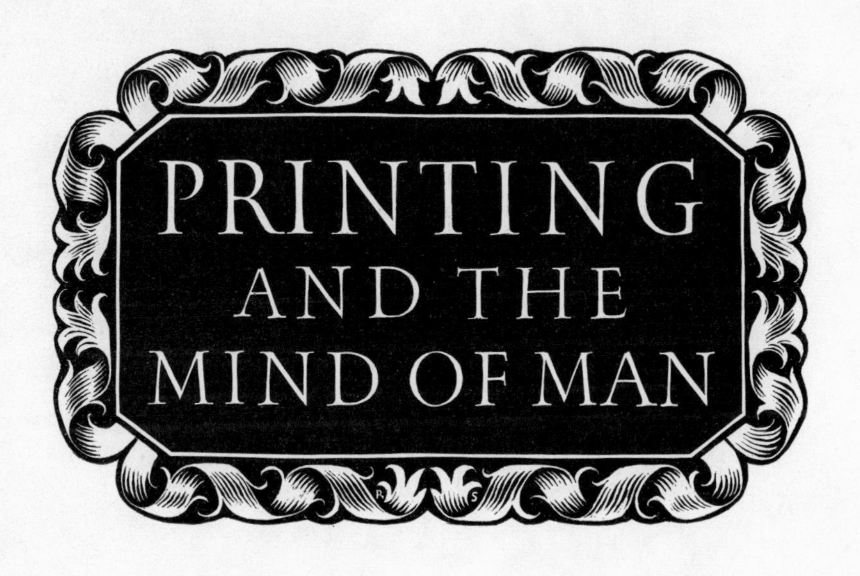

ASSEMBLED AT

THE BRITISH MUSEUM

AND AT

EARLS COURT

LONDON

16–27 JULY 1963

PUBLISHED BY

MESSRS F. W. BRIDGES & SONS LTD AND

THE ASSOCIATION OF BRITISH MANUFACTURERS OF

PRINTERS' MACHINERY (PROPRIETARY) LTD

COPIES OBTAINABLE FROM THE BRITISH MUSEUM

PRINTED IN GREAT BRITAIN

PRINTING AND THE MIND OF MAN

PATRON: HER MAJESTY THE QUEEN

COMMITTEE OF HONOUR

THE PRIME MINISTER
THE DUKE OF WELLINGTON, K.G.
THE EARL SPENCER, *President of the Roxburghe Club*
THE EARL OF CRAWFORD and BALCARRES, K.T., G.B.E.
THE EARL OF DROGHEDA, O.B.E.
THE VISCOUNT ESHER, G.B.E.
LORD KENYON, *Chairman, Friends of the National Libraries*
THE RT. HON. LORD ECCLES OF CHUTE, K.C.V.O.
THE RT. HON. SIR EDWARD BOYLE, BT., *Minister of Education*
SIR DENIS TRUSCOTT, G.B.E., *President of the Institute of Printing*
SIR FRANCIS MEYNELL, R.D.I.
SIR GEOFFREY KEYNES
SIR SYDNEY ROBERTS
KARL BAEDEKER, *Freiburg*
W. BEATTIE, *Librarian of The National Library of Scotland*
JOHN BETTS, *Master of the Stationers' and Newspaper Makers' Company*
PALLE BIRKELUND, *National Librarian, The Royal Library, Copenhagen*
ROBERT BIRLEY, C.M.G., *Head Master of Eton*
JOHN BOON, *President of The Publishers' Association*
VERLAG F. A. BROCKHAUS, *Wiesbaden*
MONSIEUR JULIEN CAIN, *L'Administrateur Général, Bibliothèque Nationale, Paris*
H. R. CRESWICK, *University Librarian, Cambridge*
BROOKE CRUTCHLEY, C.B.E., *University Printer, Cambridge*
BERN DIBNER, *Burndy Library, Norwalk, Connecticut*
CHRISTOPHER DOBSON, *House of Lords' Library*
SIGNOR FILIPPO DONINI, *Cultural Attaché and Director, The Italian Institute, London*
IAN FLEMING
D. H. FOLLETT, *Director, The Science Museum*
DOTT. GIORGIO DE GREGORI, *Direttore, Centro Nazionale per il Catalogo Unico delle Bibliotheche Italiano e per le Informazioni Bibliografiche, Rome*
DR. HAENISCH, *Universitäts-Bibliothek, Marburg*
L. W. HANSON, *Keeper of Printed Books, Bodleian Library, Oxford*
JOHN HAYWARD, C.B.E.
DR. G. HOFMANN, *Generaldirektor, Bayerische Staatsbibliothek, Munich*

COMMITTEE OF HONOUR

PROFESSOR W. A. JACKSON, *The Houghton Library, Harvard University*

JOHN JARROLD, *Past President of the Federation of Master Printers*

A. F. JOHNSON, *The British Museum*

E. D. JONES, *Librarian of The National Library of Wales*

I. KAYE, *Librarian of the Royal Society*

A. N. L. MUNBY, *Fellow and Librarian, King's College, Cambridge*

J. N. L. MYRES, *Bodley's Librarian, Oxford*

SIMON NOWELL-SMITH, *President of the Bibliographical Society*

DR. H. W. PARKE, *Vice-Provost and Librarian, Trinity College, Dublin*

GRAHAM POLLARD

F. N. L. POYNTER, *Wellcome Historical Medical Library*

DAVID A. RANDALL, *Lilly Librarian, Indiana University*

VIVIAN RIDLER, *Printer to the University of Oxford*

WILLIAM H. SCHEIDE, *Princeton, New Jersey*

VICTOR SCHOLDERER, C.B.E.

JOHN SPARROW, O.B.E., *Warden of All Souls, Oxford*

THE EDITOR of *The Times Literary Supplement*

DR. L. VOET, *Curator, Plantin-Moretus Museum, Antwerp*

JAMES M. WELLS, *Curator, The Newberry Library, Chicago*

R. A. WILSON, C.B., *Principal Keeper of Printed Books, British Museum*

THOMAS WRAGG, M.B.E., T.D., *Keeper of the Collections, Chatsworth*

PREFACE

THE Eleventh International Printing Machinery and Allied Trades Exhibition (IPEX) is the largest and most comprehensive display ever mounted under these auspices.

The purpose of the main exhibition is to assemble in London, at Earls Court and Olympia, the latest machinery, equipment, materials, and services available to the many crafts practised and processes employed in the printing and allied trades. IPEX brings together from all over the world professionals in the industries which produce, service, or buy printed matter. It is also expected to attract considerable numbers of the interested general public.

IPEX 1963 was early recognized by its sponsors as presenting an opportunity, not to be missed, of illustrating to the printing industry its own historical evolution, and of reminding the general public what Western civilization owes to print. They further aspired to offer a survey of the history of printing through five hundred years as one of the most important applied arts of the Western world, thus demonstrating, by means of a multiple display, the printing industry's debt to its historic past and the debt of civilization to typography.

Accordingly, with the enthusiastic support of the Association of British Manufacturers of Printers' Machinery and of Messrs. F. W. Bridges & Sons Ltd., organizers of the main exhibition, the preparation of these historical annexes, under the general title of PRINTING AND THE MIND OF MAN was entrusted to a supervisory committee, whose members are named on page 10.

SCOPE

The invention of printing with movable type was crucial to the whole development of Western civilization. The purpose of the historical exhibitions annexed to IPEX 1963 is to illustrate the internal development of that invention, in the technical progress of printing as a craft; the external development, in the finest achievements of printing as an art; and, beyond the limits of the art and craft of printing, to demonstrate the impact of printing on the mind of man and the effect it has had on the history of the last five hundred years. This threefold aim has been approached in three complementary displays, the first and last at Earls Court and the second in the King's Library of the British Museum.

The scope, then, is large, and the task of reducing the mass of significant material to a representative microcosm has been a harrowing one, even within the generous space afforded. The word Western will already have been noted in the preceding paragraphs. Printing has only come lately to the whole world, and in this retrospective exhibition we have deliberately restricted ourselves (with few exceptions) to Greek and Latin, the foundation tongues of Western civilization, and the languages of Europe (of which in this context the British Isles may be considered to form a part, and the Western Hemisphere an extension).

One probably general criticism we must forestall. Creative literature has elevated and inspired the *spirit* of man. But examples here have been restricted to the propagation of ideas (e.g. *Candide, Alice in Wonderland*) or characters (e.g. Hamlet or Faust) which have sensibly affected his *thinking* and actions—though in fact the accident of typographic distinction has earned a number of pieces of pure literature a place in the aesthetic section.

Our task has necessarily been that of exclusion rather than inclusion, and no doubt each visitor will make his own list of deplorable omissions. One in particular is a matter for regret: we have been compelled to exclude what could at best have been a sadly unrepresentative selection from the category known as 'jobbing' printing, which has come to take so large a place in the output of the printing industry. There is one exception: the Caxton *Indulgence* of 1476. This is the first known piece of printing in England; and it is probable that the last will be a piece of jobbing work too, since Armageddon is more prone to proclamations than to sonnet sequences.

EXECUTION

The retrospective survey of technical processes was delegated by the Supervisory Committee to Mr. Charles Batey, O.B.E., Printer Emeritus to the University of Oxford and a member of the Council of the Institute of Printing, assisted by a sub-committee of specialists.

The demonstration of the impact of print on the mind of Western man during the past five hundred years—religion, philosophy, history, politics, economics, sociology, education, scholarship, the arts, criticism—was entrusted to Mr. P. H. Muir, bibliographer and antiquarian bookseller, supported by a team of experts.

The third component is the aesthetic. The selection of fine printing (including illustrated books, but excluding bindings) has been made and annotated by members of the staff of the British Museum under the direction of Sir Frank Francis, K.C.B., its Director and Principal Librarian.

Liaison between the three sub-committees was effected by the presence on both the technical and historical sub-committees of a senior member of the British Museum's staff, and the attachment to the aesthetic sub-committee of Mr. John Dreyfus, typographical adviser to the Monotype Corporation and to the Cambridge University Press, who also acted as chairman of the editorial sub-committee responsible for the production of the two catalogues.

ARRANGEMENT

The selection of 194 examples of fine printing is displayed in the King's Library of the British Museum. Since this exhibition will outlive by some months the technical–historical display at Earls Court, its catalogue is also available in separate form.

At Earls Court the evolution of printing techniques is illustrated, in a series of functional groupings on a broadly chronological base, by actual implements and machines, by enlarged illustrations, and by characteristic products. The impact on the mind of Western man, for which the developing capacities of the printing press made increasing provision over the centuries, is indicated by a selection of significant printed matter arranged in a stricter chronology (with a small section for newspapers).

The visitor to Earls Court may thus follow in a single perambulation both the technical course which runs from Gutenberg and the first movable type, through Blaeu, Stanhope, Koenig, Mergenthaler, Lanston, to the pioneers of filmsetting without the use of any type at all, and also a selection, drastically constricted by the space available, of those printed works—from Thomas Aquinas and Copernicus to Einstein and Rutherford—which might be called the decisive battles against ignorance and darkness in the history of man.

ACKNOWLEDGEMENTS

We, and all visitors to the exhibition PRINTING AND THE MIND OF MAN, owe a great debt to the initial vision and enthusiasm, the confident generosity, and the steady administrative support of the organizers.

To the Trustees of the British Museum we are indebted not only for their cordial reception of a project which involved the whole exhibition space in the King's Library, but also for accepting the responsibility for housing, in transit, loans from the many institutional libraries and private collectors to the Earls Court exhibition.

To the generous lenders, from Her Majesty the Queen onwards through a distinguished international list, we offer our heartfelt thanks for making the Earls Court exhibition possible at all by entrusting to us precious and often fragile contributions essential to our theme.

We salute Mr. John Lansdell, O.B.E., who brought an imaginative eye and a skilled hand to the lively visual presentation of much inherently intractable material, and Mr. Reynolds Stone, C.B.E., whose engravings adorn the covers and the title-page of this catalogue.

We pay tribute to the organizers of the Gutenberg Quincentenary Exhibition of Printing, assembled at Cambridge in 1940 (and prematurely disassembled because of the risks from enemy bombing). It was our original inspiration for several sections of our display, and its invigorating catalogue has been our constant friend.

Finally, we wish to record our grateful admiration for the arduous and unremitting labours of the members of the four executive sub-committees whose names are given on the following page. They have somehow found time in the midst of busy professional lives to fulfil every demand imposed upon them by their indefatigable chairmen at the behest of an exacting general staff.

For the Supervisory Committee:

FRANK FRANCIS
STANLEY MORISON
JOHN CARTER

PRINTING AND THE MIND OF MAN

CONTENTS

LIST OF ILLUSTRATIONS

LIST OF LENDERS

Her Majesty the Queen 134, 179

His Grace the Duke of Devonshire and the Trustees of the Chatsworth Settlement 136, 138, 157, 193, 208, 223, 249, 268, 272, 340, 380, 437, 447, 506, 511, 522
The Rt. Hon. the Earl of Crawford and Balcarres 154
The Rt. Hon. the Earl of Powis 256

All Souls College, Oxford 195, 228
American Pressman, Washington 429
American Red Cross 125
Ampleforth Abbey 139
Architectural Association 459
Herzog August Bibliothek, Wolfenbüttel 353

Dr. Karl Baedeker, Freiburg 513
Nicolas Barker 296, 484, 556, 592
Bayerische Staatsbibliothek, Munich 137, 184, 239, 282, 386, 449, 452, 456, 477, 520, 536, 596
Alfred C. Berol, New York City 543
Biblioteca Communale, Treviso 148
Biblioteca Marciana, Venice 145, 151
Biblioteca Nazionale (Braidense), Milan 551
Biblioteca Nazionale Centrale, Florence 140
Biblioteca Nazionale Centrale Vittorio Emanueleii, Rome 247, 591
Biblioteca Universitaria Alessandrina, Rome 144
Biblioteca Universitaria, Bologna 147
Bibliotheek der Rijksuniversiteit, Leiden 230, 243, 258, 300.
Bibliothek des St. Nikolaus-Hospitals, Bernkastel-Kues 174
Bibliothèque Nationale, Paris 5, 6, 192, 289, 339, 483, 539, 600, 603
Bodleian Library, Oxford 3, 89, 98, 131, 133, 158, 175, 205, 210*a*, 240, 242, 278, 302, 312, 333, 354, 389
Boston Public Library 308
Bristol Baptist College 187
British Dental Association 332
British and Foreign Bible Society 135, 181, 213, 309
The British Museum 86, 310
Dr. F. A. Brockhaus, Wiesbaden 390
Burndy Library, Norwalk, Conn. 238, 245, 301, 329, 348, 351, 361, 381, 476, 480, 517, 545, 558, 578
Col. A. D. Burnett-Brown 505

Cambridge University Library 153, 212, 439, 557, 640
H. G. Carter, Oxford 3, 80
Matthew Carter 12*a*, 18
Caslon Machinery Ltd 25, 36
Christ Church, Oxford 253
C. E. R. Clarabut 532
Clarendon Press, Oxford 133
Curwen Press 397, 627

J. Irving Davis 215
Wm. Dawson & Sons Ltd. 442
Dawson, Payne & Elliott Ltd. 422, 430

Edinburgh University Library 209
Antiquariat Fritz Eggert, Stuttgart 491
Heinrich Eisemann 163, 569
Sir Arthur Elton 518
Encyclopaedia Britannica Ltd. 360
Eton College 169, 203, 204, 219, 236, 250, 279, 292, 322, 366, 376
Eyre & Spottiswoode Ltd. 55

Fitzwilliam Museum, Cambridge 155
Ian Fleming 341, 350, 395, 432, 479, 481, 487, 496, 499, 500, 501, 509, 510, 521, 524, 527, 530*b*, 542, 550, 553, 554, 560, 563, 564, 567, 568, 571, 573, 575, 577, 579, 580, 581, 587–9, 590, 593–5, 598, 599, 601, 602.
Dr. Desmond Flower 345, 347
Fry's Metal Foundries Ltd. 90, 91

The Hon. Robert Gathorne-Hardy 271
The General Post Office 494*b*
Geological Society of London 388, 450
J. S. L. Gilmour, Cambridge 357, 486, 561
Glasgow University (Hunterian Library) 199
Gloucester City Libraries 371
Cosmo Gordon, Insch 218
W. P. Griffith & Sons Ltd. 617
Grolier Club of New York 96

Miss P. M. Handover 644
Harvard University (Houghton Library) 489, 504, 533, 562
Carl Haverlin, New York City 540
Georges Heilbrun, Paris 291
Howard League for Penal Reform 366

Illustrated London News 636
Indiana University (Lilly Library) 1, 143, 146, 162, 166, 171, 220, 244, 246, 275, 286, 355*a*, 362, 382, 441, 482, 493, 494*a*, 503, 514, 515, 519, 525, 530*a*, 537, 541, 547, 548, 566, 597, 606

André Jammes, Paris 197, 613, 618, 637, 638
Jesus College, Oxford 216
John Johnson Collection, Oxford 628

Sir Geoffrey Keynes 264, 276, 383
King's College, Cambridge 142, 150, 152, 165, 170, 182, 201, 225, 233, 235, 251, 259, 261–3, 273, 280, 287, 294, 295, 297, 298, 305, 306, 321, 328, 330, 335, 337, 338, 342, 352, 363, 364, 368, 378, 379, 384, 385, 387, 391, 393, 394, 438, 446, 451, 453, 458, 531, 534, 609
Dr. Frieder Kocher-Benzing, Stuttgart 435
Koenig & Bauer, Würzburg 403, 404, 405, 407, 409, 410

Lambeth Palace Library 198, 206
Wilmarth S. Lewis, Farmington, Conn. 355
Lincoln Cathedral Library 178, 189
Linnaean Society of London 299
Linotype & Machinery Ltd. 33, 61
The London Library 326, 478, 485, 507, 516, 546
Lorilleux & Bolton Ltd. 127
H. D. Lyon 343

Maggs, Bros. Ltd. 160
H. Bradley Martin, New York City 377
Elkin Mathews Ltd., Takeley 559, 582, 604, 610
Merton College, Oxford 85
Monotype Corporation Ltd. 11, 26, 28, 29, 33, 62, 84, 471, 472
Stanley Morison 645
Dr. A. N. L. Munby, Cambridge 320, 433, 526
Sir John Murray 255

National Library of Scotland 177, 188, 190, 211, 248, 288, 313, 323, 331, 373, 448, 605
National Maritime Museum 234
Thomas Nelson & Sons Ltd., Edinburgh 421
Newberry Library, Chicago 8, 270
New College, Oxford 176
New York Public Library 472
Newcastle-upon-Tyne Public Library (Pease Collection) 614
Niedersächsische Staats- und Universitäts-bibliothek, Göttingen 358, 444, 552
Nordisk Museum, Stockholm 460

Offentliche Bibliothek der Universität, Basel 194, 333*a*, 538

Dr. W. Pagel 269
Boies Penrose, Devon, Pa. 207
Peterborough Cathedral Library 217
Pierpont Morgan Library, New York City 222
Plantin–Moretus Museum, Antwerp 19, 20, 21, 40, 41, 46, 47, 48, 53, 77, 78, 85, 91, 92, 93, 97, 116, 231
Press Club Library 641, 642, 649
Public Record Office 2, 94

Queen's College, Oxford 132, 214, 257

Sir Sydney Roberts, Cambridge 344
Charles J. Rosenbloom, Pittsburgh, Pa. 512
Royal Aeronautical Society 369, 584
Royal Anthropological Institute 492
Royal Asiatic Society 374
Royal Astronomical Society 167
Royal College of Physicians 168, 173, 185, 260, 293
Royal Geographical Society 365, 544
Royal Horticultural Society 200, 254
Royal Institute of British Architects 180, 224
Royal Institute of International Affairs 607
Royal Library, Copenhagen 285, 443, 457, 490, 502
Royal National Institute for the Blind 483
Royal Scottish Museum 100, 399
The Royal Society 226, 281, 307, 327, 346, 359, 370, 431, 434, 436, 440

St. Bride Foundation Library 4, 7, 85, 95, 96*a*, 99, 122, 123, 125, 315, 316, 317, 319*a*, 401, 615, 621, 624, 625, 631, 635
St. Paul's Cathedral Library 265
St. Thomas's Hospital, London 528
William H. Scheide, Princeton, N.J. 290
Science Museum, 116, 196, 375, 396, 398, 416, 423, 461, 469, 473, 474, 475, 535, 570, 583, 608
Scott Polar Research Institute, Cambridge 572
Louis H. Silver, Wilmette, Ill. 227, 267
Simson Shand Ltd. 400
The Smithsonian Institution, Washington, D.C. 629, 630, 632, 633, 634, 639
The Society of Friends 284
Stadt- und Universitäts-Bibliothek, (Schopenhauer-Archiv), Frankfurt am Main 454
Lady Stenton, Reading 221
Stephenson Blake & Co. Ltd., Sheffield 17, 24, 36, 75
Dr. F. W. Stoyle, Wolverhampton 129, 130
Thomas W. Streeter, Morristown, N.J. 186, 549

THE TIMES 318, 319, 646, 647, 648
TRINITY COLLEGE, DUBLIN 274
FL. TULKENS, BRUSSELS 156, 372

UNIVERSITÄTS-BIBLIOTHEK, MARBURG (LAHN) 488, 491*a*, 498
UNIVERSITÄTS-BIBLIOTHEK, TÜBINGEN 508
UNIVERSITETSBIBLIOTEKET, UPPSALA 336
UNIVERSITY COLLEGE LONDON 277
UNIVERSITY OF LONDON (INSTITUTE OF GERMANIC LANGUAGES AND LITERATURE) 334
UNIVERSITY OF LONDON (SCHOOL OF ECONOMICS AND POLITICAL SCIENCE) 576, 586
UNIVERSITY OF LONDON LIBRARY 325, 356, 495
UNIVERSITY OF TEXAS (HUMANITIES RESEARCH CENTER) 555
UNIVERSITY PRESS, CAMBRIDGE 27, 30, 32, 57, 59, 311
UNIVERSITY PRESS, OXFORD 9, 12–16, 22, 23, 31, 34, 35, 37–40, 42–45, 49–52, 54, 56, 58, 60, 64–66, 68–74, 76, 79, 81–83, 85, 87, 88, 91, 92, 96*b*, 101–15, 117–19, 120, 121, 133, 252, 314, 611, 612, 619, 621, 643

VICTORIA AND ALBERT MUSEUM 10, 616, 620, 622, 623

DR. E. WEIL 523
WELLCOME HISTORICAL MEDICAL LIBRARY 141, 149, 159, 164, 202, 210, 229, 241, 283, 303, 304, 349, 367, 392, 455, 565, 574, 585
WESTMINSTER ABBEY 161
WESTMINSTER SCHOOL 232
THE WESTOVER FAMILY 656*a*
B. WINSTONE & SONS, LTD. 128
WIENER STADTBIBLIOTHEK 600*a*

YALE UNIVERSITY LIBRARY 191

ZENTRALBIBLIOTHEK, ZÜRICH 172, 497

THE MAINZ PSALTER 1457

[NO. 134]

A PLATE IN COLOUR

PSALTER, in Latin, *Johann Fust and Peter Schoeffer, Mainz, 14 August 1457*

This famous masterpiece of printing surpasses even the 42-line Bible in the beauty of its type and the richness of its ornament. It is the first printed book to give the name of its printer and the date of printing.

The colophon at the end may be translated from the Latin as follows: 'The present volume of the psalms, adorned with beautiful initial letters and with the proper rubrics in red, has been given this form artificially by means of a contrivance for printing and inscribing without any use of a pen, and laboriously brought to completion for the service of God by Johann Fust, citizen of Mainz, and Peter Schöffer of Gernsheim in the year of our Lord 1457 on the Eve of the Assumption'.

This, the Queen's copy, from the Royal Library at Windsor, has exceptionally big margins and is very clean. It has corrections skilfully made by hand at a time not much later than the printing.

(*see also p. 31*)

Dnicis noctibus Inuitatorium.

Regē magnū dnm̄ Venite ad o remus. ps Venite. hymnus

Nocte surgentes. An. Seruite domino. Euouae. post festū venerabilis sacramenti Antiphona

Pro fidei meritis Euouae. Psalmꝰ dauid.

Beatus vir q̄ non abijt in consilio impiorū: ⁊ in via peccōꝝ nō stetit: ⁊ ī cathedra pestilētie nō sedit. Sed in lege dn̄i volūtas eiꝰ: et in lege eius meditabit' die ac nocte. Et erit tanq̄ lignū qd̄ plātatū est secus decursus aquꝝ: qd̄ fructū suū dabit ī tp̄e suo. Et foliū eiꝰ nō defluet: et oīa q̄cūq; faciet pspe͛rabūtur. Non sic impij non sic: sed tanq̄ puluis quē proicit ventus a facie terre. Ideo nō resurgūt impij ī iudicio: neq; peccōres in ɔsilio iustoꝝ. Quoniā nouit dn̄s viā iustorum: et iter impioꝝ peribit. Gloria. Ps dd

DESCRIPTION OF THE EXHIBITS AT EARLS COURT

'In the beginning was the Word'

1 BIBLE, in Latin. *[Johann Gutenberg, Johann Fust, & Peter Schoeffer, Mainz, c. 1455]*

The first substantial volume to come from a printing-press in the Western world was, appropriately, the Bible.

This edition of the Latin text as established by St. Jerome and known as the Vulgate was planned and printed (whether wholly or in part only) by Johann Gutenberg of Mainz, the inventor (between 1440 and 1450) of the process of printing with movable types which is still in use today.

History can show no more pregnant mechanical innovation than Gutenberg's. Its potentiality for infinite multiplication of the written word revolutionized man's capacity for the exchange of ideas. PRINTING AND THE MIND OF MAN tries, as far as space allows, to give expression to our debt to the first printer.

Note. The leaf here shown is thought by some authorities to be a printer's proof, but considered by other incunabulists to be a sheet (with only one of its four pages printed) discarded at the press. In either case it is the only example of its kind known to survive. A copy of the Gutenberg Bible, one of twenty-one surviving, is on exhibition in the King's Library, British Museum.

The Earliest Piece of English Printing

2 A LETTER OF INDULGENCE by John Sant, Abbot of Abingdon, dated 13 December 1476.

The form is set in William Caxton's types—his second and third, the first of which he had already used at Bruges. Caxton was employed in Bruges as late as 1475 and probably moved to England in the middle of the following year: his tenancy of a house in Westminster began at Michaelmas 1476. The first of his books dated at Westminster was finished by 18 November 1477. No other printer worked in England until 1478.

This form, therefore, ranks as the first recorded piece of printing done in England. Its existence in the Public Records was noticed in 1928.

TYPEFOUNDING

INSTRUCTIONS TO PUNCHCUTTERS

3 Handwriting used as the model for Garamond's Royal Greek Types, c. 1539–50

To judge by the result, the instructions given to Claude Garamond must have been to reproduce the handwriting of the Cretan scribe, Angelos Vergetios, who was employed by Francis I to copy books for the royal library. The types were cut at the king's expense mainly for use by his Printer for Greek.

The manuscript is the 'Bestiary of Manuel Phile' written by Vergetios for Francis I.

The printed book is the first that was set in one of the royal Greek types (for the body of Gros Romain): Eusebius, *Ecclesiastical History*, Robert Estienne, Paris 1544.

4 A Writing Manual with hints for Punchcutters, 1553

The early writing masters gave instruction in the formation of letters from which, no doubt, punchcutters among others benefited. Wolffgang Fugger, in his *Nützlich und wohlgegründt Formular*, first published at Nüremberg in 1553, gives examples which, he says, are meant partly for the information of those who make type.

A page is shown from a recent facsimile reprint: *Wolffgang Fuggers Schreibbüchlein* (with an introduction by Fritz Funke, Leipzig 1958.

5 Plantin's request for a New Hebrew Type, c. 1563

(A photograph of the original in the Bibliothèque Nationale, Paris.)

The legend in Christophe Plantin's handwriting means: 'This is the kind of type for which I should like to have punches for the letters in various widths, such as . . . &c., and for points and accents of all kinds needed to go with the letters, &c.'

Under it Guillaume Le Bé has added: 'This is a

message that Plantin wrote me for a face that he wanted and wanted me to cut for him, but I had no time to do it then.'

The printed leaf on which the notes are written was taken from a commentary on the Pentateuch by Baḥya ben Asher printed by Daniel Bomberg at Venice in 1546.

6 Woodcut Models for Hebrew Letters, 1573

(A photograph of the original in the Bibliothèque Nationale, Paris.)

The manuscript note by Guillaume Le Bé means: 'Portrayed and drawn in 1573 and partly cut, and got the rest cut by Mahiel du Boys and another, on wood.'

The 'portraits' preserve a model worked out by Le Bé during thirty years' practice in cutting Hebrew faces and may have been meant for the guidance of his descendants in cutting and judging punches for this script. *Plate 2*

7 A Design for Letters recommended by the Académie des Sciences, 1698

A plate made to accompany a report to Louis XIV on the best forms of Latin letters for use at his Royal Printing Office in the palace of the Louvre. The Académie des Sciences, consulted in 1692, appointed a committee of three who produced six years later a report headed 'Des Arts de construire les caractères, de graver les poinçons de lettres, d'imprimer les lettres et de relier les livres'. It recommended pattern letters drawn by geometrical means on squared paper which, they wrote, 'would enable artificers to execute to the smallest detail the letters that we have decided on'.

The report has not been published, but during the 18th century the drawings were engraved and some were published. They were followed (with large variations sanctioned by the committee in the light of experience) in a series of roman and italic types made for the royal press in the years 1694–1745. The types, named 'Romains du roi', have undoubtedly influenced type-design since then.

8 Drawings for the Doves Press Type, 1899

These were made in 1899–1900 by an artist in Emery Walker's studio drawing over enlarged photographs of pages printed by Nicolas Jenson at Venice in 1479. The work was supervised by Walker in consultation with T. J. Cobden-Sanderson. *Plate 2*

9 Edward Johnston's Experiments for Robert Bridges, 1909

One of several experimental pen-made models by Johnston for a type contemplated about 1909 by Robert Bridges for his enlarged alphabet for the English language.

10 Johnston's Designs for the Cranach Press, 1930

Letters from Edward Johnston to G. T. Friend about cutting italic sorts designed by Johnston for the Cranach Press at Weimar, 1930–1.

11 Drawings by Eric Gill, 1926

Gill's finished drawing for his Felicity italic and a letter asking for slight changes to be made in some letters as they were first cut for the Perpetua roman. *Plate 2*

A WORKING TYPEFOUNDRY

PUNCHCUTTING

Mechanization, the introduction of optical magnifying and measuring instruments, and increasing use of photography and electrotyping for reproduction have very much altered typefounding in recent years, and the few firms engaged in making type for sale differ so widely in their practices that it is hardly possible any longer to describe techniques as being universal.

The exhibits here represent the equipment generally used for cutting steel punches, making copper matrices, and casting and dressing type some sixty years ago. The methods in use then had survived with little alteration since the sixteenth century, and may have been even older.

12 A Punchcutter's Bench

A punchcutter works at a 'peg', a firm piece of wood with a notch at the hither end with a powerful magnifying glass fastened above it at eye-level.

A table to hold the tools and oil-stones within reach is usually combined with the peg.

Besides these the punchcutter needs fire and water for hardening the finished work.

The tools on this bench are enough for cutting punches by traditional methods. Most of them are also used by engravers, die-sinkers, and jewellers; that is to say gravers, files, a facing tool, a vice, oil-stones, and slates. Gauges for measuring are made by punchcutters for themselves. A candle or oil-lamp serves for proofing the punch in soot. *Plate 3*

Among the tools to be seen are the following.

a A Facing Tool

A tool of this kind is needed for holding the punch upright while its face is ground flat on an oil-stone or slate.

b A Gas Blowpipe and a Wig

A common means of heating finished punches as a preliminary to hardening them by plunging them red-hot in water. The 'wig' or a piece of asbestos holds heat and reflects it on to the punch.

13 A Blank

Until the nineteenth century punchcutters had often to forge blanks of a suitable size or get blacksmiths to forge them from iron of high quality.

Since the nineteenth century they have been able to buy steel bars of convenient dimensions. Sheffield steel of the best quality is favoured in Germany as well as in England.

The blank is filed true on two faces so as to fit accurately in a facing tool, and with this tool the face at one end is ground true and flat on a stone. The 'hammer end' is rounded.

Many of the earlier punchcutters favoured cigar-shaped blanks.

Punchcutting Technique

14 Two Stages in Punchcutting by Hand

The first has the counter of the letter cut out with engraving tools: the second has been completed by filing the shoulders but has not been hardened. Proofs made with soot from a flame enable the punchcutter to judge the progress of his work.

15 Counterpunches

These were the normal means of making hollows in the faces of hand-cut punches to form the spaces enclosed or nearly enclosed by the strokes of a letter. Some sixteenth-century counterpunches have survived at the Museum Plantin-Moretus with the punches they served to make.

16 Punches Fitted with Accent Punches

Matrices for letters with diacritical marks were often struck with two punches fitted together. One example is a punch for Hebrew *aleph* bought by the University of Oxford at Leiden in 1637 made with a step in the shoulder in which a small punch for *ḥolam ḥaser* is fitted and clipped on.

17 Letters cut in Type-metal for forming Matrices by Electrolysis

In 1845 T. W. Starr of Philadelphia patented a process for making matrices in this way, and it has largely superseded the cutting of steel punches in typefoundries, especially for type of the bigger bodies. The cathode is made of a letter in relief projecting from a plane surface of the right area to form the upper face of the matrix.

18 Punchcutter's Tools

a A facing tool for holding a punch perpendicular while its face is ground smooth on an oil-stone.

b Gravers and scorpers for cutting hollows in the face.

c Files for shaping the shoulders.

d Emery sticks and emery powder.

e Gauges for measuring the face and one for the inclination of the italic.

Plate 3

Punches of the Sixteenth to Twentieth Centuries

19 Punches by Garamond for St. Augustin (English-bodied) Roman

These were bought by Christophe Plantin from Guillaume Le Bé in Paris in 1562–3. Claude Garamond, who died in 1561, is the most celebrated of all punchcutters.

20 Punches by Granjon for Ascendonica (Double Pica) Italic, 1570

Commissioned by Plantin and cut at Antwerp in 1570. Robert Granjon was cutting punches for type in Paris by 1543. Later he worked in Lyons, Antwerp, Frankfurt, and Rome, where he is believed to have died in 1603. He ranks second only to Garamond in this art.

21 Punches by Le Bé for Hebrew, 1559

Guillaume Le Bé died in Paris in 1599. He specialized in cutting Hebrew types and was one of the greatest artists among punchcutters. He left his own account of this type: 'In the year 1559 I cut this big Double Canon Hebrew in my house. It was done before the start of the troubles; and I sold the punches, the set of matrices, and the mould to Monsieur Christoffe Plantain cheap because of the troubles.' Le Bé wrote this over smoke-proofs of the punches preserved in the Bibliothèque Nationale in Paris, of which a photograph is shown.

22 Punches probably by Van Hoogenacker for Hebrew

Bought by the University of Oxford from the executor of this typefounder at Leiden in 1637. The elongated forms of certain letters were added in London about 1670 by Nicholas Nicholls.

23 Punches cut in Amsterdam for Runic

Commissioned about 1660 by Francis Junius, the philologist, and later given by him to the University of Oxford.

24 Punches by Moxon for Irish

Cut to the order of Robert Boyle, the natural philosopher, about 1680. Joseph Moxon had not been taught this art, and his performance was not of a high order.

25 Punches by Caslon for Arabic

The first type made by this well-known English typefounder, who had been apprenticed as an ornamental engraver to an armourer. It was cut for the Society for Promoting Christian Knowledge and used for an edition of the Psalms in 1725.

26 Punches by Caslon for Pica Roman

The famous 'Caslon Old Face', now cast on 12-point body. Its earliest appearance was in books printed in 1725. The records of the Caslon firm in later years attributed the punches to 'Caslon I and II'. Matrices struck with these punches are in use today.

27 Punches cut for Baskerville's Canon Roman

One of the earliest of Baskerville's types, used by him in 1754. These punches for Canon roman capitals were cut by John Handy to the design of John Baskerville. *Plate 3*

28 Punches by Bessemer for a Diamond Type

Anthony Bessemer, the father of the inventor of a process for manufacturing steel, worked as a punchcutter in Holland and then in France; he came to London about 1794 and cut a range of modern-face types for the firm of Caslon. This was the second face cut in England for the diminutive body of Diamond (about 4½ points).

29 Punches for Bourgeois Modern Wide

Cut by an unknown punchcutter for H. W. Caslon & Co. about 1865. English punchcutting at this time enjoyed a high reputation abroad.

30 Punches by E. P. Prince for Morris's Golden Type

Morris drew the characters for his Golden type on enlarged photographs of the roman of Jacobus Rubeus, and altered many as he saw smoke-proofs. The punches were cut under the supervision of Emery Walker in 1891.

Prince died in 1923, the last regular independent punchcutter in England. He cut the punches for nearly all the proprietary types of the private presses and those designed by George W. Jones, besides some for the London typefounding firms of Caslon and Shanks.

31 Punches by E. P. Prince for 'Otter' Greek, 1903

Cut to the design of Robert Proctor of the British Museum.

32 Punches by Charles Malin for Perpetua, 1926

An experimental face cut by hand at Paris in 12 point (Didot) before Eric Gill's design was reproduced by the Monotype Corporation in a range of sizes.

33 Linotype and Monotype Punches

The machines used to cut these punches are adaptations of the invention of the American, Linn Boyd Benton, patented in Great Britain in 1885. They can be adjusted to reproduce a design in the size required for the type face. The punches are cut by a series of diminutive routers controlled by an operator following the contours of a pattern in relief.

MATRIX-MAKING

34 A Striking Press for making Matrices

Until recent times punches were struck into copper with a hammer. A press enables an experienced man to drive the punch to the required depth with an even, continuous pressure. *Plate 4*

35 Justifier's Tools

The struck piece of copper is made into a matrix of the required shape and dimensions almost entirely by being rubbed backwards and forwards on a big file. Gauges are used in the early stages of the process to test the depth of the strike and the angle and distance of the strike in relation to the sides and head, but the final tests are made on trial types cast in the matrix fitted, generally, in a hand mould.

36 Justifier's Gauges

A needle gauge serves for a preliminary rough test of the depth of the strike.

An overlap gauge is used to measure the distance of the strike from the head and sides of the matrix.

A turning gauge is used in making the sides of the matrix parallel.

A type-high gauge shows whether type cast in the matrix has a level face and is of the right height-to-paper.

Matrix-Making Technique

37 A Typefounder's Matrix

The matrix has to be so made that, when fitted to a typefounder's mould of the appropriate size, it will give the character cast in it the right height, thickness, alignment, and angle with the perpendicular.

The oldest existing matrices are made of copper or bronze, but some were made of brass in the sixteenth and seventeenth centuries, and some, for big characters, of lead.

Those that were made for use in a hand mould have a notch at the back to receive the point of the spring of the mould which fastened them in position. They also have grooves filed in two of their surfaces to make it easier to tie them to the 'leather' which attached them to the mould (see no. 80).

38 A Small Anvil or 'Stake' for striking Matrices

This tool, stuck in a bench, provided a surface on which to hammer punches into copper. The example shown is probably one recorded in 1693 as part of the equipment of the typefoundry at Oxford bequeathed to the University by John Fell, Bishop of Oxford.

39 A Punch stuck in the Copper

40 Unfinished Matrices, 1570, 1886

Pieces of copper struck with punches but not yet 'justified' (trued up). Punchcutters normally sold their work in this form, i.e. as a 'strike' of all the characters needed for a fount.

a A strike sold to Christophe Plantin about 1570. This is for a face cut by Robert Granjon and named by him 'La Gaillarde', of which he printed a specimen at Antwerp in 1570. Plantin bought four strikes of it, of which two have been justified.

b A strike bought in 1886 by the University of Oxford from Messrs. Theinhardt of Berlin.

41 Lead Matrices, c. 1580

These were made to avoid the difficulty of striking large punches into material as hard as copper. Such matrices were still being made in the eighteenth century.

Those shown are for a set of roman capitals left incomplete by Garamond at his death in 1561. Plantin bought it and had it completed and copper matrices made by Jacob Sabon in 1565. Lead matrices for this face, lacking the O, were recorded as belonging to Plantin in 1588.

42 Electrotyped matrices

Since Starr's application of electrolysis to matrix-making in 1845 the process has been much used to produce new faces and copy old ones.

A nickel deposit has been riveted to a backing of copper.

43 Engraved Matrices

Machines on the pantograph principle were adapted to this purpose about 1890. They are used especially to make type for complicated designs, such as trade marks.

The specimens were made in 1924–7 by W. J. Bilton, using a Benton-Waldo punchcutting machine. They are for Egyptian hieroglyphs designed by Sir Alan Gardiner.

44 Justifier's Tools

The work was formerly done by rubbing the unfinished matrices on files, testing them meanwhile first with set-squares, turning gauges and overlap gauges and then by casting trial letters and testing those with height-to-paper gauges and lining gauges.

Recently, optical instruments for magnifying and measuring and milling machines have been applied to the earlier stages of justifying.

Matrices of the Sixteenth to the Twentieth Centuries

45 Matrices for a Typeface first used in 1520

These well-made matrices, bought by the University of Oxford from a typefounder at Leiden in 1637, correspond with the type printed in Ḳimḥi's *Rudimenta hebraica* (Augsburg 1520).

The face is of a rather primitive cut and has not been found in later printing. It seems probable, therefore, that the matrices were made as early as 1520. On that assumption, they are evidence that the technique of matrix-making by typefounders remained unchanged since then until the nineteenth century. *Plate 4*

46 Matrices by Le Bé in 1551 for a Hebrew face

The punches for this Great Primer Hebrew were cut in 1551 by Guillaume Le Bé for Claude Garamond, another famous French punchcutter. Plantin bought them soon after Garamond's death in 1561.

47 Matrices by Le Bé for the 'Parangonne' Roman Cut by Garamond, 1573

Plantin bought these from Le Bé to replace older matrices for the same face but seems hardly to have used them.

48 Old Matrices rejustified in 1564 by Guyot for Plantin

A Hebrew face of unknown origin. The Antwerp typefounder François Guyot repaired many of the matrices in 1564 and fastened strips of copper to their sides. Some, in the original state, have no margins on either side of the strike. They have been drilled from side to side, presumably so that they could be tied to the leather which attached them to the mould.

49 Matrices for Hebrew and Arabic

These matrices were bought by the University of Oxford at Leiden in 1637. The seller was the executor of Arent van Hoogenacker who probably cut the faces and made the matrices not long before he died in 1636.

50 Matrices for the Gothic of Junius

These were made at Amsterdam about 1660 to 1665. Francis Junius gave them to the University of Oxford in 1677.

51 Matrices for Great Primer Cyrillic

Made at Amsterdam in 1694, probably by Johann Adolf Schmidt, to the design of H. W. Ludolf.

52 Matrices for the 'Elstob' Anglo-Saxon

Made by a London typefounder about 1714 for William Bowyer to print Elizabeth Elstob's *English-Saxon Grammar*. The workmanship is rough by continental standards.

53 Matrices by Rosart for a big Long Primer Roman

Jacques François Rosart of Brussels was an extremely skilful punchcutter and typefounder. He sold the punches and matrices for this face to the firm of Plantin–Moretus in 1758.

54 Matrices by Figgins for Greek Capitals

In 1796 the Delegates of the Press at Oxford ordered Greek capitals of five sizes from Vincent Figgins, a London typefounder. These matrices are beautifully made.

55 Matrices by Howard for the 'Basle' Roman

The face was cut to the design of the younger Charles Whittingham about 1854 by William Howard, a typefounder in a small way in London. Presumably he made the matrices.

56 Matrices by Schelter & Giesecke for English Medieval

The face was cut for the London firm of Reed & Fox and finished in 1868. It was a copy of the Old Style of Miller and Richard which had been completed in 1860. These matrices were bought for the University Press at Oxford in 1886 from Schelter & Giesecke, the Berlin typefounders, who had acquired punches or strikes from Reed & Sons.

57 Matrices by Reed & Sons for the 'Troy' Type

The face was cut by E. P. Prince in 1892 to the design of William Morris, for use at the Kelmscott Press.

58 Matrices by Miller & Richard for Proctor's 'Otter' Greek

These were made in 1903 with punches cut by E. P. Prince.

59 Matrices by Ribadeau-Dumas for Eric Gill's 'Perpetua'

These were made in 1926 by Ribadeau-Dumas of Paris using punches cut by Charles Malin for the Monotype Corporation Ltd.

60 Matrices by H. W. Caslon & Co. for Eric Gill's 'Joanna'

These were engraved in steel to Gill's design for the firm of Hague & Gill, who began to print with the type in 1931.

61 Linotype Matrices

These are struck with steel punches in the edges of brass stampings. The matrices are afterwards justified in milling machines.

The serrated V of the stamping is adapted to the mechanism for raising it to the magazine after use and dropping it into a particular channel there.

The present techniques of the makers of the English Linotype are substantially those adopted about 1900 incorporating inventions by Robert Barr.

62 Monotype Matrices

These are made of bronze and are struck in an enclosed die with punches of the same section. The punches have the characters so placed on them as to give the characters the proper alignment and distances. Justification is limited to correcting the depth of the strike by milling the struck surface.

CASTING AND DRESSING

63 A Caster's Furnace

A furnace like this is described and illustrated in Joseph Moxon's *Mechanick Exercises*, vol. ii (London 1683–4), and can be seen in Plantin's house at Antwerp, where a typefoundry was set up late in the seventeenth century. Illustrations of the eighteenth and early nineteenth centuries show similar appliances.

The fuel was charcoal or coal. The metal-pot fitted in a hole in the top plate. On either side of the caster was a bank on which he laid his tools and the type as he ejected it from the mould.

Plate 5

64 Hand Moulds

A different mould is needed for each of the bodies on which type is cast. A typefounder, even in a small way of business, had to have at least a dozen ranging from Pearl (or 5 point) to Canon (or 48 point).

Plate 1

65 Caster's Ladles

These were of various sizes to suit the volume of the casting. The mould and jet should be filled at every cast, and an overflow of metal should be avoided because it makes the mould hard to open.

66 A Typometer

A gauge of this kind is a simple but reliable means of measuring the body and thickness of type and comparing them with a standard. The caster is told how many pieces of type of a given sort should fit exactly in the gauge when laid bodywise and setwise.

Fournier le Jeune recommended this tool in his *Manuel typographique* (Paris 1764–6).

67 Red Ochre

Casters coated the inner surfaces of their moulds with this powder when casting very small sorts to make the metal flow more readily.

68 Rubbing Stones

Type cast in hand moulds or pivotal machines needs to be rubbed on the top and bottom sides to make the surfaces true and even. Gritstones are used. The rubber wears a leather finger-stall.

The stones are grained from time to time with wet sand ground between a pair of them.

69 Letter Sticks

Strips of hardwood with rabets are used to hold type in the intervals between the processes of dressing.

70 A Wooden Dressing Bench

A replica of the bench illustrated in printer's manuals of the seventeenth and eighteenth centuries and described by Fournier le Jeune in his *Manuel typographique* (Paris 1764–6). It served to hold type feet-uppermost in a straight line while the unevenness where the jet had been broken off was grooved out with a plough. Other ploughs were used for bearding and cutting additional nicks. The plough was guided by a projection on its under-side fitting in a channel in the dressing-rod. The rod is in two pieces which grip the type firmly when it is fastened in the bench with a quoin.

71 An Iron Dressing Bench

The type is compressed lengthwise by a thumb-screw at the end of the dressing-rod and sideways by a long vice.

This specimen was probably made about 1850; but the invention is said to date back to the early seventeenth century, when the first of the kind was made by the French typefounder Jean Jannon to save his invalid wife from being disturbed by the noise of knocking up the quoin of the wooden bench.

72 Ploughs

These are fitted with irons for dressing the feet, bearding the shoulders, and cutting extra nicks in the shanks of type.

73 A Kerning File

Sorts whose faces overhang the top or bottom sides of the type have to be rubbed on an appliance of this kind which has a slide protecting the overhanging part.

74 A Galley and Slice

These old-fashioned wooden galleys are convenient for making new type into pages roughly justified, tied up, and finally wrapped in paper for delivery to the printer. Printers used these galleys also (no. 110).

75 Instruments used in a Contemporary Typefoundry

A show-case made up by Messrs. Stephenson, Blake & Co. of Sheffield to illustrate modern techniques in making type for sale.

Besides punches and matrices made in the traditional way, the collection includes the drawing and pattern used for cutting a punch mechanically. Similar patterns with the character in recess are used for machines for engraving matrices. Engraved matrices and soft metal originals on which matrices are formed by electrolysis are also shown.

TYPE MOULDS

76 A Typefounder's Hand Mould

Probably made in the first half of the nineteenth century. The bottom half has been taken to pieces to show the construction.

This mould is made to cast type of Bourgeois body.

77 A Description of the Type Mould by Plantin in 1567

In his *Dialogues françois pour les ieunes enfans* Plantin clearly refers to a mould of the kind shown as no. 76.

78 A Mould that probably belonged to Christophe Plantin

Of surviving moulds likely to be of early date, those whose age is best attested are some that have been kept in Plantin's house with his punches and matrices. Many moulds were included in lists of his equipment made in the years 1556–89. Some of those that have been preserved in his house are likely to have been among them. This, and several others, are made of brass.

79 An Old Mould

This mould made of steel and iron is in all respects like the pattern described by Joseph Moxon in *Mechanick Exercises*, vol. ii (1683–4). It lacks the woods to protect the caster's hands from heat and the spring which clips the matrix on. The body is Pica (0·166 in.).

80 An English Typefounder's Mould of about 1800

The style of workmanship looks rather early. It is stamped with the name 'Figgins', a firm of London typefounders in the years 1792–1908.

A matrix is shown clipped in position. When released from the spring it was held to the bottom half of the mould by a piece of leather.

81 A Trigger Mould

The addition to the hand mould of a contrivance for tilting the matrix so as to release the casting without undoing the spring is attributable to a Scotsman, Archibald Binney, who patented it in America in 1811. This improvement almost doubled the speed of production to some 800 medium-sized castings in an hour.

82 A Rule Mould

Simple moulds of this kind were used to make rules, leads, quotations, and metal furniture.

83 A Pivotal Machine Mould

The mould in these casting machines (see no. 460), largely used from 1840 until recent years, does not differ in principle from the hand mould. The mould made for the machine is of heavier construction, and therefore less liable to fluctuation of temperature, than the hand mould and has a smaller jet. The big jet designed to accommodate the hand caster's comparatively erratic aim is not needed on a mould filled, as this is, by a spurt of metal from a fine nozzle under pressure from a pump.

84 A Thompson Mould

This mould was patented by J. S. Thompson in 1909 and is fitted to the casting machine of his invention. The mould delivers 'perfect' type, i.e. type that needs no breaking, rubbing, or dressing. Unlike the older moulds, it is adjustable for body within a range of 5 point to 48 point. The adjustment is made by changing the mould-blade, a sliding part which determines the body, shears off the jet, carries the casting between dressing knives, and delivers it to a race.

Typographical Standards

85 Standardization of the Dimensions of Type

Mould-making was complicated in the past by the want of agreed standards for height of type, depth of strike in matrices, and body. The gradual approximation to universal standards for these is an important technical advance.

a Pattern Types, 1757.

Before the introduction of standards for the dimensions of type, founders had to cast founts matching those they had previously delivered. The patterns exhibited were kept by the firm of Moretus at Antwerp to be sent to the founder with a repeat order. The inscription is: '28 sbre 1757. Petit Rommain rommain a gros oëil de Mr Rosa alfabet et accent et pontiaison et Légature'. The face is a large Long Primer roman cut by Jacques François Rosart of Brussels.

b Height to paper, 1540.

In the book exhibited (*Pirotechnia*, Venice 1540) Vanocchio Biringuccio wrote that type, after being cast, was cut to the desired length.

On the other hand, an impression from a piece of type lying on its side in a *Justinian* printed at Venice in 1490 is evidence that moulds made to cast type of a given height were in use by then.

c Old moulds of different shoulder-heights, *c.* 1675?

Two halves of old moulds made of brass probably in Holland late in the seventeenth century. If fitted with the same matrices, these moulds would cast type differing in height by 0·15 in.

d Type of various conventional heights, seventeenth to nineteenth centuries.

A collection made about 1895. At the present time only two standards are in general use, 'Didot Normal' height on the continent of Europe (0·9278 in.) and 0·917 in. in North America, Great Britain, and the former British dependencies.

e Type of the common bodies used in London in 1850–1900.

The bodies found by experience to be the most useful had been very roughly standardized by the middle of the sixteenth century and were known by names. Attempts to give the named bodies precise values in lawful measures go back as far as 1683–4, when Joseph Moxon printed a list of the conventional bodies in his *Mechanick Exercises* and related them to the foot.

f Fournier's point-system, 1737.

'Table des proportions des differens caracteres de l'imprimerie.' Pierre Simon Fournier, typefounder of Paris, introduced a series of bodies approximating to those in common use but all multiples of an ideal unit which he named the 'typographical point'. This leaf, bound in a copy of Fournier's *Modèles des caracteres de l'imprimerie* (Paris 1742), is probably the proposal which he said that he published in 1737. Measurements in Fournier's units could only be made by reference to a scale which he printed on paper and a metal gauge which he sold.

g The standard bodies of F. A. Didot, *c.* 1784.

A specimen book of the types from the typefoundry of Pierre Didot at Paris, 1819. The bodies, named by their measurements in points, are, as Didot explains in his preface, those introduced by his father, François Ambroise Didot. This printer began about 1784 casting type for his own use on bodies precisely related to the royal foot, the standard linear measure in France at the time. They were multiples of a unit, which Didot called the 'metre', equivalent to the seventy-second part of an inch. This unit was later renamed the 'Didot point'. Didot's scale of bodies, which had the disadvantage of differing considerably from conventional practice based on experience, was generally adopted in France early in the nineteenth century and by German typefounders between 1840 and 1879.

h The American Point-system, 1878.

An advertisement of '*The American System of Interchangeable Type Bodies* published in 1880 by Marder, Luse & Co. of Chicago. After a fire at their typefoundry in 1872 this company adopted bodies which were multiples of the twelfth part of a typical Pica measuring 0·166 in. Following Fournier, they called their unit a 'point'. Marder, Luse & Co. began to sell type on these bodies in 1878, and in 1886 their system was recommended to its members by the United States Type Founders' Association. British typefounders conformed with the American point-system in the early years of this century.

CASTING TYPE

86 A Typefounder in 1545

Behind the printers a typefounder can be seen holding a ladle in his right hand and in his left hand a mould something like the one shown above with the spring at the bottom.

This is an illustration in a book of religious and moral instruction to men of all conditions printed by Joos Lambrecht at Ghent in 1545 (Cornelis van der Heyden, *Corte Instruccye ende Onderwys*). It illustrates the 'Admonition to the Skilled Tradesman'. Lambrecht was a punchcutter and typefounder as well as a printer.

87 Casting in a Hand Mould in 1926

A photograph of Sidney Squires, formerly typefounder at the University Press, Oxford. As lately as this, the old 'Fell' types were cast by hand to give them a slight irregularity which was thought becoming to them.

88 Founder's Ladles

Found in a hole in a wall of an old house in High Street, Oxford. These may have been made for a silversmith; but ladles adapted in capacity to the volume of the sort of type being cast were also used for typefounding.

89 Constituents of Type-metal in 1540

A page of *Pirotechnia* of Vanocchio Biringuccio (Venice, first published in 1540) giving a recipe for printer's metal. The ingredients, lead, tin, antimony, are substantially those still in use, but their proportions are now very different.

90 Ingredients of Type-metal

a Lead, tin, and antimony in the forms used to prepare the alloy at the present time.

b Materials used to make typemetal in the sixteenth and seventeenth centuries. These are described in Plantin's accounts for 1563, in Joseph Moxon's *Mechanick Exercises*, vol. ii (1683–4), and in the accounts of the University Press at Oxford, 1699–1700.

Antimony was bought in the form of the sulphide and refined by typefounders by heating it and skimming the dross, adding iron filings or old nails and sometimes copper filings. Lead was mixed with the product, old (i.e. calcined) lead being preferred.

91 Analyses of the Metal in Old Type

The examples assayed were taken from founts at the Museum Plantin-Moretus and the University Press, Oxford, whose age is attested by documentary proof.

92 Processes in the Finishing of Type

a Unbroken type.

Type cast in hand moulds and in most pivotal machines is ejected with the jet attached to it. The first step in finishing the type for use is to break off the jet.

b Type before and after rubbing.

The top and bottom sides of the type are rubbed on a millstone to get rid of fins of metal due to imperfect fitting of the mould and a slight rounding of the corners in cooling.

c A kerning file.

Sorts whose faces overhang adjoining type cannot be rubbed in the ordinary way. Their kerned sides must be smoothed on a file fitted with a guard to protect the face.

d Type set up for dressing.

After being rubbed, type is assembled in letter-sticks to undergo further processes.

e A bearding plane and type before and after bearding.

In former times the type was secured face-uppermost in a dressing block and had the angle of the shoulder trimmed off.

If the forme was inked by hand and the impression was deep, the shoulders of the type often printed, especially at the head and foot of a page. Bearding prevented this.

f Type before and after dressing at the feet.

The row of newly cast type is dropped into a dressing rod and locked up in a dressing bench with the feet uppermost so that the roughness left at the break of the jet can be planed away leaving the type to stand truly on its feet.

g Type with distinguishing nicks.

Most moulds are fitted with one wire to form the indispensable nick to indicate the 'front' of a letter to the compositor. Moulds with two or more wires to form extra nicks are expensive to make, and founts or sorts were often distinguished by nicks cut with a plane at the dressing block.

h A dressing knife.

In former times the dresser pared the front and back of type to lessen inequality of body due to variation in the heat of the metal and mould inevitable in primitive typefounding and so make the type stand more truly in line.

i Schemes for the proportions of sorts to a fount.

The first of those exhibited here was made by Laurent van Everbroeck about 1573 for a fount of Paragon Greek cast for Plantin. He charged for the number of pieces of type cast and separately for the metal.

The second was drawn up about 1870 in the typefoundry at the University Press, Oxford. The proportions are given in terms of weight.

TYPEFOUNDERS' SPECIMENS

La Gaillarde, 1570

93 Epreuve de la Petitte Antique ou romaine de Rob. Granion nommee la Gaillarde. *Antwerp 1570.*

Perhaps the oldest dated specimen of a typeface offered for sale to printers. Granjon is not known to have sold type: the offer is rather of a 'strike', i.e. unfinished matrices.

As well as the roman face he shows some of the arabesque ornaments in the form of type of which he was the originator. At the head is his *fleuron de douze pièces* (12-piece flower composition), and at the foot four units of his *fleuron de six pièces.*

94 The Earliest English Type-specimen

The oldest of known specimens by British typefounders is this miniature example annexed by Nicholas Nicholls of London to his petition for an appointment as royal letter founder in 1665.

The intention behind this 'specimen of his art' was to prove his competence as a punchcutter and founder by displaying type that he had made for very small bodies (the roman is about 4½ point). There is no reason to think that Nicholls completed the Greek and exotic faces—Hebrew, Syriac, Samaritan, Ethiopic, and Arabic—of which some letters are shown.

Baskerville's first Type-Specimen, 1754

95 A Specimen by John Baskerville of Birmingham in the County of Warwick, Letter-founder and Printer. *Birmingham 1754*

The specimen of the types is combined with proposals for publishing to subscribers a *Virgil* intended to be set in them.

Historic London Types

96 A Catalogue and Specimen of the Printing-Type-Foundery of . . . Mr. John James. *1782*

Thomas James established this business in 1710, and he and his son after him bought the stocks of all the typefounders who had worked in London before that time. Soon after the death of John James in 1772 the material came into the hands of the antiquary Edward Rowe Mores, who prepared this specimen of types but died before he had completed it. The punches and matrices were then put up to auction, and the specimen was finished and included in the sale-catalogue.

The type faces are those that London printers used before Caslon's became available, some of sixteenth-century origin, and many cast in matrices brought from abroad.

At the sale in 1782 some of James's matrices were bought by Joseph Fry for his typefoundry and have descended to Messrs. Stephenson, Blake & Co. Ltd., of Sheffield, but most went for scrap.

Only two copies of the *Catalogue* are known, both belonging to owners in U.S.A.

The First Sanserif

96a A Specimen of Printing Types &c. by Blake, Garnett & Co. (successors to Mr. W. Caslon, of London), Letter-Founders. *Sheffield, c. 1819*

Largely a reissue of leaves previously published by William Caslon IV in 1816, whose foundry was bought by the Sheffield firm in 1819. Among Caslon's types was one of the kind afterwards called 'Sanserif', which he named 'Egyptian'. It was the earliest of its kind. *Plate 21*

The First All-bold Type

96b Specimen of Printing Types by Vincent Figgins, Letter-Founder, West Street, West Smithfield. *London 1815*

Typefaces named 'Antique' cut by Figgins, of which four of different sizes are shown for the first time in this book, are believed to be the earliest of the design now generally known as 'Egyptian'. It is peculiar in giving equal emphasis to the up and down strokes and serifs. In historical perspective the design is of importance as the precursor of the 'Clarendon' typefaces, with only slight contrast of up and down strokes, which came to be used for distinguishing headings and emphasized words. The usefulness of 'Clarendon' for this purpose led to a general demand for bold faces which now obliges printers to stock a third Latin alphabet added to the roman and italic. *Plate 21*

PRINTERS' TYPE SPECIMENS

Plantin, 1567

97 Index sive specimen characterum Christophori Plantini. *Christophe Plantin, Antwerp 1567*

One of two surviving copies, differing slightly. The book was probably made for use by the Spanish Government in specifying type for liturgical books. Plantin secured a monopoly of supplying such books to Spain three years later.

Oxford, 1693

98 (University of Oxford), A Specimen of the Several Sorts of Letter given to the University by Dr. John Fell, late Lord Bishop of Oxford. *Oxford, at the Theater, 1693*

Probably designed chiefly to acknowledge publicly the munificence of Fell in adding a great many typefaces to the University's equipment for printing, which, when it was let to him in 1672, was very small.

As a result of Fell's bequest and of a somewhat earlier gift by Francis Junius of type for Icelandic and dead northern languages, together with some later purchases, the University's press in 1693 had few rivals for the diversity of the scripts that it could print.

Moncur, Edinburgh, 1709

99 A Specimen of the Types in John Moncur's Printing-house, being a Sermon, &c. *J. Moncur, Edinburgh 1709*

An early example (for Great Britain) of type specimens meant to advertise a printer's equipment and help customers to make good use of it.

PRINTING

A Reconstructed Early Printing House

100 A Wooden Press

A typical press of the kind known in the eighteenth and early nineteenth centuries as 'the common press' to distinguish it from one with slight improvements attributed to W. J. Blaeu (who died in 1638).

Representations of the printing-press in *La Grant danse macabre des hommes* (Lyons, 1499) and in sixteenth-century printers' devices show the essential features of the later common press. Joseph Moxon's full description in *Mechanick Exercises*, vol. ii (London 1683–4) fits this specimen, apart from variations in the dimensions.

The wooden press was made to hold a forme of twice the area covered by the platen. A full-sized sheet, therefore, was printed by two pulls of the press for each side.

Iron presses with larger platens actuated by compound levers superseded these in the first quarter of the nineteenth century. In 1840, according to T. C. Hansard, wooden presses could still be found in old offices, where they were used for pulling proofs.

This specimen lacked the platen when it was bought for preservation, and that part of it is a reproduction.

Wooden presses were fastened to the ceiling with struts, called 'braces', to prevent their being distorted by the constant pulling of the bar.

101 An Ink Block

A piece of beech-wood fastened to the hind-rail of the press was used for spreading the ink. From it the pressman picked up ink with the balls. This has been made recently following the drawing in Stower's *Printer's Grammar* of 1808.

102 A Brayer

Used for working ink on the block to an even depth and consistency.

103 A Ball

This tool for dabbing ink on the forme was used as early as the fifteenth century and was the only implement for the purpose until it was superseded by rollers about 1820. The pad was made of a piece of sheepskin stuffed with wool, and it was nailed to the wooden stock.

Balls were used in pairs. The pressman held one in either hand and distributed the ink thinly and evenly on them by rolling one against another with an expert spinning motion of his hands.

Plate 7

104 A Laystool

White paper and printed sheets were laid on big boards, which were put on stools ready to the pressman's hand.

By the nineteenth century a 'horse' with a sloping top had been evolved to take the white paper and make it easier to pick sheets off the heap.

105 A Peel

Paper made of rag was printed wet and after printing was hung on 'poles' to dry. These were horizontal rails hung from the ceiling. The peel was used for lifting sheets on to the poles and getting them down again.

106 Frames

The oak frames for supporting compositor's cases were in use for a long time at the University Press, Oxford, and are believed to have been made in 1668 for the University's first equipment for printing in the Sheldonian Theatre. Their panelled backs and turned legs suggest that they were designed to harmonize with the dignified interior of the Theatre. The typical printer's frame of the time was, no doubt, less elaborate.

The height of these frames was increased about a hundred years ago by fitting blocks on the ends of the legs. *Plate 7*

107 Compositor's Cases

Some chosen from the stock at the University Press, Oxford, for their antique look. Their age is, however, not known.

A diagram in Joseph Moxon's *Mechanick Exercises*, vol. ii (1683–4), is the earliest to show the construction of the pair of cases used in England. The division of the cases into boxes has hardly changed since his time.

108 A Pair of Greek Cases

Until late in the eighteenth century three pairs of cases were needed to lay a fount of Greek; but since the disuse of ligatures and compendia all the sorts have been fitted into one pair with rather more divisions than are required for Latin types.

109 Stanhope's Lower Case

The 3rd Earl Stanhope was one of many to propose improvements in the construction and lay of the pair of cases. His plan, published about 1810, provided for eight logotypes for the most frequent combinations of letters in the English language.

Two lower-cases are believed to be the only survivors of a number of pairs made for the earl, whose proposed reform met with no support.

110 A Galley and Slice

This is the only kind of galley described by Joseph Moxon in 1683–4. It has a detachable bottom, called the 'slice', sliding in the frame. A page of type made up and tied up on the galley was carried on the slice to the imposing-stone. *Plate 7*

111 Wooden Column Galleys

Long galleys of this kind were probably introduced first in newspaper offices early in the nineteenth century.

112 An Imposing Stone

The flat surface on which pages of type were made into a forme was traditionally a piece of stone. The steel surface now used for the purpose is still called 'the stone'. The stone surface and metal surround of this example are known to have been made before 1830.

Printer's Sundries

113 A Pair of Chases

A forme is given rigidity by being wedged in a metal frame called a chase. Chases are made in pairs of identical dimensions so that the two formes needed to print the two sides of a sheet may be interchanged on the press with the least adjustment to make them 'register'.

114 A Printer's Candlestick and Tallow Candle

Before the days of gas-lighting, each compositor had a candle fixed to his case and each press was equipped with four candles.

115 The Lay used before the Long ſ was discarded

The disposition of the sorts in the case has altered hardly at all since it was shown in a diagram of 1683–4. A minor rearrangement took place, however, early in the nineteenth century when the boxes previously needed for the long ſ and its combinations with other letters could be used to improve the accommodation for spaces.

116 Wooden Composing-sticks

A wooden stick in which a mortise has been cut and lined with brass to fit a given measure may be taken as the earliest tool used by compositors for assembling type in lines. The age of these specimens is not known, but the stick in this form is believed to have been superseded by adjustable composing-sticks made of iron during the seventeenth century. Plantin mentions only the wooden stick in his description of printing in *Dialogues françois pour les ieunes enfans* of 1567.

117 A Set of Brass Measures

These were standards for setting adjustable composing-sticks so as to secure conformity among all the compositors in a room.

118 An Old Bodkin

The tool used for picking pieces of type out of set matter.

119 Shooting-sticks

These sticks are made to be put against wooden quoins and hit with a mallet in the process of locking up a forme. One of these is made of lignum vitae, the other of gun-metal.

120 A Small Forme

Two pages locked up in a chase with wooden furniture, sidestick, footstick, and quoins to make a miniature forme. The pages are set in type of Diamond body and are part of an *Apocrypha* printed at Oxford in 1909.

121 Hand-made Wooden Furniture

Gutter-sticks used to separate pages of type in the formes. These are relics of handwork by printer's joiners.

PRINTING INK

Exhibits selected by Colin Bloy

It was an essential part of the invention of typographical printing that an ink should be found which would stick to a metal surface, and the first printers at Mainz gave striking proof of their technical competence by making oil-bound colours of high quality which answered the purpose and have hardly been bettered since. This was within fifteen years of the first use of oil paints for pictures, at a time when the ability to make them fine and durable enough for such a purpose seems to have been confined to a school of artists in the Netherlands.

It is likely that the ink of the earliest printers was based on heat-bodied linseed oil, kept for a year to allow the mucilage, or 'foots', to settle; rosin may have been added. The black would have been made by collecting the soot from burning pitch and roasting it several times to rid it of tarry oils. Ink-making was a disagreeable and troublesome process in which the risk of fire was always present, and there were no short cuts which did not result in loss of quality.

As late as 1850 many printers were still making their own ink, but the manufacture as a separate industry was established more than a hundred years before then in some continental centres of printing.

122 The First Book about Printing Ink, 1619

This book, Caneparius's *De atramentis* (Venice 1619), is the earliest known work which gives details of the formulation of typographic inks. A translation of the section on printing ink is given.

123 Moxon on Ink, 1683–4

The *Mechanick Exercises* is the first English work to give details of ink-making, although it is the contemporary Dutch method that is described. Moxon laments the low state of English ink-making at the time.

124 The 'Sac-à-Noir', 1723

Lampblack was produced by burning pitch resin in a vessel in a tent made of sheepskins or paper. The smoke was deposited on the inside of the tent which was then beaten so that the black fell on the floor. To remove impurities still remaining the black would then be calcined several times by heating it until red-hot in an iron box with a small aperture at the top.
An engraving

125 Bad Ink on Bad Paper, 1740

Although Gessner's *Buchdruckerkunst* (1740) is about typographic printing it is, nevertheless, an example of the effect produced by bad ink on bad paper. The linseed- or nut-oil varnish may well have been boiled incorrectly, or for too short a time, and exuded into the surrounding paper. Tarry oils remaining in the lampblack, due to lack of calcination, can also cause this phenomenon.

126 Ink-making Implements from Various Sources, 17th and 18th Centuries

The illustrations mounted on the wall represent the following early ink-making equipment:

The varnish kettle and straw wreath. The elevated handles were designed to admit a pole or bar with which the kettle could be lifted from the fire safely. The straw wreath served as an insulator. The kettle was placed on it as contact with the cold earth or floor would cause the hot oil to boil over.

Iron spatula. Used for stirring the boiling varnish.

Muller and stone. For grinding the colour into the varnish.

The brayer. Used to rub out the ink on the ink-tray.

The slice. 'A little thin iron shovel (Moxon)'.

127 An Early Grinding Machine, c. 1824

This engraving of Lorilleux's factory in Paris shows a very early grinding machine which was driven by steam. These machines were introduced to meet the requirements of the new power-driven presses which demanded inks with pigments ground more finely than was possible by manual methods.

128 A Printing Ink Factory, c. 1860

A diagrammatic view of the factory of B. Winstone & Son showing not only ink production but also the manufacture of lithographic presses in which this firm was engaged for some years. By this date the making of printing ink had become industrialized.

129 A Muller with Stone and Ink, 19th Century

Until the early part of the eighteenth century the pigment was ground by hand, and this was a most laborious process. The printer who skimped this operation would very likely find that his ink filled in fine detail.

130 A Vessel of Lampblack

For a description of its preparation see no. 124 above.

EARLY PRINTER'S COPY AND PROOF

131 Copy used by Pynson in 1493

A manuscript in a fifteenth-century English hand of a *Dialogue of Dives and Pauper* attributed to the Carmelite Henry Parker (d. 1470). In 1953 Miss M. M. Morgan showed that marks made on the manuscript correspond with divisions between sheets, pages, and lines of the first edition printed by Richard Pynson in London in 1493 and were probably made by two compositors in the course of setting it. Variations between the manuscript and the printed book are negligible apart from some modernization of spelling and grammar.

132 A Proof corrected in 1526

A pull of leaves N2 and N5 of *The Grete Herball*, a book printed by Peter Treveris in Southwark, finished on 27 July 1526. The leaf is printed both sides: the recto is in the corrected state, the verso, shown here, is uncorrected and has corrector's marks on it. The corrections are made in the printed book.

A BOOK IN THE MAKING

133 Clarendon's 'History of the Rebellion' printed in 1702–4 with related Documents and Materials *Plate 23*

a A volume of the copy used by the printers.

Part of a fair copy by an unknown hand believed to have been a gift to the University of Oxford by the author's son.

b The volumes of the *History* printed by the University at its press in Oxford in 1702, 1703, and 1704.

This was the first edition of the work. Most copies (including the one exhibited) were printed on Medium paper, but a small number were printed on larger and finer paper.

c The Warehouseman's accounts.

The Warehouseman was, at that time, responsible for the management of the press and rendered accounts to the University.

d Punches and matrices for the typeface used for the text.

The face is one of those commissioned by the partnership of four headed by John Fell, Dean of Christ Church and Bishop of Oxford, which rented the University's right to print during the years 1672 to 1690. It is the Great Primer roman and italic for which a German, Peter de Walpergen, cut the punches and made the matrices while he was employed by the partners at Oxford as their typefounder. His faces for the bigger bodies of Canon and Double Pica are also used in the book.

e Copper plates for the frontispiece and ornaments.

These were engraved by Michael Burghers, a Dutchman who worked in Oxford from *c.* 1673 until his death in 1727. Burghers was at first an assistant to David Loggan and succeeded him in the appointment of Engraver to the University.

f The artist's drawings for the ornaments.

Burghers engraved the plates for the *History* from his own designs. Some of these are preserved in an album which once belonged to Horace Walpole, Earl of Orford.

The Mainz Psalter

134 PSALTER in Latin, *Johann Fust and Peter Schoeffer, Mainz, 14 August 1457*

This famous masterpiece of printing surpasses even the 42-line Bible in the beauty of its type and the richness of its ornament. It is the first printed book to give the name of its printer and the date of printing. One of the printers, Johann Fust, had been in partnership with Gutenberg and had advanced money for the first essays in printing. It is supposed that a lawsuit between the partners in 1455 led to the dissolution of the partnership and that thereafter Fust exploited Gutenberg's invention with the help of his son-in-law, Peter Schoeffer, the other printer named in this book.

The colophon at the end may be translated from the Latin as follows:

'The present volume of the psalms, adorned with beautiful initial letters and with the proper rubrics in red, has been given this form artificially by means of a contrivance for printing and inscribing without any use of a pen, and laboriously brought to completion for the service of God by Johann Fust, citizen of Mainz, and Peter Schoffer of Gernsheim in the year of our Lord 1457 on the Eve of the Assumption' [i.e. on 14 August].

It is an extremely elaborate book, set in two founts of type, excellently cut and cast, with 292 impressions of initial letters cut in metal and printed in colours. The text was printed in black and red and the big initials in red and blue or grey and printed for the most part at one pull, but here and there by two impressions and some stamping by hand. The inking was remarkably laborious: the red and blue letters were picked out of the forme before each impression and separately inked; in the case of the two-colour initials, the block for the letter was pulled out of the closely fitting block for background ornament, given its colouring, and put back (probably fastened in also) before each copy was printed. Many changes were made in the formes during the run, so that no two of the surviving ten copies, all on vellum, are alike.

Some authorities contend that Gutenberg had a hand in the early stages of the printing; but this can be no more than conjecture.

This, the Queen's copy, from the Royal Library at Windsor, has exceptionally big margins and is very clean. It has corrections skilfully made by hand at a time not much later than the printing.

Colour reproduction between pp. 16–17.

The Bible in the Vernacular

135 Bible, in German. *[Johann Mentelin, Strassburg, before 27 June 1466]*

The first Bible to be printed in any vernacular language, this was the first of not fewer than fourteen German Bibles which appeared before Luther's New Testament of 1522 (no. 181). The text was based on the Latin Vulgate and the translation is believed to have been largely the work of Andreas (or Stephen) Rüdiger. Bibles in Bohemian, Dutch, French, and Italian were also circulating more or less freely in the fifteenth century.

God's Government on Earth

136 St. Augustine, De civitate Dei. *Conrad Sweynheym & Arnold Pannartz, Subiaco, 12 June 1467*

St. Augustine, Bishop of Hippo, was one of the four great fathers of the Latin Church. While in his *Confessiones* (no. 139) he described the influence of God's action on the individual, in this book theology is shown in relation to the history of mankind and God's action in the world is explained. Written as an apologia answering the pagans who attributed the fall of Rome to the abolition of pagan worship, St. Augustine explains the Christian Church as an organization arising from the declining Roman Empire. The work is our earliest treatise on the philosophy of history, and its influence on political thinking has been considerable.

Roman Law

137 Justinian, Institutiones. *Peter Schoeffer, Mainz, 24 May 1468*

Justinian I (483–565) was responsible for the code of Roman law known as the *Corpus juris civilis* which is the basis of the form, as well as of much of the content, of modern law. It consisted of the *Codex*, the essence of the confused mass of statute law; the *Pandects*, a similar abridgement of juristic opinions; and the *Novellae*, new ordinances made since the *Codex*. Both Justinian and his principal adviser Tribonian brought the passion for rationalization to their task which it demanded. The clarity which they achieved gave the *Codex* its permanent value. The *Institutiones* were the first body of law to be given printed form.

The First Complete Natural History

138 C. Plinius Secundus, Naturalis Historia. *Jenson, Venice 1472*

The *Naturalis Historia* of Pliny the Elder (A.D. 23–79) is more than a natural history: it is an encyclopedia of all the knowledge of the ancient world set out in an orderly fashion. It was the source of much of medieval knowledge—and legend—and the model for such works as the *Speculum majus* of Vincent of Beauvais. The high regard in which it was held in the world of the

Renaissance can be seen by its early appearance in print. The copy shown is one of a few printed on vellum. It has an especially illuminated title-page, the arms of the original donor and historiated capital letters.

The First Great Autobiography

139 St. Augustine. Confessiones. *[Johann Mentelin, Strassburg not after 1470]*

The first great autobiography in which personal confession and revelations are linked with the spirit of Christian piety and devotion. It was written soon after Augustine became Bishop of Hippo in 397, and none of his other writings, apart from the *City of God* (no. 136), has been more universally read or admired. Its strength of thought and confession of weakness have been a constant support to Christians ever since.

The Greatest Latin Epic

140 *[*Publii Vergilii Maronis Opera cum Servii commentariis. *Bernardo Cennini, Florence 1471–2]*

The *Aeneid*, the greatest of Latin epics, written by Virgil (70–19 B.C.) in honour of the Emperor Augustus, describes the fall of Troy and the foundation of Rome. Its place in the mind of man is as firm as it is indefinable, and even in this age of small Latin and less Greek, phrases and lines are known to all who have the slightest knowledge of the past. Of its continuing impact, the fourth-century commentary of Servius, the earliest textual commentary to survive, is evidence; it was frequently printed with the early editions, and is an invaluable aid to interpretation. The edition shown is one of the few books, all of great beauty, printed by the goldsmith Bernardo Cennini who himself cut the punches and cast the type for this book.

The Medieval Standard Encyclopedia

141 Isidore of Seville, Etymologiarum sive Originum libri XX. *Günther Zainer, [Augsburg], 19 November 1472*

For nearly a thousand years the Spanish bishop's encyclopedia (completed in 623) preserved for medieval western Europe the modes of thought and the factual knowledge of the ancient world, of which it is a primary source. More than a thousand manuscripts have survived, and its early appearance in print shows its undiminished appeal down to the seventeenth century. Later encyclopedias, such as the *Catholicon* (printed by Gutenberg, 1460), derived much of their material from Isidore, whose influence can hardly be overrated.

This is the first book to contain a printed map or diagram of the whole world.

The Earliest Technical Illustrations

142 Robertus Valturius, De re militari. *Johannes Nicolai de Verona, Verona 1472*

This is the first book printed with illustrations of a technical or scientific character, and also the first book with woodcuts by a native Italian artist (probably Matteo de Pasti, a pupil of Alberti). The illustrations show the equipment necessary for the military and naval engineer, such as apparatus for assault and defence, cannon, bridges, a battleship, &c. It was the handbook of the military leaders of the Renaissance, and Leonardo da Vinci, when acting as chief engineer to Cesare Borgia, possessed a copy. *Plate 25*

The Imitation of Christ

143 Thomas à Kempis, De imitatione Christi. *Günther Zainer, [Augsburg, before 5 June 1473]*

An expression of the mystical German-Dutch school of the fifteenth century and intended for monks and anchorites, the book has become one of the greatest spiritual forces in the life of Christians of all denominations. Its purpose is to instruct the soul in Christian perfection.

Over 2,000 editions have been published and it has been translated into over fifty languages. First written in 1418, its authorship, having been in dispute for hundreds of years, is now definitely attributed to Thomas à Kempis, a German monk in the Augustinian convent of St. Agnes in Zwolle.

Renaissance Baedeker

144 Mirabilia Urbis Romae. *[Rome c. 1473]*

Conceived on the basis of late classical guides to temples and of medieval prototypes, the *Mirabilia* were intended as a guide for the pilgrims to Rome. Besides information about the churches and their reliquaries, they included an increasing number of descriptions of their art treasures, followed by a guide to ancient Rome. Innumerable editions were published from 1472 onwards, including a block book of 1480, and Italian, English, and German translations. They were the basis for the large series of Italian guide-books to the country's art treasures throughout the seventeenth and eighteenth centuries, until their role was taken over in modern times by the publication of Baedeker (no. 513).

Arabic Medicine

145 AVICENNA, Canon. *Philippus de Lavagua, Milan, 12 February 1473*

Avicenna's *Canon* remained the most important medical textbook in Europe until the end of the seventeenth century, and is still in use in parts of the Arabic world. The book is an encyclopedia of medicine containing virtually the whole of ancient and Muslim knowledge. Like Rhazes, Avenzoar, and other Arabic writers, Avicenna's work transmitted to the West the ideas of Galen, Hippocrates, and Aristotle (no. 165), in some respects superseding them.

The Venerable Bede

146 [BEDE], Historia ecclesiastica gentis Anglorum. *Heinrich Eggestein, Strassburg 1475–8*

The greatest work of the greatest medieval English historian was one of the first historical books to be printed. Before Bede's death in A.D. 735 contemporary and near-contemporary Anglo-Saxon scholars and missionaries such as Boniface, Lullus, and Alcuin had carried manuscripts of his work into Germany. The early Strassburg printers specialized in publications for the laity, and Bede's history was among the books that had an obvious appeal to educated, non-academic readers. Part of the edition may have been destined for export to England.

The Universal Doctor

147 ALBERTUS MAGNUS, De mineralibus. *Petrus Maufer for Antonius de Albricis, [Padua,] 20 September 1476*

Albertus Magnus, who died in 1280, was the most learned scholar of his age, the 'Doctor Universalis' of the Middle Ages. He was active in practically all departments of learning—theological, philosophical, and scientific. His influence in all these directions was immense, for hundreds of years rivalling that of Aristotle (no. 165). His collected works appeared in 1651 in 21 folio volumes and again in Paris in 1890 in 36 volumes edited by the Abbé Borgnet. He wrote on nearly all branches of science, many of his works being the first extensive studies of their subjects. The present book contains his studies of mineralogy and chemistry.

The First Bilingual Dictionary

148 Dizionario Tedesco–Italiano. *Adam von Rottweil, Venice, 12 August 1477*

Venice, the economic metropolis of the Mediterranean, with a large German colony of businessmen, was the predestined place for the publication of the first dictionary of two living languages. It is not a philological work, but the ancestor of modern conversational dictionaries.

The Earliest Medical School

149 *[*Regimen sanitatis Salernitanum. *J. de Paderborn, Louvain, Cologne 1480]*

This popular work on diet and hygiene emanated from the medical school in Salerno which flourished from the ninth to the fourteenth centuries. Salerno was the earliest university in Europe, and medicine was here first treated as a separate science. Greek, Arabic, and Hebrew works were collected and translated into Latin. Written in doggerel Latin verse and addressed to a mythical king of England—thought by some to be Robert of Normandy, the Conqueror's son —this book was memorized by generations of physicians. About 300 editions are thought to have been published including many translations.

The Divine Comedy

150 DANTE ALIGHIERI, La Divina Commedia. *Nicolaus Laurentii Alemannus, Florence, 30 August 1481*

The *Divine Comedy* is one of the few works of which it may truly be said that its influence has no limits. Its writing was a turning-point in the life of Dante (1265–1321) and in the Renaissance of the fourteenth century. It is not only a fascinating summary of the knowledge of its time; it is also the finest expression of the depth and originality of Dante's political thinking; its subtle thought and imaginative power have made it universally read and loved since it was written.

This edition is famous for the remarkable series of engravings by Baldini from drawings made by Botticelli for a manuscript of this work probably commissioned by Lorenzo di' Medici. Only nineteen engravings were made and only two or three were printed with the text. The others were printed separately and pasted in. This copy contains eighteen of them—an unusually high proportion.

An Arabic Interpreter of Aristotle

151 ABDUL-WALID MOHAMMAD AVERROES, Colliget. *Laurentius de Rubeis, Ferrara, 5 October 1482*

Averroes of Cordova, the twelfth-century Arab philosopher and physician, is famous chiefly for his interpretation of Aristotle (no. 165). He attempted to reconcile the Aristotelian view of an eternally changing and self-renewing world with Muslim theology and the orthodox theories of creation. This and his theory of the twofold truth—one for the philosophers and another more literal one for the masses ('teach the people as they can understand')—led to extensive attacks on his works, and their reading was forbidden by the Holy See, although Thomas Aquinas (no. 156) made an effort at a reconciliation. In spite of this, Averroism deeply influenced both Christian and Jewish thought, and he initiated the schoolmen into the knowledge of Aristotle, whose works from the earliest editions of 1472–4 onwards were published with his commentaries. It should be noted that these were translations. The earliest Greek edition was in 1495–8 (no. 165). He is represented here by his chief medical work.

The Elements of Geometry

152 EUCLID, Praeclarissimus liber elementorum Euclidis in artem geometriae. *Erhard Ratdolt, Venice, 25 May 1482*

The oldest scientific textbook in the world—and still in use because of the simplicity of its definitions and theorems. Over 1,000 editions have been published, and its system remained unchallenged until Lobatchewsky's work was published in 1829 (no. 558). This, the first edition, is an outstandingly fine piece of printing, and the care and intelligence with which diagrams are combined with text made it a model for subsequent mathematical books.

The Common Law

153 SIR THOMAS LITTLETON, Tenures. *William de Machlinia, London [1482]*

The first codification of English law of the Middle Ages and the principal authority on English real property until almost our own day. It was based on the method and materials of Bracton (no. 221), but it was the first classic law book written in law French instead of Latin, and was little influenced by Roman law. Much of the common law was derived from it, and it remained the basic law book—particularly in the form of 'Coke upon Littleton' (no. 259) published regularly until the nineteenth century—both in England and America.

Aesop's Fables

154 AESOP, Fabulae. *Francesco del Tuppo, Naples, 13 February 1485*

Aesop (supposedly *c.* 610–*c.* 560 B.C.) is not perhaps the first moral fabulist, but no other has been so often quoted, copied, parodied, or reprinted. At any age since his lifetime, few readers can have been unfamiliar with his tales, and the imitations of La Fontaine and Thurber have given new life to the form and become famous in their own right. This edition is a fine example of the early illustrated book.

The Revival of Classical Architecture

155 LEON BATTISTA ALBERTI, De re aedificatoria. *Nicolaus Laurentii, Florence, 29 December 1485*

Alberti was a true humanist of great learning and a practising architect. His book on architecture was the first original Renaissance treatise on the art. It was partly based on Vitruvius (no. 180) and spread the revival of classical architecture throughout Italy and Europe. Translations were published in French, Italian, and Spanish.

The Sum of the Knowledge of God

156 THOMAS AQUINAS, Summa theologica. *Michael Wenssler, Basel 1485*

Thomas Aquinas (*c.* 1227–74) was the greatest of medieval philosophers and theologians. From Albertus Magnus (no. 147) he learnt the Aristotelian theory of knowledge derived from reason, but to it he added his own concept of the higher knowledge derived from revelation. All his writings develop this quality, but in the *Quaestiones* of the *Summa*, his last and greatest work, the nature, attributes, and relations of God and Man—the sum of all learning—were finally discussed and laid down. His teaching was decreed by Leo XIII to be the basis of Catholic theology; it underlies all subsequent political and social inquiry into the position of man in the state or in the universe. This is the first complete edition.

The Greatest Greek Epic

157 HOMER, Opera. *Bernardus & Nerius Nerlius & Demetrius Damulas, Florence, not before 13 January 1489*

The *Iliad* and the *Odyssey* are the first perfect poetry of the Western world. The legend of the Trojan War and of the return of Odysseus are the common heritage of all; the form, in some cases the words, of the two epics have determined the composition of, to name but a few, the *Aeneid*, *The Divine Comedy*, and *Paradise Lost* (nos. 140, 150). Their popularity is perennial; they have been frequently translated; more than a million copies of a recent version of the *Odyssey* (that by E. V. Rieu for the Penguin classics) have been printed. This, the *editio princeps*, is a magnificent example of early printing in Greek. This first Greek text was preceded by Latin translations.

The Greatest Humanist

158 Angelo Ambrogini Poliziano, Miscellaneorum centuria prima. *Antonio Bartolommeo Miscomini, Florence, 19 September 1489*

Politian in his short life (1454–94) saw the movement of humanistic scholarship reach its climax; in him, through his friendship with Lorenzo the Magnificent, it found its finest form. This *Miscellany* consists of translations and fragments of the classics in which his penetration and understanding of them may be seen. It is characteristic that he should have attempted a Latin version of the *Iliad*, which earned him the title of *Homericus juvenis*. His poems gave new impetus to the use of the vernacular and may be considered the real beginning of modern Italian literature.

The 'Bible' of Classical Medicine

159 Galen, Opera. *Philippus Pincius, Venice 1490*

Galen was the greatest physician of antiquity after Hippocrates (no. 185) and the number of his writings covering the whole field of medicine is vast. For 1,500 years his authority was unassailable: every medical question was automatically referred to his works from which there was no appeal. Though a careful observer his mania for teleology and the deductive method spoiled much of his work and retarded in many ways the progress of medicine in more modern times. The first really effective break with Galenic tradition was made by Paracelsus (no. 241), but Galen's influence remained incalculable until the end of the seventeenth century.

The Theory of Music

160 Boethius, Opera. *Johannes & Gregorius de Gregoriis, Venice 1492 [1491]*

This includes the first printing of his treatise *De institutione musica*, the first work on musical theory in the Christian West. His contention that music must have not only a scientific but also an ethical basis affected all medieval musical theory.

The Ideal Universe

161 Plato, Opera. *Bernardo de Choris de Cremona & Simone de Luere for Andreas Torresanus, Venice, 13 August 1491*

That Plato (428–347 B.C.) should be the first of all the ancient philosophers to be translated and broadcast by the printing-press was inevitable. Plato's central conception of a universe of ideas, Perfect Types, of which material objects are imperfect forms, and his ethical code based on action according to human nature, developed by education, which represents the authority of the State, fitted in as well with the religious and constitutional ideas of 15th-century Italy as it did with those of the Byzantine Greeks, by whom Plato was reintroduced to the Western world. It is fitting that the first translator and commentator was the Florentine Marsilio Ficino (1433–99), one of the central figures in the humanistic movement. This, the second edition, was a best-seller.

The Discovery of America

162 Christopher Columbus, Epistola Christofori Columbi . . . de Insulis Indie supra Gangem nuper inventis . . . *Stephen Planck, Rome, [after 29 April 1493]*

The modern age begins with the discovery of America, which enormously expanded the known world and encouraged exploration, colonization, navigation, the knowledge of a new flora and fauna, and of meteorology, quite apart from its political and economic consequences. The voyage was prepared with great scientific method, and during it the variation of the compass needle was first observed.

Columbus's dispatch to his patrons, King Ferdinand and Queen Isabella of Spain, was first written in Spanish and printed in Barcelona in April 1493, but only one copy of that edition survives. Five other editions of his report, one in Spanish and four in Latin, were published in the same year. It is ironic that the continent was eventually named after Amerigo Vespucci, who had travelled to South America in 1499 and 1501. Waldseemüller, in his *Cosmographiae introductio*, St. Die [1501], named part of South America after him, and in 1538 the name America was applied to the whole continent by Mercator (no. 234) (*see also* no. 237).

The Ship of Fools

163 Sebastian Brant, Stultifera navis. *Johann Bergmann, Basel, 1 August 1494*

In this satire Brant, under the form of an allegory—a ship laden with fools and steered by fools to the fools' paradise of Narragonia—vehemently criticizes the weaknesses and vices of his time. The book achieved immense popularity and influence throughout Europe. Although essentially conservative Brant was aware of abuses in the Church, and his book helped effectively to prepare for the Protestant reformation. It has inspired many imitators and has been very frequently reprinted. The woodcuts illustrating the book greatly helped its popularity.

Dissection First Illustrated

164 JOHANNES DE KETHAM, Fasciculus medicinae. *Johannes & Gregorius de Gregoriis, Venice 1495*

A collection of important medical texts, some of which had already been in use for centuries and were to remain influential for a long time; among them is the *Anatomy* of Mundinus, composed about 1300, which is the first modern treatise on the subject. Other sections are on surgery, pregnancy, uroscopy, epidemiology, &c. This is also the first medical text illustrated with realistic figures. The woodcuts are of the school of Bellini and have been attributed to the Polifilo Master. Among them is the first printed representation of a dissection scene.

The Master of Those Who Know

165 ARISTOTLE, Opera omnia. *Aldus, Venice 1495–8*

Aristotle (384–322 B.C.) is not only one of the greatest classical philosophers, the master of every branch of ancient knowledge: his method still underlies all modern thinking, and has spread outside the bounds of Western civilization. To him all things are substances, unlike the Platonic ideas (no. 161), and the universe consists of substances and the relations between them. Aldus's great edition of all Aristotle's work was, predictably, the first major Greek prose text to be reintroduced to the Western world by the invention of the printing-press.

The Far East made known to the West

166 MARCO POLO, Delle maravigliose cose del mondo. *J. B. Sessa, Venice, 13 June 1496*

Dictated in prison at Genoa in 1298–9, this account of Asia and eastern Africa became by far the most important travel book of the Middle Ages. Travelling overland from Acre in 1271, Marco Polo stayed in China with Kublai Khan until 1295. Taking part in the administration of the country, he had unique opportunities enabling him to give this earliest first-hand account of the Far East, eastern Africa, Siberia, and some Arctic regions. The first practical charts—the Portolani—and the Catalan Atlas of 1375 are based on his work, and his influence on the geographical conceptions of the age of discovery is incalculable.

The Universe of Ptolemy

167 JOHANNES MÜLLER REGIOMONTANUS, Epitoma in almagestum Ptolemaei. *Johannes Hammann, Venice 1496*

This work contains the first printed edition of Ptolemy's *Almagest* which is the consummation of Greek astronomy. It establishes the geocentric system of astronomy which Hipparchus and Ptolemy had worked out and which remained the basis of all astronomy from ancient times until Copernicus (no. 201). Peuerbach, Regiomontanus's teacher, began this translation of an abbreviated *Almagest*, and after his death it was completed by Regiomontanus, thereby reintroducing Greek astronomy into the modern world. Regiomontanus also did important work in mathematics, established the first observatory in Europe, at Nüremberg, and set up his own printing-press. The first complete edition of the *Almagest* appeared in Venice in 1515.

Modern Surgery born in the Middle Ages

168 GUY DE CHAULIAC, Chirurgia. *Bonetus Locatellus for Octavius Scotus, Venice, 21 November 1498*

Written in the fourteenth century, this work began the development of modern surgical techniques and was the standard surgical textbook in Europe for several hundred years. The descriptions of early surgical procedure were of great importance. He explained a system of narcotic and soporific inhalation; he was one of the first to operate for hernia and cataract, and cut out cancer with the knife at an early stage.

The Beginning of Medical Botany

169 DIOSCORIDES, De materia medica. *Aldus, Venice 1499*

This was the first authoritative work of antiquity on the *Materia medica*, and Dioscorides was the first to write on medical botany as an applied science. It remained the standard work until the eighteenth century—though modified by many commentators—and of the 600 plants it describes with their medical properties, 90 are still in use today. In his classification of plants he recognized natural families before Bauhin and Linné (nos. 254, 336), and his book also contains important material on early chemistry.

The Father of History

170 HERODOTUS, Historiae. *Aldus, Venice 1502*

Herodotus (484–?424 B.C.) is the first historian; his predecessors were by contrast chroniclers. He was the first to collect his materials systematically, to test their accuracy as far as he could, and arrange his story in such a way as to appeal to, as well as inform, his readers. The struggle between Persia and Greece, which is his main theme, is the stuff of legend, quoted and translated over and over again by ancient and modern writers. This is the first edition, one of the series of Greek and Latin classics which owed their first appearance to the Venetian printer Aldus.

The Route to the Indies

171 FRANCAN DA MONTALBODDO, Paesi novamente retrovati. *Henricus Vicentinus, Vicenza 1507*

Apart from the *Libretto*, 1504, this is the earliest collection of voyages. It contains reports of the voyages of Vasco da Gama, Pedro Cabal, and Ca da Mosto, all concerning the circumnavigation of Africa and the route to the Indies, also the first three voyages of Columbus (no. 162), the third voyage of Vespucci, and others. Published in numerous editions this book more than any other made Renaissance Europe familiar with the great discoveries and voyages—both East and West—and has remained one of our chief sources of knowledge for their history.

Satire on Tyranny

172 DESIDERIUS ERASMUS, Moriae encomium. *Paris 1511[1512]*

The Praise of Folly was written during Erasmus's stay in England in the house of Thomas More (no. 175). It is a brilliant, biting satire on the folly to be found in all walks of life. Neither kings nor princes, popes nor bishops are spared, and it is a constant wonder that in that age of authority he remained unscathed. Whenever the threat of tyranny was in the air, Erasmus's work was read; Milton found it 'in every hand' at Cambridge in 1628. It is still read today.

Renaissance Chemistry

173 HIERONYMUS BRUNSCHWIG, Das Buch der Kunst zu distilliren. *Strassburg 1512*

The most important early work on chemistry and pharmacology, which greatly influenced other writings on the subject for 300 years. It explains the processes of distilling and the composition of remedies for a large number of diseases. The book marks a considerable advance over medieval pharmacology by separating medical remedies from inessential matter. It is famous also for its beautiful illustrations of chemical apparatus and medicinal plants.

The Last of the Medievals, the First of the Moderns

174 NICOLAUS DE CUSA, Opera. *Badius Ascensius, Paris 1514*

Though a good medieval Catholic, Nicolaus de Cusa's philosophy marks the beginning of modern philosophical and scientific thought. He influenced Giordano Bruno, Spinoza, Leibniz and Hegel (nos. 287, 324, 458). Opposed to scholasticism and the excessive veneration of Aristotle (no. 165), his philosophy is characterized by an optimistic enthusiasm for knowledge: human wisdom consists in recognizing one's ignorance. With this scepticism he combined the practical spirit of scientific investigation based on mathematics and observations. He recommended a reform of the calendar; recognized that the earth rotates on its axis and propounded a limitless universe.

Utopia

175 THOMAS MORE, Utopia. *Louvain [1516]*

More's *Utopia*, his most famous literary work, which was intended, like *Gulliver's Travels*, to be a satire on contemporary states, has become a symbol of the ideal state. This is an irony that he would have enjoyed. The book is, in fact, a satire by contrast, but the passages in which the Utopian toleration was contrasted with the authoritarian states which More knew became so famous that they dwarfed the original theme. The plea for universal education (which undoubtedly expressed More's real wish) has also had great influence, and the communistic form of government enjoyed by the Utopians made Marx (no. 547) acclaim the work as one of the forerunners of his own system. 'Utopia' added a word to every European language.

The New Testament in the original Greek

176 NEW TESTAMENT, Greek and Latin. Edited by Desiderius Erasmus. *Johann Froben, Basel 1516.*

The first attempt to produce a scientifically correct text of the Greek New Testament to be published, although the New Testament in the Complutensian Polyglot (no. 182) had been printed two years earlier. The text was not a very good one as the materials at Erasmus's disposal were defective, but its success among Biblical scholars was immediate and it formed the basis of the translations of both Luther (no. 181) and Tyndale (no. 187).

Plutarch's 'Lives'

177 PLUTARCH, Vitae Romanorum et Graecorum . . . *Philip Giunta, Florence, August 1517*

Plutarch, born about the beginning of the first century B.C., lived when the ancient world was passing through its major climacteric. The vicissitudes of the great suggested his peculiar moralistic method of comparing similar lives, a method which gave his work a scope greater than that of a collection of biographical facts. Early translated, by Amyot in France and North in England, its influence has constantly been manifest in the lives of the modern great and in the authors who have been inspired by them.

Shakespeare (no. 255) relied almost exclusively on Plutarch for the historical background of ancient Rome.

The Reformation is Established

178 MARTIN LUTHER, An den christlichen Adel deutscher Nation; von des Christlichen Standes Besserung. *Melchior Lotter, Wittenberg [1520]*

One of the three great tracts which constitute the manifesto of the Reformation. This is Luther's appeal addressed to the Emperor and the rulers of the Holy Roman Empire. Anti-clerical propaganda is combined with an anti-Roman political movement. The book attacks the doctrine of the supremacy of the spiritual power over the worldly one (the theory of the two swords); in fact the book calls for the renunciation of the temporal power of the Pope and indicates numerous reforms which Luther maintains should be carried out. The propaganda value of this tract was enormous, 4,000 copies were sold within a few days and seventeen further editions were published in the sixteenth century.

'Defender of the Faith'

179 HENRY VIII, Assertio septem sacramentorum. *Richard Pynson, London 1521*

This book, which earned for the English Crown the title *Fidei defensor*, had one of the most fateful impacts upon Western civilization of any printed book. For had not Henry, in answering Luther (no. 178), made so absolute an admission of Papal authority—despite the advice of Thomas More (no. 175), it is unlikely that he would have felt so personally slighted by the Pope's refusal in his 'great matter', and then—but there speculation must stop. Suffice it to say, that the *Assertio* must be considered a cardinal, if not a motive, force in the history of the English Reformation.

The Survival of Classical Architecture

180 VITRUVIUS, De architectura. *Como 1521*

This handbook of classical architecture is the oldest original work on art to survive in its entirety from late classical times. It transmitted the rules of classical architecture and aesthetics and of civil and military engineering to the Middle Ages and the Renaissance and became the basis for the work of Alberti (no. 155), Bramante, Michelangelo, Ghiberti, Palladio (no. 224), Vignola, and others. First published in Rome in 1486, this is the first Italian translation by Cesare Cesariano, a pupil of Bramante. The beautiful illustrations are now attributed in part to Leonardo da Vinci.

Plate 26

The Reformation Bible

181 NEW TESTAMENT, German. Translated by Martin Luther. *[Melchior Lotter], Wittenberg [1522]*

Luther's translation of the New Testament into German was based mainly on the Greek text of Erasmus (no. 176) and was accompanied by introductions and some marginal comments in which many of the ideas of the Reformers were expressed. It greatly influenced the translations of the Bible made by other Reformers, including Tyndale (no. 187) and has remained the standard German reformed Bible to this day. The literate German language of our day derives from the Middle German dialect used here by Luther.

The First of the Polyglot Bibles

182 BIBLE, Polyglot. 5 volumes. *Arnald Guillen de Brocar, Alcalá de Henares 1522*

The so-called 'Complutensian Polyglot' was the first of the great multi-lingual Bibles of the sixteenth and seventeenth centuries and was edited by a party of scholars headed by the learned Stunica at the University of Alcalá (Complutum) at the instigation of Cardinal Ximenes. The text of the Old Testament is given in Hebrew, Aramaic, Greek, and Latin. Printed between the years 1514 and 1517, it was not published until 1522.

Renaissance Reflections

183 DESIDERIUS ERASMUS, Colloquia. *Basel 1524*

If a single figure had to be chosen to typify the spirit of the Renaissance, there are few who would deny the claim of Erasmus (1466–1536). The *Colloquies*, more than any other work except perhaps his *Letters*, are the basis of this opinion.

They are a series of dialogues, first written for pupils in his early days at Paris as formulas for polite address, but later expanded into conversations in which all the major topics of the day were discussed with a freedom which ensured their popularity. For long afterwards they were read in schools, and there are lines in Shakespeare (no. 255) which directly recall Erasmus's words. He has been called the father of eighteenth-century rationalism, but his rationalist attitude is that of perfect common sense, to which tyranny and fanaticism were alike abhorrent.

The Science of Perspective

184 ALBRECHT DÜRER, Vnderweysung der Messung. *Nuremberg 1525*

The object of this book, intended for painters, sculptors, goldsmiths, stonemasons, and others, was to explain the theoretical and practical problems of perspective. Dürer had already partly solved some of these in his paintings, notably the 'Martyrdom of the 10,000 Christians' of 1508, which is cited in the second edition of the first printed book on the subject, Jean Pelerin's *De artificiali perspectiva*, Nuremberg, 1509. Dürer had studied Euclid (no. 152), Piero della Francesca, and probably Uccello and Alberti (no. 155) on the subject, and he illustrated the mathematical explanations in his book with woodcuts showing the instruments he invented to transfer the perspective image to paper. By this means Dürer introduced methods of geometrically correct drawing to the countries north of Alps, which remained a principle of artistic representation until new art forms began in the nineteenth century.

The Father of Medicine

185 HIPPOCRATES, [Operum] Octaginta volumina. *Franciscus Minitius Calvus, Rome 1525*

The first complete Latin edition of the works of one of the greatest clinical physicians of all time. Hippocrates freed medicine from superstition and the influence of the priestcraft and based his system of medicine on the accumulated empirical knowledge of Egypt, Cnidos, and Cos. The 'Hippocratic oath' has remained until today the most valid expression of the duties and ethics of the medical profession. He created diagnostic medicine—Laennec (no. 455) admits that his idea was suggested to him by Hippocrates—and many of the famous *Aphorisms* have passed as proverbs into our everyday life.

First Voyage Round the World

186 FRANCISCO ANTONIO PIGAFETTA, Le Voyage et navigation fait par les Espagnols aux isles de Molluques. *Paris 1525*

Magellan conceived the idea of reaching the Orient by finding a passage round South America. He accomplished the first voyage round the world from 1519 to 1521, proving that the East Indies could be reached via the Pacific. Magellan died on the journey and Pigafetta, who had accompanied him, wrote this account which has remained the most authoritative.

Tyndale's New Testament

187 NEW TESTAMENT. Translated by William Tyndale. *[Peter Schoeffer, Worms 1525 or 1526]*

From the days of Wyclif in the fourteenth century the dissemination of the Scriptures in English had been frowned on by the ecclesiastical authorities, and Tyndale had to take refuge in Germany in 1524 to complete his translation of the New Testament, the first to be printed in the English language. A number of editions of this, as well as his translation of the Pentateuch, were printed in Germany and Antwerp before Tyndale's martyrdom in 1536. Only one other fragment of this first published edition is known to survive, most of the copies of all editions of his translations having been burned as heretical. This copy is extensively illuminated.

Manifesto of the Reformation

188 ULRICH ZWINGLI, Commentarius de vera et falsa religione. *Froschauer, Zürich 1527*

This Swiss humanist became one of the leaders of the Reformation. In many ways he was more radical than Luther (no. 178), with whom he had a famous quarrel on the nature of communion, rejecting the theory of the Real Presence. He also disagreed with Calvin's doctrine of original sin as punishable guilt; he regarded it as simply a moral defect. His desire was to go back to the principles of primitive Christianity, to abolish the Mass and images in the Church, to reform government as well as the Church, and to 'preach the Gospel'. In importance and influence his book ranks with that of Calvin (no. 194).

The Perfect Gentleman

189 BALDASSARE CONTE DI CASTIGLIONE, Il Cortegiano. *Aldus, Venice 1528*

Based on the author's reminiscences of his stay as a member of the Court of Urbino, this book gives a picture of the ideal courtier, prince, and enlightened ruler. The highest moral aspirations of the Renaissance are expressed and the rules for courtly behaviour have remained until today those governing the conduct of a gentleman. It is indeed the prototype of the genus 'courtesy book'.

In 1561 Sir Thomas Hoby published an English translation which was one of the most popular books of the Elizabethan age; and the book was translated into most other European languages.

Scholarship in France

190 GUILLAUME BUDÉ, Commentarii Linguae Graecae. *Paris 1529*

Budé (1467–1540) was the most influential of the French humanistic scholars at the beginning of the sixteenth century. The Collège de France and the Bibliothèque Nationale both owe their origins to him; he also pursuaded Francis I not to enforce the interdiction on printing suggested by the Sorbonne in 1533. This *Commentary* had a notable influence in spreading the study of Greek. It is a monument of the new learning.

Education for Government

191 THOMAS ELYOT, The Boke named the Governour. *Thomas Berthelet, London 1531*

The *Governour* is at once the first book in modern English prose, an influential advocacy of the study of the classics, and a treatise on education and politics which was immensely popular throughout the sixteenth century. It inculcates the moral principles which alone fit those in authority for the performance of their duties. While there was nothing very revolutionary in its thought, it remained the textbook for behaviour for generations and had a lasting effect on the writing of English.

Scientific Lexicography

192 ROBERT ESTIENNE, Dictionarius sive Latinae linguae thesaurus. *Robert Estienne, Paris 1531*

Robert is the greatest member of the greatest family of scholar-printers of all ages. Among his many claims to immortality, that based on the *Thesaurus* is perhaps the most secure. Contrary to his medieval predecessors, Estienne established the principle that a Latin dictionary must be based on classical authorities—he himself used the vocabulary of some thirty authors; he relied for grammatical points on Budé (no. 190). The *Thesaurus* has not yet been superseded.

Machiavellianism

193 NICCOLO MACHIAVELLI, Il Principe. *Antonio Blado, Rome 1532*

The Prince of Machiavelli (1469–1527) is the perfect statement of the ruler's task in the sixteenth century. The lack of scruple which is traditionally associated with it is but one side of a work in which for the first time the practical is paramount to the theoretical. Directed to the unification of Italy, the main theme is that with such a goal in view, all means to attain it are possible and legitimate. It is the work of a great political thinker with an equally clear insight into the facts. Immensely popular in its own time, it influenced the politicians of the European Renaissance, and its influence continues to this day.

Calvinism

194 JOHANNES CALVIN, Christianiae religionis institutio. *Basel 1536*

This was the first published systematic statement of the fundamental doctrine of the Reformed Church. The cardinal points are the absolute sovereignty of God, the theory of predestination, and the strong awareness of original sin in all mankind with the resultant feeling of guilt. Calvin's view that the king's power derives from the people, and the people are justified in overthrowing a ruler who defies God, contributed to the rise of democracy. He influenced Presbyterianism, penetrated many sects of the Reformed Church, and is still very influential in Scotland, England, America, and some parts of the continent of Europe.

The book was somewhat revised in the 1559 edition, but essentially it has remained unchanged, and has been published in innumerable editions and translations.

Cicero and Latinity

195 PIETRO VETTORI (Petrus Victorius). Castigationes in Ciceronem. *Venice 1536–7*

Throughout the hundreds of years when Latin was the *lingua franca* of thought and communication, the works of Cicero (106–43 B.C.) were the universal model for style. Thus, as well as giving the most vivid of all pictures of ancient Rome, Cicero's speeches and letters have had more influence, if indirectly, on the means of expression than any other writer. When Latin was superseded by the vernacular tongues, this influence was transmuted into the new languages. Pietro Vettori, or as he is better known, Victorius (1499–1585) was the foremost Latin scholar of his day in

Italy. His edition and commentary on the *Letters* fully revealed this; the feeling for meaning and style, and the sureness of his emendations opened a new era in textual criticism.

The Course of Projectiles Defined

196 NICCOLO TARTAGLIA, Nova scientia. *Venice 1537*

Gunnery and surveying were Tartaglia's special subjects. He applied mathematical laws of the free motion of projectiles to the flight of cannon-balls and mortar-bombs. He proved that the trajectory of a cannon-ball was not straight—as hitherto believed—but a continuous curve, and determined its maximum range to be at the gun's elevation of 45°. His important mathematical discoveries were communicated by him to Cardanus, who published them in his famous *Artis magnae sive de regulis algebraicis liber unus*, 1545. Tartaglia also claimed the invention of the gunner's quadrant.

The First Practical Dictionary

197 ROBERT ESTIENNE, Dictionarium latino-gallicum. *Robert Estienne, Paris 1538*

Inspired by the success of his Latin *Thesaurus* (no. 192), Robert Estienne undertook the compilation of a series of Latin–French and French–Latin dictionaries including a *Dictionariolum* for schoolboys. These dictionaries helped to create the classical French language (eventually fossilized in *Dictionnaire de l'Académie*, 1694), were translated into German (1568), Dutch (by Plantin, 1573), and English (1552 and 1565), and were the progenitors of all bilingual dictionaries.

Lily's Grammar

198 WILLIAM LILY, Institutio compendiaria totius grammaticae. *T. Berthelet, London 1540*

William Lily (*c.* 1468–1522) is famous as the first High Master of Colet's new school of St. Paul's. 'Lily's Grammar', of which this is the first complete edition, was the standard Latin Grammar used by St. Paul's, Eton, and other schools until well into the nineteenth century. The original *Brevissima Institutio* was sketched by Colet, amended by Erasmus, and completed by Lily, who wrote the sections on the gender of nouns and the conjugation of verbs which have been the foundation of all subsequent grammars. This edition is thought to have been produced for the young Prince Edward, and is commonly known as 'King Edward's Grammar'. This copy was printed on vellum especially for him.

The First Treatises on Physiology and Pathology

199 JEAN FERNEL, De naturali parte medicinae. *Adam Saulnier for Simon de Colines, Paris 1542*

Fernel was one of the most influential representatives of the new humanist school in medicine and insisted on personal observation and experiment. The above is the first part of his great work, completed in his *Medicina*, 1554. These two parts contain the first explicit treatises on pathology and physiology and gave both these subjects their names in their present-day meaning. The *Universa medicina*, 1567, contains the first description of appendicitis. His books were published in numerous editions, and in our own day he inspired Sir Charles Sherrington, the greatest modern neurologist (no. 585), who wrote a brilliant monograph on his work.

A Famous Classic Herbal

200 LEONHARD FUCHS, De historia stirpium commentarii. *Officina Isingriniana, Basel 1542*

This most celebrated herbal contains about 400 German and 100 foreign plants illustrated by 512 superb woodcuts. Many new plants, especially those from America, are here described for the first time, and there is the first vocabulary of botanical terms. The fuchsia is named after him. Many editions were published and it long remained the pattern for herbals. *Plate 25*

The Heliocentric Universe

201 NICOLAUS COPERNICUS. De revolutionibus orbium coelestium. *Johannes Petreius, Nuremburg 1543*

Copernicus, Newton (no. 295), and Darwin (no. 530) produced three fundamental works that destroyed the anthropocentric view of the universe. Copernicus made the first step by propounding the theory of the planetary orbits. His mathematical proof of this made his conclusion inescapable.

Modern Anatomy begins

202 ANDREAS VESALIUS, De humani corporis fabrica. *Oporinus, Basel 1543*

In this most important book in the history of medicine since Galen, Vesalius broke with the traditional authority of Aristotle and Galen (nos. 165, 159). Dissection gave him an accurate knowledge of the human body, its structure, and functions. Illustrated with wonderful illustrations by Calcar, the book started a revolution by its insistence on independent observations in anatomy and clinical medicine. It prepared the way for Harvey's discoveries in physiology (no. 260).

'Give me a place to stand, and I will move the earth'

203 ARCHIMEDES, Opera. *Hervagius, Basel 1544*

Archimedes was the greatest mathematician, physicist, and engineer of antiquity. Some of his most enduring work was done in geometry, but he also laid the foundations of theoretical mechanics and demonstrated the principles of hydrostatics ('principle of Archimedes'). He found the laws determining the centres of gravity, floating bodies, and specific gravity. Many machines were constructed by him; the compound pulley, ship-launching mechanism, the screw for raising water (now known by his name), burning mirrors, an orrery, &c. His book also includes for the first time the description of the heliocentric system of Aristarchus, who had conceived this centuries before Copernicus (no. 201) but this discovery was quite unknown to him.

The First Modern Book about Books

204 CONRAD GESNER, Bibliotheca universalis. *Zürich 1545*

This is the first of the bibliographies of which Gesner published a series. These were the earliest systematic 'books about books', although preceded to some extent by Tritheim's *De Scriptoribus*, Basel, 1494, and are the beginning of all modern bibliography. This is the *Author* bibliography. The authors are arranged under their Christian names, the list of their books is given together with the various printed editions, as well as critical notes. In 1548–9 there followed the *Subject* index in twenty volumes each of which was dedicated to a contemporary printer, a list of whose productions is added.

The Inspiration of the Society of Jesus

205 IGNATIUS LOYOLA, Exercitia spiritualia. *Antonio Blado, Rome 1548*

The most famous of modern textbooks on the nature of sin and its consequences. St. Ignatius's manual of ascetic discipline is informed by a remarkable fixity of purpose. He created a dynamic system designed to enable the human soul to conquer inordinate passion and reach perfection by Grace. The exercises are spread over four consecutive weeks. Their essential characteristic and novelty lie in the importance attached to the hygiene of the will, its healthy activation and effective formulation, without neglecting stimulation of the imagination. The *Exercises* became the handbook of the Society of Jesus, the militant religious order which St. Ignatius founded, and has exerted a uniquely powerful influence outside the Society.

The English Liturgy

206 THE BOOKE OF THE COMMON PRAYER. *Edward Whitchurch, London, 6 June 1549*

The English *Book of Common Prayer* was the first single manual of worship in a vernacular language directed to be used universally by, and common to, both priest and people. It has been substantially altered since this, the first prayer book of Edward VI, but its form has remained the same, and it has been a source of spiritual inspiration in England second only to the Bible.

The Science of Navigation

207 MARTIN CORTES, Breve Compendio de la sphera y de l'arte de navegar. *Anton Alvarez, Seville 1551*

The most complete statement of navigational science that had thus far appeared. It contains splendid descriptions of the making of navigational instruments, particularly the cross-staff and astrolabe—to which Bourne in 1576 (inspired by Cortes to write his *Regiment of the Sea*, the first English treatise on navigation) added instructions for their use. Cortes gave instructions for making charts and for plotting the courses of ships on them; most important of all, he first understood and described the magnetic variation of the compass, suggesting that the magnetic pole and the true pole of the earth were not the same.

Medina's similar but less correct work of 1545 was widely used in France and Italy, but Stephen Borough, the man behind Queen Elizabeth's measures to advance Britain's maritime power, brought Cortes's book back from Seville and persuaded the Muscovy Company to have it translated into English. This was published in 1561 and reached its eighth edition in 1615. It was one of the most decisive books printed in the English language, as it supplied to the British navigators their key to the mastery of the sea, which remained in English hands for centuries.

Modern Zoology Begins

208 CONRAD GESNER, Historia animalium. *Zürich 1551–87*

The starting-point of modern zoology, this great compilation gives an account of all animals then known; their names are given in ancient and modern languages; detailed biological as well as literary information is supplied. The splendid illustrations, some by Gesner himself, are the earliest attempt at the representation of animals from nature, and many are astonishing for the realism of their delineation. This work remained authoritative until John Ray published his classification of fauna in 1693.

Unitarian and Martyr

209 MICHAEL SERVETUS, Christianissimi restitutio. *[Vienne 1553]*

Servetus had aroused the opposition of both Papists and Protestants by his statement of the Unitarian doctrine. Following Cellarius, *De operibus Dei*, 1527, he rejected the orthodox and generally accepted theory of the Trinity; he believed in the essentially intellectual recognition of sin and disapproved of infant baptism. He was a forerunner of modern Biblical criticism and one of the founders of comparative geography. The present book includes his description of the lesser circulation of the blood through the lungs, first observed by him. He had also probably at least an inkling of the greater circulation long before Harvey (no. 260). He died a martyr's death in Geneva in 1553. Calvin (cf. no. 194) wanted him beheaded but he was burned. Servetus's books were burned with him and are therefore among the rarest in the world. There are good reasons for believing that the copy shown belonged to Calvin.

Pioneer of Modern Geology

210 GEORGIUS AGRICOLA, De re metallica. *Isingrinius, Basel 1556*

Agricola's most widely known work, this is the first systematic treatise on metallurgy and mining and is one of the first technological books of modern times. Many chemical processes, such as the preparation of saltpetre and nitric acid, are here explained for the first time. There are sections on glassmaking, the magnet, the divining rod, surveying, and the first picture of a railway (for trucks of ore on wooden rails). It is illustrated with fine woodcuts, by Hans Rudolf Manuel Deutsch, and remained a standard work for a very long time with great influence on the development of metallurgy, chemistry, geology, and the technology of mining. The book was translated into English in 1912 by Herbert Hoover, afterwards President of the United States.

The English Epic

210a. THOMAS MALORY, The Story of the most noble and worthy Kynge Arthur newly imprynted. *W. Copland [1557]*

The *Morte d'Arthur* is the most famous version and the first in English prose of all the legends which have collected about King Arthur. It is the only true English epic; its matter is 'the Matter of England'. The matchless style of the first English prose version, the humour, magnificence, the magic that takes away the breath, combine in a story which is known to all. Each century has produced its own version, but Malory's will never be forgotten.

The first edition was printed by Caxton in 1485, but of that printing only one perfect copy and a fragment have survived, and neither was available to us.

Onslaught on Female Monarchy

211 JOHN KNOX, The First Blast of the Trumpet against the Monstrous Regiment of Women. *J. Crespin, Geneva 1558*

The argument is that government by a woman is contrary to the natural law and to divine ordinance. While Knox wrote against Mary Queen of Scots his argument, expressed in characteristically violent terms, was felt to apply to both Mary and Elizabeth, successive queens of England. The *First Blast* was disowned by Calvin who felt obliged to respect Elizabeth's strong objection to being ranked with Roman Catholic queens as an 'idol and an idolatrous idol'. But his book, and its author, found a welcome in his native land among those with whom Knox later organized the Scottish Reformation.

Censorship of Books

212 Index librorum prohibitorum. *Antonio Blado, Rome 1559*

The *Index* is the classic example of censorship. From late Roman times onwards there had been censorship of books considered to be dangerous to religion and morals, but its real influence was not widely felt until the invention of printing. Bishops, universities, and inquisitions soon began to circulate lists of prohibited books, but censorship was not made really effective until Rome took a hand with the publication of this list of books prohibited to Christians of the Roman Catholic faith. In 1558 the Congregation for the *Index* was created and is still responsible for its publication.

The Geneva Bible

213 THE BIBLE AND HOLY SCRIPTURE, [Translated by William Whittingham, Anthony Gilby, Thomas Sampson and possibly others]. *Rouland Hall, Geneva 1560*

This version of the English Bible produced in Geneva by the Marian exiles was never sanctioned by the Archbishop of Canterbury, and the so-called 'Bishops' Bible' of 1568 was the version used in churches in Elizabethan times. But after Archbishop Matthew Parker's death in 1575 the Geneva version was openly printed in London and this—the so-called 'Breeches Bible'—remained the Englishman's private Bible until Cromwellian times. The General Assembly of the Scots Kirk adopted the Geneva Bible (1579) as its official version.

It was the first English Bible printed in roman type and therefore had a powerful influence in conditioning the English reading public to roman face. It was the first printed English text with division into verses.

'Gresham's Law'

214 By the Quene. [A Proclamation for the valuation of testons. *London, 27 September 1560*]

In 1558, shortly after the accession of Queen Elizabeth I, Gresham wrote to her on the evils of a debased coinage. This proclamation, with measures for currency reform, was the sequel. 'Gresham's Law'—'bad currency drives out good'—is a recognized principle in economics.

The First History of Europe

215 FRANCESCO GUICCIARDINI, Dell'istoria d'Italia libri xii. *Torrentino, Florence 1561*

Guicciardini, a Florentine and papal diplomatist and friend of Macchiavelli (no. 193), wrote his book after he was dismissed in 1527 because the Curia wrongly held him responsible for the sack of Rome by the Spaniards and Germans. Guicciardini is the first 'universal historian', as he sees the history of Italy in the larger context of the European system of States, with sound political instinct and devoid of ecclesiastical bias.

The Theory of Modern Music

216 GIOSEFFO ZARLINO, Istitutioni armoniche. *Venice 1562*

Zarlino (1517–90) enjoyed a long and successful career as a composer, but his compositions have largely disappeared. However, his principal theoretical work, the *Istitutioni*, remains and it is a crucial work in the transformation of music which took place in the seventeenth century. Ancient and medieval musical theory and (at least until the invention of counterpoint) practice had been based on the Pythagorean mathematical proportion of the tetrachord. Zarlino uncompromisingly rejected the mathematical analogy, and claimed that the now universally used diatonic scale was the only form that could reasonably be sung. On this theory all subsequent music theory has been based, and even the mechanically tuned, keyed, and fretted instruments have been adjusted to the octave of twelve semitones which Zarlino first put forward.

Foxe's Book of Martyrs

217 JOHN FOXE, Acts and Monuments of these Latter Perilous Times touching Matters of the Church. *Day, London 1563*

Foxe's *Book of Martyrs* was for more than two centuries one of the most widely read books in England. Foxe was an exile for religion 1554–9 (he was employed as a reader by the Basel printer Oporinus), and it was then that his famous work was written. It is a history of the Christian Church from the earliest times, and of the Christian martyrs of all ages, more particularly the Protestant martyrs of Mary's reign. Written in a simple homely style, with lively dialogues between the persecutors and their victims and with gruesome illustrations, it was well calculated to appeal to ordinary unlearned people for whom it was for long their only secular reading.

Epicureanism and Scholarship

218 LUCRETIUS, De rerum natura. Edited by Denis Lambin. *Rouille, Paris 1564*

The atomic theory of the universe, vivid depictions of nature, and a sense of the beauty and rhythm of the words, combine in the most astonishing way to produce one of the grandest and most moving poems in the Latin language. Never widely popular, Lucretius' work has delighted inquiring minds in every generation. Lambin, its first proper editor, was ideally fitted for his task. Scholarly and yet passionate, his editorial work is a monument of erudition and fine vigorous Latinity.

The Great Historian of Athens

219 THUCYDIDES, Historia. Edited by Henri Estienne. *Estienne, Geneva 1588.*

The historical methods of Thucydides, who lived in the fifth century B.C., have never been bettered. His severe standard of historical truth, coupled with his passionate belief in the general significance of particular events, have given his history of the tragic war between Athens and Sparta a universal value to statesmen and historians alike. Estienne, perhaps the best scholar of his learned family (no. 192), edited the Greek text of this edition, which was first published in 1564. This edition was improved by the addition of a translation, and notes by another great French scholar Isaac Casaubon.

This copy was inscribed by Casaubon to Sir Henry Wotton, scholar, diplomatist and Provost of Eton but Casaubon's name is written in a different hand, which is probably that of Henri Estienne himself. *Plate 27*

The Beginnings of Art History

220 GIORGIO VASARI, Le vite de' piu eccellenti pittori scultori ed architetti. *I Giunta, Florence 1568*

Though a painter and architect, Vasari's most abiding influence is through this work, the first attempt to give scientific, historical accounts of artists and a critical appreciation of their art based on documents and personal knowledge. It became a model for subsequent writings on the history of art, and for its period has remained—in spite of inaccuracies and critical shortcomings revealed by modern research—the chief authority. First published in 1550, this is the first illustrated and first complete edition bringing the biographies up to 1567.

Precedent and Common Law

221 HENRY DE BRACTON, De legibus et consuetudinibus Angliae. *London 1569*

The treatise of Bracton (*d.* 1268) is the first formulation of the laws of England. He sought to lay down jurisprudential maxims of universal validity, but the important element in his book is the citation of the 'precedents', judgments based on the common law of the land as opposed to local customs or royal prerogative, an element decisive in the development of English law.

Humanity in Education

222 ROGER ASCHAM, The Scholemaster. *Day, London 1570*

This book, by which Ascham (*c.* 1515–68) is best known, was not published until after his death. It is neither, as is supposed, a complete system of education, nor a wholly original work. It was designed by its author—tutor to the Princess Elizabeth—to teach children 'to understand, write and speak in Latin tong': the plea for gentle coercion, as opposed to flogging, as an educative force had already found support in England. But the expression of this humane spirit, and the spirited defence of the vernacular in it—and perhaps the touching description of Lady Jane Grey—made the book famous.

The Popularization of Geography

223 ABRAHAM ORTELIUS, Theatrum orbis terrarum. *Plantin, Antwerp 1570*

Ortelius (1527–98) was a scholar first (one of the notable group who dominated learning in the later sixteenth century) and a geographer second. Nevertheless, the great series of atlases, of which this is the first, represent his most important achievement. While they made no great advances in the theory of geography nor recorded any new discoveries, they demonstrated—and the quantities in which they were produced drove it home—Ortelius's belief that no literate person should be without knowledge of geography.

Palladian Architecture

224 ANDREA PALLADIO, I quattro libri dell'architettura. *Domenico de Franceschi, Venice 1570*

Palladio as a young man studied Alberti and Vitruvius (nos. 155, 180). He eventually created a style of his own—now universally described as 'Palladian'. This greatly influenced Inigo Jones (1573–1632) whose copy of Palladio was copiously annotated. These notes were incorporated into the first English translation made by Giacomo Leoni and published 1715–16. Among the subscribers to this were Wren, Vanbrugh, Hawksmoor, and Lord Burlington's mother. It became the architectural inspiration of the age and had an enduring influence on English and American architecture.

The Idea of Constitutional Government

225 JEAN BODIN, Six livres de la république. *Jacques du Puy, Paris 1576*

Bodin first put clearly the argument round which most political discussion centred during the seventeenth and eighteenth centuries that law is merely an expression of the sovereign will. He was, nevertheless, a firm believer in the sovereignty of the monarch. He approved, therefore, of absolute government, but he first recognized that there is a customary or natural law, and when the lawgiver's law becomes unjust, it ceases to be valid and can be resisted, i.e. the idea of constitutional law is here propounded. In economics Bodin was a mercantilist (*see* no. 278). This work was issued in many editions and translations and was studied in the principal European universities.

Algebraic Trigonometry

226 FRANCISCUS VIETA, Canon mathematicus seu ad triangula. *Paris 1579.*

Vieta's greatest innovation in mathematics is the denoting of general or indefinite quantities by letters of the alphabet instead of mere abbreviations of the words for those things as used hitherto. He obtained the value of π as an infinite product. He applied algebra to trigonometry, and his work on the nature and general solution of equations is fundamental.

'C'est icy un livre de bon foy'

227 MICHEL EYQUEM DE MONTAIGNE, Essais. *S. Millanges, Bordeaux 1580*

Montaigne devised the essay form in which to express his personal convictions and private meditations, a form not anticipated in either ancient or modern literature. The most elaborate essay, the *Apologie de Raimond Sebonde*, is second to no other modern writing in attacking fanaticism and pleading for tolerance. He was an enlightened sceptic. In 1588 a new edition of the *Essais* included a third volume and the definitive text on which all later editions are based.

The Beginnings of Rationalism

228 FRANCISCO SANCHEZ, Quod nihil scitur. *Lyons 1581*

Sanchez was one of the first to develop a full system criticizing the scholastic philosophy. Though recognizing the importance of Aristotle (no. 165) as a natural scientist, he opposed the uncritical acceptance of his views, the unquestioning belief in authority, and the syllogistic methods of reasoning still prevailing from the Middle Ages. Only by experiment, observation, and rational judgement can knowledge be obtained. These views were soon to be taken up by Bacon (no. 251) and later by the rationalist philosophers and scientists of the seventeenth and eighteenth centuries. The author, a Portuguese-Jewish physician, appears to have been distantly related to Montaigne.

Plant Classification

229 ANDREAS CAESALPINUS, De plantis. *Florence 1583*

This is the first book in which an attempt was made to classify plants in a systematic manner based on a comparative study of forms. The traditional division into trees, shrubs, half-shrubs, and herbs is retained but these are subdivided into different categories according to their seed, fruit, and flower. There are important passages on the germination of flowers and their sexual distinctions. Caesalpinus was a source for the work of Jung and Ray, but in particular for Linnaeus (no. 336) who studied the book closely and was greatly indebted to it.

Historian and Scholar

230 TACITUS, Opera cum notis, Justi Lipsii. *Antwerp 1584*

Lipsius—the 'learned Lipsius' of *Stalky & Co.* was one of the great scholars of his day. He was a pioneer in the advance from conjectural emendation to emendation by collation. His fame rests on his edition of Tacitus (*c.* 55–120) whose works he could recite by heart. In a life vexed by the violence of governments, Lipsius found much, as his notes declare, in common with Tacitus's ironic and cynical records of first-century Rome, written in an epigrammatic style of great force.

The Decimal System

231 SIMON STEVIN, De Thiende. *Plantin, Leiden 1585*

Though he made many most important contributions to statics, hydrostatics, and military and civil engineering, Stevin is best remembered for the introduction of the system of decimal fractions. He urged the general introduction of his system, which replaced a system of sexagesimal fractions. It was eventually used in coinage, and after the French Revolution it was adapted for weights and measures, as 'the metric system'.

Britain Described

232 WILLIAM CAMDEN, Britanniae descriptio. *London 1586*

If Camden is not the first English historian (in the modern sense), topographer, and antiquarian, he was certainly the first to relate the three studies, and his *Britannia*, primarily topographical, is the first book which shows a modern sense of the need to evaluate sources. It was enormously successful, and edition after edition, augmented by later scholars, followed; it was at once the model and vehicle for research on these subjects for the next 250 years. Camden fully realized the originality of his work, and did much to put it on a permanent footing, the most important step being the foundation of what is now the Camden chair of Ancient History at Oxford. This copy comes from the library at Westminster School, of which Camden was headmaster (1593–7).

Politics and the Church

233 RICHARD HOOKER, Of the Laws of Ecclesiastical Politie. *London 1594–7*

The great work of Richard Hooker (1554?–1600) was intended as a defence of the Church of England as established in the reign of Elizabeth I. But, since the temporal Head of the Church is the Sovereign, it constitutes a full discussion of authority, spiritual and secular. In it the theory of the 'original contract' as the basis of sovereignty, which originated in France, was first made known in England, where it became a major issue in the political struggles of the seventeenth century. The *Ecclesiastical Politie* is in fact the first English work of political theory.

Mercator's Projection

234 GERARDUS MERCATOR, Atlas sive Cosmographicae meditationes de fabrica mundi. *Düsseldorf [1585]–1595*

This work is the first collection of maps to which the name Atlas was applied. It was composed in three parts in 1585, 1590 and 1594, and was issued after the author's death by his son Rumold Mercator in 1595, and dedicated to Queen Elizabeth.

Mercator's fame rests chiefly on the projection known by his name. First used by him for a world map in 1569, it made navigation by dead reckoning easier, enabling the sailor to lay off a compass course on the chart as a straight line. As developed by Wright (see no. 237), it has been used for all nautical charts ever since and has only very recently been partially abandoned, chiefly owing to the requirements of the aeroplane. Mercator together with Ortelius (see no. 223) first freed geography from the domination of Ptolemy which had lasted 1,200 years. Modern geography and map-making date from Mercator.

The Queen's Captains

235 RICHARD HAKLUYT, The Principal Navigations, Voyages and Discoveries of the English Nation. *London 1598–1600*

The most complete collection of voyages at that date. As early as 1583 Hakluyt advocated the colonization of America by the English and became one of the chief promoters of the development of Virginia. He was the historian of the achievements of the Elizabethans at sea, and became an expert on maritime economic enterprise. His book intensified the desire for British expansion overseas. The Hakluyt Society founded (1846) is named in his honour.

The Great Scaliger

236 JOSEPH JUSTUS SCALIGER. De emendatione temporum. *Leiden 1598*

Scaliger has been described as 'the founder of historical criticism'. His penetrating criticism and powerful gift of analysis were first demonstrated in his famous edition of one of the most difficult of Latin texts, the *Astronomica* of Manilius, and his greatest work, *De emendatione temporum*, followed in 1583. In it he revolutionized ancient chronology by insisting on the equal value of Jewish, Persian, Babylonian, and Egyptian historical material, and thereby set a new standard in the treatment of ancient sources. The copy shown is of the second edition, and is of especial interest for it was presented by the author to Isaac Casaubon, brother-in-law of Henri Estienne and a scholar of almost equal critical faculty.

Mercator's Projection and the Navigators

237 EDWARD WRIGHT, Certain Errors in Navigation . . . Detected and Corrected. *London 1599*

With Gilbert (no. 238), Hakluyt (no. 235), and Wright we reach the highest achievement of English navigational science. They solved practical problems of the compass, latitude, and geography. Wright published a set of tables for the construction of the network known as 'Mercator's projection' (no. 234) and made its use practicable. There are instructions in the use of the compass and cross-staff. In 1618 Wright translated Napier (no. 248) into English.

Electricity Named

238 WILLIAM GILBERT, De magnete. *London 1600*

The first really modern scientific book published in England. In this work on electricity Gilbert established that the earth itself was one great magnet. He worked out the variation and declination of the compass and he distinguished magnetic mass from weight. He first used the terms 'electricity', 'electric force', and 'electric attraction', invented the first electric measuring instrument the 'electro-meter', considered the static quality of amber as an electric force, &c. His book influenced Kepler, Galileo, and Newton (nos. 244, 245, 295) and became one of the basic works of modern physics.

Il Bel Canto

239 GIULIO CACCINI, Le Nuove Musiche e nuova maniera di scriverle. *Marescotti, Florence 1601*

Caccini frequented the salon of artists and scholars under the patronage of the Conte di Vernio in Florence from which the opera as we know it emerged. Peri's *Euridice*, 1600, the first opera, included songs by Caccini, who was himself a gifted singer. No single inventor of solo singing can be named, but Caccini, by example and precept and notably by the publication of the *Nuove Musiche* produced what Grove describes as 'one of the most illuminating treatises of the time and one of the most important in the history of singing'.

The People's Rights

240 JOHANNES ALTHUSIUS, Politica methodice digesta. *Herborn 1603*

It is arguable that the modern meaning of the word 'politics' is due to Althusius (1557–1638). The basis of his theory lies in the Calvinistic doctrine of determinism (no. 194) on which he constructed a rational system of political and social theory. In it he defended the theory of the social contract, the sovereignty of the people, and their right to rebel against a tyrannical authority. Spinoza (no. 287) directly, and Rousseau (no. 350) indirectly, show his influence.

The End of the 'Philosopher's Stone'

241 THEOPHRASTUS PARACELSUS, Opera medico–chemico–chirurgica. *Frankfort 1603*

Paracelsus made the startling assertion that 'The true use of chemistry is not to make gold but to prepare medicines.' He thus founded what is known as 'iatrochemistry' which added greatly to the knowledge of compounds. He also reformed medicine through a new theory of the causation of disease. He knew ether and its narcotic action which he tested on chickens, and used mercury as a diuretic. His scientific views and discoveries are bound up with religious and mystical ideas. His medical and philosophical works fill 11 quarto volumes in this edition, and his theological works, now being published from the manuscript, are planned in 14 volumes. He was a colourful character, being at one time or another as an itinerant doctor and chemist, theologian, and lay preacher.

Quixotism

242 MIGUEL DE CERVANTES SAAVEDRA. Primera Parte d'el ingenioso hidalgo Don Quixote de la Mancha. *Madrid 1605*

Very few books can be said to have added a new field to human imagination, but *Don Quixote* is one of them. Cervantes began it simply as a satire on the tedious romances of the time. It found immediate fame, and within months Don Quixote and Sancho Panza had become legendary. The first part was pirated by three different publishers immediately after publication and two further authorized editions also appeared in 1605. In 1614 a spurious 'second part' appeared, anticipating Cervantes' own continuation by one year. The realization of its pathos and deep insight into life came later, and its influence since has been unbounded. There are very few who have not at one time or another felt themselves to be Don Quixote confronting the windmills or Sancho Panza in the inn.

The First Encyclopedia

243 JOHANN HEINRICH ALSTED, Encyclopaedia cursus philosophici. *Herborn 1608*

Alsted's book, later (1630) expanded to the seven-volume *Encyclopaedia . . . distincta*, was the first of its kind to bear the term 'encyclopedia' as its title. It was one of the last encyclopedias written in Latin and designed on a systematic plan, as had been the custom from Isidore to Bacon (nos. 141, 251); the future belonged to the vernacular and alphabetical type of which Harris's *Dictionary* (no. 305) was an early specimen.

The Laws of Planetary Motion

244 JOHANNES KEPLER, Astronomia nova aitiologetos. *Prague 1609*

In this book and in his *Harmonices mundi*, published in 1619, Kepler discovered the three laws of planetary motion. Copernicus (no. 201) had referred planetary motion to the centre of the earth's orbit, but Kepler referred it to the sun itself, thereby paving the way for a real centre of force and making possible the Newtonian celestial mechanics (no. 295). Modern astronomy is founded on these two books.

The Telescope Discovers New Worlds

245 GALILEO GALILEI, Sidereus Nuncius. *Venice 1610*

In this work the use of the newly invented telescope by Galileo with the improvements he had made to it led to revolutionary discoveries. The most important was the existence of the satellites of Jupiter. The observation of this system convinced Galileo finally of the truth of the Copernican system (no. 201) and has remained ever since one of its powerful demonstrations. Galileo further observed that the Milky Way and the great nebulae were composed of countless stars.

The Authorized Version

246 THE HOLY BIBLE ... newly translated out of the original tongue. *R. Barker, London 1611*

This, the most famous of English vernacular translations of the Bible, is also known as the King James version, since the king summoned the Hampton Court Conference at which it was first discussed and took an active part in the selection of the six companies of scholars who prepared it between 1607 and 1610. It was based on existing printed translations rather than on a study of the best original manuscripts, and although its title-page bears the words 'Appointed to be read in Churches', no record remains of its authorization by King, Parliament, or Convocation. Nevertheless, it soon began to supersede all other English translations and to assert its unrivalled influence on the minds, and still more on the language, of the English-speaking peoples.

Standard Italian

247 Vocabolario dell' Accademia della Crusca. *Florence 1612*

Founded in 1582 with the express purpose of cultivating and purifying the Italian language, the Academy propagated in its dictionary the Tuscan dialect as the norm of literate Italian. In this it was completely successful, and no other dialect has achieved the authority or the circulation of 'pure Tuscan'. In its insistence on a single correct form, it laid the foundations of what is now considered one of the essentials of a dictionary—an approved uniform spelling—and had considerable influence on the morphology of language.

The Discovery of Logarithms

248 JOHN NAPIER, Mirifici Logarithmorum canonis descriptio. *Edinburgh 1614*

The discovery of logarithms is announced in this book. Napier explains their nature and gives a logarithmic table of the natural sines of a quadrant from minute to minute. Logarithms provided a most important advance in mathematics, because they reduced multiplication and division to a process of addition and subtraction, and extraction of roots to division. The new method was immediately applied to mathematical and astronomical calculations by Briggs, Kepler (no. 244), and others.

Napier also invented 'Napier's bones' as a help in calculation which made possible the construction of machines for mechanical addition and subtraction—the precursors of our modern calculating machines and computors.

History as the Teacher of Politics

249 SIR WALTER RALEIGH, Historie of the World. *London 1614*

Written while Raleigh was imprisoned in the Tower, this masterpiece of noble Elizabethan prose—a creditable specimen of the historical scholarship of the age—gained its immense popularity mainly as a treasury of political ammunition for the opponents of Stuart absolutism. For the *Historie* is as much a political tract as an historical narrative (ending in 130 B.C.). With an eye on the 'divine-right' pretensions of James I, Raleigh passed severe strictures on ancient rulers who set themselves above the law, and assessed the value of political institutions according to what he considered the eternal standards of right and justice.

The Council of Trent

250 PIETRO SOAVE POLANO [i.e. PAOLO SARPI], Istoria del Concilio Tridentino. *London 1619*

The Council of Trent, the turning-point of the Counter-Reformation, created the modern

Roman Catholic Church. It represents not merely one of the decisive moments of the sixteenth century, but a moment whose influence is still felt, all over Europe, by Catholics and non-Catholics alike. The history of it written by Sarpi, besides being of great importance in the development of historiography, is memorable as the touchstone by which the value and effect of the Council were debated. Written by a member of the Servite Order, hated yet never excommunicated by the Papal See, whose first loyalty was to the Republic of Venice, the *Istoria* was printed pseudonymously in London. Its ambivalent position typifies a controversy which is still alive.

The Advancement of Learning

251 FRANCIS BACON, Instauratio magna. *London 1620*

Bacon had an immediate and lasting influence upon philosophy and natural science. In the major part of his greatest work, the *Instauratio magna*, he outlines what was to be a reorganization of the sciences and the restoration of man to the command of nature he had lost by the Fall. The impetus to the foundation of the Royal Society (no. 281) came from Bacon's writings; to Voltaire he was 'le père de la philosophie expérimentale'.

AN IMPROVED HAND PRESS

252 The Blaeu Press

A wooden press embodying improvements attributed to Willem Janszoon Blaeu (1571–1638), the Dutch cartographer and printer.

The main improvement was the substitution of two iron pillars passing through bearings in the till instead of the earlier box-shaped hose, to guide the downward movement of the platen. This and some lesser changes in the press are attributed to Blaeu on the authority of Joseph Moxon (*Mechanick Exercises*, vol. ii, 1683–4).

These improvements to the wooden press are about the earliest advances in the design of printer's equipment of which there is a record. They seem not to have been generally adopted.

This particular specimen is of unknown age. It has features not ascribable to Blaeu: screw pillars instead of cords to hang the platen and 'side boards' to the carriage to prevent its jarring against the uprights of the staple. *Plate 6*

Anatomy of Melancholy

253 ROBERT BURTON, The Anatomy of Melancholy. *Oxford 1621*

All the learning of the age as well as its humour—and its pedantry—are in this book. It has something in common with such books as Brant's *Ship of Fools* (no. 163), Erasmus's *Praise of Folly* (no. 172). More's *Utopia* (no. 175), Rabelais and Montaigne (no. 227), and like all these it had considerable influence on the thought of the seventeenth century; it was forgotten in the eighteenth, but revived by Charles Lamb in the nineteenth and has remained a popular work ever since. This copy is inscribed by the author to his College, Christ Church, Oxford by whom it is lent for this exhibition.

Classification of Plants

254 CASPAR BAUHIN, Pinax theatri botanici. *Basel 1623*

At this time great confusion reigned in botanical nomenclature, as different names had been given to the same species by different authors. Bauhin first established a system of nomenclature in this work, which described 6,000 species. Each plant was given a generic and a specific name, and this was the first appearance of the binary nomenclature, later universally adopted after Linnaeus. Bauhin's system was followed by Ray and other botanists, and Linnaeus used the book extensively when composing his own great system (no. 336).

The First Folio

255 WILLIAM SHAKESPEARE, Comedies, Histories, and Tragedies. *Isaac Jaggard and Ed. Blount, London 1623*

The magic of Shakespeare's poetry is potent only in his own tongue; but the great theatrical scenes, the great dramatic figures are universal. Hamlet's doubts, the doomed love of Romeo and Juliet, Brutus's dilemma, the Falstaffian image, the characters of Iago, Petruchio, and Lady Macbeth, are part of the fabric of Western civilization. Henry V's summons to Agincourt, Othello's stand before the Signoria, Portia at Shylock's trial: these are more real to us than the history books or Hansard. This first collected edition of Shakespeare's plays, commonly known as 'The First Folio', was published seven years after his death.

The Father of English Metaphysics

256 EDWARD HERBERT, LORD HERBERT OF CHERBURY, De veritate. *[Paris] 1624*

This is the earliest metaphysical treatise by an Englishman. It is based on a theory of knowledge derived from the neo-Platonists. Though not directly denying the Church's doctrine, Herbert establishes five articles which became the fundamental principles of English Deism. He was the English precursor of both natural theology and rationalist philosophy as expressed by Descartes (no. 262). The copy shown is lent by the Earl of Powis, the present head of the Herbert family.

'America, my new-found land'

257 JOHN SMITH, A Generall Historie of Virginia, New England, and the Summer Isles. *London 1624*

Captain John Smith (1580–1631) set out with the Virginia colonists in 1606 and eventually became head of the colony. His *Generall Historie* was the first sizeable work written in English about the new found continent, and though not wholly reliable, it remained a standard work, the foundation of England's knowledge of America during the early period of colonization.

This is the dedication copy to Frances Duchess of Richard and Lennox.

International Law

258 HUGO GROTIUS, De jure belli ac pacis. *Paris 1625*

Grotius (1583–1645) began his famous work in 1604 but was not able to complete it until his release from imprisonment for advocating religious tolerance. Though it brought him no gain, it won him a great and enduring reputation. It was the first attempt to find a principle of right and a basis for law and society outside Church or Scripture. The practical distinction between religion and a combination of law and morality was not in fact fully made by Grotius, but his attempt made it easy for his followers to grasp it. *De jure belli ac pacis* is the first and greatest treatise of international law; its influence is still potent. The International Court at the Hague is based on the ideas of Grotius.

Law and Democracy

259 EDWARD COKE, Institutes. *London 1628*

If Bracton (no. 221) first began the codification of the common law, it was Coke who completed it. Ranging over the whole field of law, in comment, report, argument, and decision—it is a disorderly, pedantic, masterful work in which the common thread is a national dogmatism, tenacious of its continuous self-perpetuating life. With it the lawyers fought the battle of the constitution against the Stuarts; historical research was their defence for national liberties. In the *Institutes* the basis of the constitution in the law of the land was firmly established.

The Foundation of Modern Physiology

260 WILLIAM HARVEY, De motu cordis. *Frankfurt 1628*

The circulatory movement of the blood had been little understood until Harvey's time. Michael Servetus's discovery (no. 209) had been suppressed as heretical. It was believed that the blood 'irrigated' the tissues by a kind of tidal motion. Galen believed that blood was continually produced by ingested food and the heart's porous system. Harvey proved experimentally that the blood in animals is impelled in a circle by the beat of the heart and the volume of blood-flow calculated. With this work all Galenic and other doctrines which had largely dominated medicine before were swept away and modern physiology began.

'Eppur si Muove'

261 GALILEO GALILEI, Dialogo . . . dei massimi sistemi del mondo tolemaico e copernicano. *Florence 1632*

In this book Galileo maintained that the earth moves round the sun. Written in the form of a dialogue, two interlocutors argue, one for Copernicus, one for Ptolemy (nos. 201, 167). Galileo disproves the two chief objections to heliocentricity—the stellar parallax and the vertical fall of terrestrial bodies. He also introduces here his important theory of tides.

Published in January 1632 its sale was forbidden in August, and on 1 October the author was brought before the Inquisition for one of the most famous trials in history. The book remained on the *Index* (*see* no. 212) until 1822.

'Cogito, ergo sum'

262 RENÉ DESCARTES, Discours de la méthode. *Leiden 1637*

The purpose of the *Discours* of Descartes is to find the simple indestructible point which gives to the universe and thought their order and system. Three points are made; the truth of thought, when thought is true to itself (thus, *cogito, ergo sum*), the inevitable elevation of its partial state in our finite consciousness to its full state in the infinite existence of God, and the ultimate reduction of the material universe to extension and local movement. From those central propositions in logic, metaphysics, and physics came the subsequent inquiries of Locke, Leibniz, and Newton (nos. 297, 294, 295). This great work also contains scientific material of fundamental importance—his invention of analytical geometry which is the basis of geometry as we know it, treatises on optics and meteors, and the first mention of Harvey's discovery (no. 260) by a prominent foreign scholar.

Mechanics and Motion Examined

263 GALILEO GALILEI, Discorsi e dimostrazioni matematiche, intorno a due nuove scienze attenenti alla Mecanica & i movimenti locali. *Elzevier, Leiden 1638*

By many scientists this is considered Galileo's most important book. It is the first modern textbook of physics and a great many fundamental problems are solved here for the first time by the application of experimental and mathematical methods. The first law of motion, that of 'inertia', replaced Aristotle's (no. 165) conception which had been accepted for 2,000 years; the motion of falling bodies, the demonstration of the parabolic curve of projectiles, and the laws of cohesion, and of the pendulum are explained. Newton (no. 295) said that he was able to deduce the first two laws of motion from this book. As his books were banned in Italy, Galileo had this published in Holland.

Religio medici

264 SIR THOMAS BROWNE, Religio medici. *London 1642*

'To pursue my reason to an O Altitudo!' is perhaps the underlying theme of *Religio medici*. Endlessly imitated, its influence lies in its plea, not to differ from the rest of mankind, but for the mind to reach its conclusions in its own way. Browne (1605–82) was a doctor, but unlike subsequent *apologiae*, this is not a defence of his calling, but of the right to that individuality of thought which is to be found in all his writings.

Truth defies Tradition

265 Acta sanctorum. *Volume 1, Antwerp, Tongerloo, Brussels, 1643 [still in progress]*

A critical collection of the lives of the Christian saints—perhaps the most remarkable collective scholarly undertaking of all ages. The work was inspired by Heribert Rosweyde, brought into being by Jan Bolland and his pupils, the first 'Bollandists', Henskens and Papebroch and carried on to the present by a group of Belgian Jesuits, never more than six at any time. The removal of St. George from the calendar is a recent example of the extra-literary effects of the Bollandists' search for truth.

Invention of the Barometer

266 EVANGELISTA TORRICELLI, Esperienza dell'argento vivo. *Florence 1643*

It had been erroneously believed that suction phenomena were due to nature's alleged abhorrence of a vacuum—the *horror vacui*. Torricelli, experimenting with mercury, first constructed the barometer: proving that the fluctuations in the height of the mercury were due to atmospheric pressure. This was finally confirmed by Boyle (no. 276), and by Pascal in his Puy de Dôme experiments in 1648 using Torricelli's barometer, and, though modified, our barometer is essentially still the same. It was first given its name by Boyle in the *Philosophical Transactions* 1665–6. Torricelli made numerous important contributions to the sciences of mechanics, optics, hydraulics, and mathematics.

The Freedom of the Press

267 JOHN MILTON, Areopagitica. *London 1644*

'Give me the liberty to know, to utter, and to argue freely according to conscience, above all liberties.' So Milton concludes his magisterial defence of the freedoms of speech, writing, and printing against the unwisdom and injustice of the order for licensing books, which constituted in fact a government censorship. His brilliant and profound argument has been quoted and repeated whenever the right of self-expression has been threatened.

The Finest Sea Atlas

268 SIR ROBERT DUDLEY. Arcano del Mare. *Florence 1646–7*

This magnificent book is the most famous of all early sea atlases. Sir Robert Dudley had left England under a cloud in 1605 and settled in Florence where he was employed by Ferdinand II, Duke of Tuscany, to whom this work is dedicated. It deals with the longitude and means of determining it, sailing directions, naval architecture, the construction of nautical instruments, naval warfare, and the principles of navigation, but it is principally an atlas, in which many of the maps and charts of ports and harbours are for the first time drawn on the Mercator projection (no. 234). Dudley had travelled widely and accompanied Henry Cavendish on some of his voyages. As an engineer he drained the marshes between Pisa and the sea, which led to the prosperity of Leghorn.

Discovery of Gas

269 JOHANNES BAPTISTA VAN HELMONT, Ortus medicinae. *Amsterdam 1648*

Helmont was the founder of bio-chemistry. He is chiefly remembered for his discovery of gas (which he named), describing various substances in gaseous form, notably carbon dioxide, and insisting on the specific character of the individual gases. His many other discoveries include gastric digestion by acid and the testing of urine by specific gravity. His extensive use of the balance facilitated many of his experiments, notably those on the indestructibility of matter by recovering metals without loss of weight after solution in acid. As in the case of his master, Paracelsus (no. 241), his achievements in chemistry and medicine had a religious and metaphysical background.

Political Nonconformity

270 JOHN LILBURNE, An Agreement of the Free People of England. *London 1649*

Out of the endless discussions of the relative importance of the State and the individual which raged throughout the Civil War came the safeguards of the freedom of the people which were finally established in 1688. These freedoms and the right to protest could not be better typified than in the life of John Lilburne. This work, the protest of the ultra-democratic 'Levellers' against authority of any kind, is the perfect expression of the nonconforming spirit which is a part of the English character.

Holy Living

271 JEREMY TAYLOR, The Rule and Exercise of Holy Living. *London 1650*

The Rule of Holy Living was written while Taylor was staying at Golden Grove in Carmarthen, where he had taken refuge during the Civil War and wrote manuals of devotion for the Anglican laity, which achieved enormous and persistent popularity. The scope of Holy Living is described on the title-page: it gives 'the means and instruments of obtaining every virtue, and the remedies against every vice . . . together with prayers containing the whole Duty of a Christian'. It has been in print ever since, and typifies, in a style at once homely and poetic, the tolerant spirit of the Church of England at its best.

That Leviathan

272 THOMAS HOBBES, Leviathan. *London 1651*

Thomas Hobbes of Malmesbury is a unique figure in the history of English political thought. His defence of absolutism, unpopular from the day it was published to the present, is based on expediency. The individual (except to save his life) should always submit to the State, because any government is better than the anarchy of the natural state. Though his ideas have never appealed to proponents of the individual rights of man or to the modern totalitarians with their mystical visions of *Volk*, the fundamental nature of Hobbes's speculation has stimulated philosophers from Spinoza (no. 287) to John Stuart Mill (no. 531). The copy shown is from Chatsworth where Hobbes was tutor to three generations of the Cavendish family.

Reason against Casuistry

273 BLAISE PASCAL, Lettres à un Provincial. *Pierre de la Vallée, Cologne [Paris] 1657*

The first important ethical work of Pascal, who was earlier distinguished as a physicist and mathematician, was the *Lettres Provinciales*, as they are generally known, written in defence of Jansenism, which had been attacked by the Jesuits, nominally on the ground that its tenets came dangerously near to the Calvinistic doctrine of predestination. Pascal's counter-attack—which exposed the real nature of the Jesuits' arguments—is a magnificent, sustained invective, after which the Jesuits never recovered their former position in France, and a noble defence of thought in religious faith.

The Foundation of Chemistry

274 ROBERT BOYLE, The Sceptical Chymist. *London 1661*

This work established chemistry as the modern science it is today and ranks in importance in the history of science with Copernicus, Galileo, and Newton (nos. 201, 245, 295). Boyle first conceived the idea of the element as the constituent of material bodies which could not be further decomposed. He explained that matter consisted of atoms and combinations of atoms in motion and that every phenomenon was the result of these bodies in motion. He coined the word 'analysis' for the process of detecting the ingredients of compounds. The publication of this book transformed chemistry into a modern science instead of an adjunct of alchemy and medicine.

Eliot's Indian Bible

275 THE BIBLE, translated into the language of the Massachusetts Indians, by JOHN ELIOT. *Samuel Green & Marmaduke Johnson, Cambridge, Mass. 1663* (N. T. *1661*).

John Eliot, 'the Apostle to the Indians', produced a Catechism in the language of the Massachusetts Indians in 1653, a New Testament in 1661, and this complete Bible in 1663. Not only was it the first Bible to be printed in the New World, but it was also the first to be printed in a new language as a means of evangelization. As such it was the forerunner of the missionary versions, which have now appeared in over 1,180 languages.

Boyle's Law

276 ROBERT BOYLE, New Experiments Physico-mechanical touching the Spring of the Air. *Oxford 1662*

Boyle's experimental proof of the basic physical property of air, namely that the volume of a gas varies inversely with the pressure, constitutes one of the greatest contributions to physical science. This is known as 'Boyle's law'. It was proved by using a greatly improved vacuum pump—first invented by Guericke in 1657—which he developed together with his assistant Robert Hooke. It was further proved that air has weight, and the function of combustion and respiration in air, the conveyance of sound and the elasticity of air are all explained.

The Beginning of Statistics

277 JOHN GRAUNT, Natural and Political Observations. *London 1662*

The statistical recording of social phenomena, now an essential feature of modern life and government, was introduced by Graunt. He studied the weekly bills of mortality showing the causes of death in the London parishes. From these he drew up statistical tables calculating the expectancy of life. France introduced birth and death registers soon after Graunt's publication, and a hundred years later the first life insurance offices were established.

The Balance of Trade

278 THOMAS MUN, England's Treasure by Forraign Trade. *London 1664*

The first clear statement of the mercantilist conception. Mun's strong pleas for favourable balances of trade, the vital necessity to increase exports and the need for new foreign markets would be approved verbatim by any modern finance minister. Written in about 1628 the book was first published by his son 'for the common good' about twenty-three years after Mun's death.

The Norse Sagas

279 [EDDA SNORRA STURLUSONAR] Edda Islandorum an. Chr. M. CC. XV. islandice conscripta per Snorronem. *Henricus Gödianus, Copenhagen 1665*

This is the first of the three great sagas to be rediscovered and published in full. The text is in Danish and Latin verse; and runic, gothic, and roman types are used in the printing. It is, like all the Eddas and Sagas, a mixture of history and mythology.

Scandinavian mythology, besides much else, is a source for the Nibelungenlied, Beowulf, and Wayland the Smith through the Arthurian legend (no. 210a) to Wagner (no. 520) as well as for the names of the days of our week—Wotan's Day, Thor's Day, and the like.

A Classic of Microscopy

280 ROBERT HOOKE, Micrographia or Some Physiological Descriptions of Minute Bodies made by Magnifying Glasses. *London 1665*

Hooke was one of the most versatile and brilliant scientists of his time, and his contributions to astronomy, all branches of physics and optics, mechanics, technology, and architecture are innumerable. The present work is chiefly devoted to microscopy and includes a description of the invention of the compound microscope. Some of the magnificent illustrations are by the author himself and others are probably by Sir Christopher Wren.

The Cradle of Modern Science

281 Philosophical Transactions of the Royal Society. *London 1665*

The foundation in 1645, under the impetus of Bacon (no. 251), of the Philosophical Society, and its later development under Royal Charter (1662) as the Royal Society, was one of the most important moments in the history of science. The catholicity of learning, which Bacon (no. 251) had advocated, was one of its most remarkable early features. Its foundation by a collection of amateurs and gentlemen seems typically English. It numbered men of letters among its first members, and demanded a plain and natural way of speaking in its transactions. Some idea of the position which the Royal Society has occupied since 1665 to the present day can be seen by reference to the number of important contributions to human thought which were first published in the *Transactions* many of them included in the present catalogue.

Latin without Tears

282 JOHANN AMOS COMENIUS, Orbis sensualium pictus quadrilinguis. *J. F. Endter, Nuremberg 1666.*

Jan Komenský, Bishop of the Moravian Brethren, was expelled from Bohemia by the counter-reformation (1620) and spent much of the rest of his life in travelling all over Europe, finally settling in Amsterdam. One of the leading educationalists of all ages, he was the first to design books specially for children of kindergarten age, to stress the value of visual education by the frequent introduction of pictures, and to base all education upon the appeal to the pupils' intelligence and co-operation rather than drill and force.

The first edition of this book was issued by the same publisher and in the same format in 1658, but it is virtually unobtainable.

The Beginnings of Blood Transfusion

283 RICHARD LOWER, Tractatus de corde. *London 1669*

As a practical consequence of the new knowledge of the circulation of the blood, blood transfusion became possible and Lower was one of the first to practise it (*see also* no. 330). When injecting dark venous blood into the lungs he found that it became immediately red in colour and concluded that it had absorbed air from the lungs. The process led to failures and was abandoned until the principle of blood groups was discovered in the twentieth century. Lower also first described correctly the heart-muscle.

The Creed of the Quaker

284 WILLIAM PENN, No Cross No Crown. *[London] 1669*

Written at the age of 24 while Penn was imprisoned for blasphemy in the Tower of London, this book is now generally accepted as the earliest and clearest exposition of the beliefs of members of the Society of Friends. Penn was a founder of the State of Pennsylvania, named after him. It is fitting that this copy should be lent by the Library of the Society of Friends.

The First Accurate Description of Fossils

285 NICOLAUS STENO, De solido intra solidum naturaliter contento. *Florence 1669*

The principles formulated in this book are fundamental to modern geology and palaeontology, our knowledge of the earth's crust. Steno first explained the true origin of fossils as being the remains of extinct animals, and was able to distinguish the various stratifications of the earth, which he divided into six categories, and their sequence in time. At the same time he was the first to describe the forms and the manner of formation of crystals. From him the path of modern geology led through Leibniz (no. 294), Lamarck (no. 440), and Hutton (no. 388) to Cuvier and the further developments of the nineteenth century.

Revelation against Rationalism

286 BLAISE PASCAL, Les Pensées. *Guillaume Desprez, Paris 1670*

Pascal had intended a full-scale defence of the Christian religion, but his early death prevented him from completing it. Fragments of it were published posthumously as the *Pensées*; the work as it stands represents only imperfectly the original plan, and several editors have attempted to arrange them in a better order. It is clear, however, that it was intended to be a defence of the faith against the contemporary forms of free-thought, and in particular against Descartes's view of the supremacy of the human reason (no. 262). Against this, Pascal set the inability of reason to deal with the ultimate metaphysical problems, and evolved his own theory of intuition. The rational appeal of the *Pensées* has found them readers from 1670 to the present day; and they remain the best-reasoned as well as one of the profoundest exercises in Christian apologetics.

The Ethics of Politics

287 BENEDICT DE SPINOZA, Tractatus theologico-politicus. *Hamburg 1670*

The famous *Tractatus* of Spinoza is the extension to political thought of his ethical views. Man is moved to the knowledge and love of God; the love of God involves love of our fellow men. Man, in order to obtain security, surrenders part of his rights to the State. But the State exists to give liberty, not to enslave; justice, wisdom, and toleration are essential to the sovereign.

Spinoza's thought, a fusion of cartesian rationalism and the Hebraic tradition in which he grew up, is a solitary but crystal-clear exposition of the theory of natural right. It is also the forerunner of modern Biblical criticism. Its original purpose as a propaganda pamphlet in support of the Dutch oligarchy against the House of Orange has long been forgotten.

The Pendulum Clock

288 CHRISTIAN HUYGENS, Horologium oscillatorium. *Paris 1673*

The pendulum clock was invented by Huygens in 1656 and is here fully described. The book further contains the theoretical exposition of the motion of bodies, theorems of their acceleration on inclined planes or given curves, the discovery of the isochronism of the cycloid, the isochronous conical pendulum, and other principles of mechanics. The work ends with thirteen theorums relating to the theory of centrifugal force in circular motion which helped Newton (no. 295) substantially in proving the law of gravitation.

The Catholic Encyclopedia

289 LOUIS MORÉRI, Le Grand Dictionnaire historique. *Paris 1674*

Deliberately designed as an apologia and defence of the Roman Catholic Church, Moréri's encyclopedia had by 1759 gone through twenty editions before it succumbed to the *Encyclopédie* (no. 343)—a useful reminder of the strength of the anti-rationalist forces in the 'age of Reason'. The book is also noteworthy for its emphasis on historical and biographical entries, neglected by Harris and Chambers as well as by Moréri's opponent, Bayle (*see* nos. 305, 331, 300).

Pilgrim's Progress

290 JOHN BUNYAN, Pilgrim's Progress. *London 1678*

For the first hundred years or more of its existence the *Pilgrim's Progress* was read only among the dissenters, the lower and middle classes; and the many early editions, like the first, were poorly printed. Now it is universally known and loved, and the parable of salvation is accepted by all denominations. Its language has become common to all, and the life of Bunyan has become the hope of all imprisoned for conscience' sake. His prose style has profoundly affected later writers.

The Christian Interpretation of History

291 JACQUES-BÉNIGNE BOSSUET, Discours sur l'histoire universelle. *Paris 1681*

Bossuet (1627–1704) was the court-preacher of Louis XIV whose Gallican policy he defended against the Roman Curia. His *Discours* is the last great successor of St. Augustine's interpretation of history as the history of the salvation of mankind (no. 136). It was originally written for the Dauphin (whose tutor Bossuet was), history, he thought, being 'the counsellor of princes'. Bossuet's theological and eschatological construction was disdained by Voltaire (no. 345) but is still influential with Roman Catholic proselytizers.

The Birth of Latin Palaeography

292 DOM JEAN MABILLON, De re diplomatica libri VI. *Paris 1681*

Conceived as a rebuttal of the hypercritical attitude towards medieval documents taken by Papebroch, the editor of the *Acta sanctorum* (no. 265), this volume created at one stroke the science of Latin palaeography. Sciences 'auxiliary to history' were greatly affected by the work—diplomacy, chronology, numismatics, &c.—and it procured for its author, a Benedictine of the Congregation of St. Maur at St. Germain-des-Près, a European reputation. Even now Mabillon's method has been superseded only in details, chiefly due to the application of technical inventions such as photography.

The English Hippocrates

293 THOMAS SYDENHAM, Tractatus de podagra et hydrope. *London 1683*

The founder of modern clinical medicine, Sydenham did much to free it from the mystical and scholastic doctrines still surviving. To him personal observation, simple remedies, and the care of the patient came first. His epidemiological researches were the forerunner of the germ theory of disease, and his contributions to pathology and therapeutics are numerous and were published all over the Continent. The present book, with its first differentiation of rheumatism and gout, is a masterpiece of clinical observation.

The Differential Calculus

294 GOTTFRIED WILHELM VON LEIBNIZ, Nova methodus pro maximis et minimis. *Acta Eruditorum, Leipzig 1684*

This work was overshadowed by the long controversy with Newton (no. 295) over the priority of this discovery, but it is now generally conceded that the invention of the differential and integral calculus, known as the infinitesimal calculus, is due to Leibniz. It is that branch of mathematics which deals with magnitudes in a state of change or growth, and Leibniz's symbols and notation have been retained until modern times. Of fundamental importance in mechanics (movement of bodies) and astronomy (movement of planets), Leibniz's concept was developed, mainly by continental mathematicians, into a great instrument of research.

The Law of Gravity

295 SIR ISAAC NEWTON, Philosophiae naturalis principia mathematica. *London 1687*

The first two books treat of mechanics, the third of the solar system. Newton states his three laws of motion which established the relationship of mass, force, and direction; he treats of the movement of bodies through gases and liquids, defines mass and force and the corpuscular theory of light. Most important of all, he refutes the then prevailing theory of the vortices of Descartes (no. 262), and establishes the principle of universal gravitation and the motion of the planets. Copernicus, Newton, and Einstein (nos. 201, 595) are the three corner-stones of our conception of the universe. Few could grasp Newton's reasoning at the time, and his fame was spread on the Continent by Voltaire's *Elémens de la Philosophie de Neuton*, 1738.

Expediency in Politics

296 GEORGE SAVILE, MARQUESS OF HALIFAX, The Character of a Trimmer. *London 1688*

The influence of Halifax, both as a practical politician and theorist, on the public opinion of his day was unrivalled. To him was due the management of the Glorious Revolution of 1688, when England finally freed herself from the authoritarian Stuarts in favour of the constitutional monarchy. Equally, his political ideas are based on the practicable: though his firm grasp of high moral generalizations is evident—often anticipating the broad concepts of Burke (no. 380), he retains his sense of what can be done: 'men should live in some competent state of freedom', he wrote. His writings provide a classic exposition of the empirical character of the British constitution.

Philosophy without Dogma

297 JOHN LOCKE, An Essay concerning Humane Understanding. *London 1690*

Locke was the first to take up the challenge of Bacon (no. 251) and to attempt to estimate critically the certainty and the adequacy of human knowledge when confronted with God and the universe. Knowledge is the perception of relations among ideas; ideas, 'neither true nor false, being nothing but bare appearances', are the only existence of which we are aware, the existence of God being demonstrated by causal necessity, without which there can be no knowledge. Locke writes with a freshness and a solid common sense which are all his own; his conceptions have remained fundamental to philosophical discussion ever since.

The Founder of Liberalism

298 JOHN LOCKE, Two Treatises on Government. *London 1690*

Locke's defence of the contract between ruler and ruled is one of the classics of English constitutional writing. Its theme, which appears in Hooker and Grotius and stems from Aquinas (nos. 233, 258, 156), is that civil rulers hold their power not absolutely but conditionally, government being essentially a moral trust, forfeited if the conditions are not fulfilled by the trustees. This presupposes an original law of the nature of reason, which was central to Locke's philosophy. Written to confute the absolutism of Hobbes (no. 272) and Filmer, his work remains as valid now as when Locke wrote it two years after the Glorious Revolution.

Seed Pollination

299 RUDOLPH JACOB CAMERARIUS, De sexu plantarum epistola. *[Tübingen 1694]*

The first experimental proof that in flowering plants the anthers are male, the ovaries and styles female organs, and that viable seeds cannot be formed without the addition of pollen.

The original edition appeared in Tübingen in 1694 and is of great rarity; no copy seems to exist in England. We show the reprint appearing in Valentini (R. J.). *Polychresta exotica*, Frankfurt 1701. Valentini was the recipient of the original letter of 1694. The copy exhibited belonged to Linné and has been annotated by him.

The Anti-clerical Encyclopedia

300 PIERRE BAYLE, Dictionnaire historique et critique. *Paris 1695–7*

Bayle, one of the most influential representatives of eighteenth-century rationalism, wrote his *Dictionnaire* as an anti-clerical counter-blast to Moréri's *Dictionnaire* (no. 289), in order, as he put it, 'to rectify Moréri's mistakes and fill the gaps'. Until the *Encyclopedie* (no. 343) became the Bible of rationalism, Bayle's encyclopedia dominated enlightened thinking in Europe.

The Discovery of Microbes

301 ANTONI VAN LEEUWENHOEK, Arcana Naturae detecta. *Delft 1696*

With the help of a simple lens Leeuwenhoek made remarkable discoveries in the anatomy of man, the higher animals, and insects. He discovered the red blood corpuscles in the blood, and the rotifera, and examined the minute structures of spermatozoa. His researches disproved the then widely held view of spontaneous generation. Leeuwenhoek himself did not apply this knowledge, his discovery of bacteria, to the aetiology of morbid infections—this had to await Pasteur's pronouncement 150 years later (no. 539). His work was described in a series of 165 letters, most of which were addressed to the Royal Society and are published in the *Philosophical Transactions* (no. 281).

Foundation of the S.P.C.K. and the S.P.G.

302 THOMAS BRAY, An Essay towards promoting all Necessary and Useful Knowledge both Divine and Human. *London 1697*

As a direct result of his visit to Maryland as a church commissioner, Bray promulgated a scheme for providing parochial libraries for the clergy both at home and abroad, the first of which was instituted at Annapolis. Direct sequels were the Society for Promoting Christian Knowledge (founded 1698–9) and the Society for the Propagation of the Gospel (founded 1701).

The 'Missing Link'

303 EDWARD TYSON, Orang-Outang, or The Anatomy of a Pigmie compared with that of a Monkey, an Ape, and a Man. *London 1699*

The earliest important study in comparative morphology. Tyson compared the anatomy of man and monkeys, and the idea that man was probably a close relative of certain 'lower animals originated with him. Known to us as the idea of the 'missing link', the idea that man had descended from the apes, was not clearly shown until the publication of Darwin's *Descent of Man* in 1871, but it was Tyson who first established this conception, which led to far-reaching changes in the thought of Western man.

Occupational Diseases

304 BERNARDO RAMAZZINI, De morbis artificium diatriba. *Modena 1700*

The first systematic treatise on the subject of industrial hygiene and trade diseases. Paracelsus (no. 241) had first called attention to this subject, but Ramazzini methodically described miners' phthisis, lead-poisoning of potters, eye-trouble of gilders, printers, and other occupations—and even the 'diseases of learned men'. His work was frequently reprinted, the latest edition (in English) appeared in 1940. He influenced Thackrah, who in 1831 published the first original English contribution to the subject, Hirt in Germany, and Sir Thomas Oliver and others in our own day.

The First True Encyclopedia

305 JOHN HARRIS, Lexicon technicum, or An Universal English Dictionary of the Arts and Sciences. *London 1704*

Harris (1667?–1719), clergyman, mathematician, and (from 1709) secretary of the Royal Society, produced the first English encyclopedia arranged in alphabetical order. He was the first lexicographer to distinguish between a word-book (dictionary in modern parlance) and a subject-book (encyclopedia proper), thereby overcoming the confusion of both which Isidore (no. 141) had introduced a thousand years earlier. It appears also to be the first technical dictionary in any language. The most famous of his contributors was Isaac Newton (nos. 295, 306).

Newton on Optics

306 SIR ISAAC NEWTON, Opticks. *London 1704*

The complete collection of Newton's optical researches since his first published paper in 1671. Newton had proved by experiments that white light was composed of a mixture of light of many colours into which it could be broken by being passed through a prism. This discovery paved the way to his construction of the first reflecting telescope. Other important sections deal with the rainbow, the nature of coloured surfaces, aberrations of lenses, the double refraction of Iceland spar which led to the theory of polarization, &c. He was aware that light is not instantly propagated but travels in a finite time. His adumbration of a corpuscular theory of light is uncannily close to the modern conceptions of Planck and J. J. Thomson (nos. 578, 582). An appendix to the book, *De quadrata curvarum*, contains Newton's method of fluxions—i.e. differential calculus—in the form that he had sent it to Barrow in 1669. This led to a regrettable quarrel with Leibniz (no. 294) on priority, which greatly embittered Newton's life for some years.

Halley and his Comet

307 EDMUND HALLEY, Synopsis of the Astronomy of Comets. *London 1705*

Halley observed that the orbits of the comet of 1531, 1607, and 1682 were very similar and concluded that there might exist a regular 75-year movement of the comet. He predicted its appearance in 1758 (sixteen years after his death) and it appeared again in 1835 and 1910. Halley saw Newton's *Principia* (no. 295) through the press, and his contributions to astronomy are numerous and very important. He also gave the first detailed description and a sketch of a circulatory theory of the trade winds and published the first star catalogue of the southern hemisphere.

The English Hymnal

308 ISAAC WATTS, Hymns and Songs. *London 1707*

Watts is the founder of modern English hymnody. There were hymns and hymn-books before him, but a comparison of the post- with the ante-Watts period in *Hymns Ancient and Modern*, for example, shows striking evidence of his influence. He was not only a prolific hymn-writer, with about 6,500 hymns to his credit, but also a master of the art. His best-known hymns include 'When I survey the wondrous cross'; 'Our God, our help in ages past', and 'Jesus shall reign'. His influence on Methodism was great and he brought to an end the 'psalm-smiting' associated with the Puritans.

STEREOTYPING

The story of the invention of stereotyping is incomplete and no authentic account of the processes of the inventors (for there were more than one) survives. It is a method of duplicating relief printing surfaces so that type (or type metal) can be released for other uses, and its wear while on the printing-machine avoided. Stereotyping also makes it possible for work to be printed from more than one set of plates, as in the case of multi-unit newspaper presses, thus increasing production. As stereotypes are only about one-sixth of the thickness of type they economize in the use of type-metal and are convenient for storage. (An alternative practice is to make moulds—after printing—and to postpone casting plates until they are needed.)

In the earlier-known method of preparing stereotypes a mould of the type surface was made in plaster of Paris which was baked before casting: this mould yielded only one plate and new moulds were required for each additional duplicate. The papier-mâché mould yields several plates. Moreover, it is flexible and will adjust itself to a shaped casting-box to produce plates curved to the radius of the plate cylinder of a newspaper rotary press. Not until the papier-mâché flong had been developed was it possible to obtain full advantage from the rotary method of printing.

309 Printed with Müller's stereotype plates

Novum domini nostri Jesu Christi testamentum Syriacum, cum versione latina; cura et studio Johannis Leusden et Caroli Schaaf editum. *Leiden 1708.*

This Syriac–Latin Testament is believed to be the second book printed from stereotyped plates. The inventor of the process was Johann Müller, a minister of the German Lutheran church in Holland, who died in 1710. In copies of an issue of the book dated 1709, his name appears in the imprint.

Müller is said to have begun his experiments with a small prayer book printed in 1701. The following surviving books are thought to have been produced by Müller's process: a Syriac lexicon (1709), editions of a Dutch Bible (quarto 1711, folio 1718), and a Greek New Testament (1716). Müller went into partnership with the bookseller Samuel Luchtmans, and a further four books, with their joint imprint, are recorded as having been printed from stereotypes.

Plates were used for later editions of some of the books. Four or five of them were kept for a long time as curiosities, but only one, in the British Museum, can now be found.

310 Plate used for Printing a Bible by the Müller Process, 1718

This photograph shows what is thought to be the oldest surviving stereotype plate beside the corresponding page of a Bible in Dutch printed by Müller's sons and Luchtmans of Leiden in 1718. This is one of the books said by contemporary writers to have been printed with stereotypes. In 1801, however, a descendant of Luchtmans asserted that the plates for this Bible had been made by soldering type together. The appearance of the plate makes it difficult to believe that it could have been made in that way. *Plate 8*

311 An Application for a Licence to print Bibles and Prayer Books by Ged's Process, 1730.

JOHN JAMES and others, To the Right Worshipful, the Vice-Chancellor, and the Masters, and Scholars of the University of Cambridge. *[London 1730]*

About 1727 William Ged of Edinburgh successfully made plates reproducing pages of type. Ged and a stationer, William Fenner, went into partnership with John James and his brother Thomas to exploit the invention, and in the spring of 1730 they applied to the University of Cambridge for the use of their privilege of printing Bibles and prayer books. A licence was granted and Ged began casting plates, but he met with many difficulties, and no book completely printed by his process at Cambridge is known to survive. In 1733 he returned to Scotland.

312 Ged's Sallust, 1739

CAIUS SALLUSTIUS CRISPUS, Belli Catilinarii et Jugurthini historiae. *Edinburgh 1739.*

In 1736 Ged published proposals for issuing to subscribers an edition of Sallust to be printed by a new process whose nature he did not reveal. The title-page of the work, which appeared in 1739, announces that it was printed 'not with movable type, as is usual, but with cast plates'. This, and the reissue of 1744, are known to have been printed entirely from plates made by Ged.

313 A Specimen Plate of Ten Pages of Ged's Sallust, 1740

This is a plate submitted by Ged to the Faculty of Advocates in 1740 in the hope that they might give their patronage to his invention. It will be seen that it is a stereotype of ten pages cast as a single plate.

Some twenty-five years after Ged's death in 1749 experiments with stereotyping began again in Scotland, but it is doubtful whether a knowledge of Ged's methods survived him for so long.

314 A Specimen of Polytypage by the Abbé Rochon, 1786

An experimental print presented to the French Academy of Sciences by Rochon. It is a specimen of printing from a plate moulded on type by the process invented two years earlier by F. I. J. Hoffman, an Alsatian. Hoffman pressed a forme of type into a wet plaster and made a stereotype plate by pouring into the resulting matrix a molten alloy of lead, bismuth, and tin.

315 Standing Rules of the Stereotype Office, London, 1804

The printer of this book, Andrew Wilson, was employed by the 3rd Earl Stanhope to develop a stereotyping process which Stanhope had bought from its inventors, Alexander Tilloch and Andrew Foulis, both of Glasgow. Their first patent, describing the process in general terms, was dated 1784. Stanhope's interest in the process brought stereotyping with plaster moulds into commercial use.

316 Invention of the Papier-Mâché Flong, British Patent, 1839

The use of paper instead of plaster of Paris for moulding was introduced in 1829 by Genoux of Lyons. This British patent, based on his method, was taken out by Moses Poole in 1839. The moulding material (later known as 'flong') was layers of paper pasted together with a mixture of paste and potter's earth. The flong, still damp, was laid on the forme and was made into a matrix by pressing and drying.

317 Kronheim's Pivotal Casting-box, 1844

Kronheim's patent employed a papier-mâché 'flanc' or flong similar to that patented by Poole except that the potter's earth appears to have been omitted. The novelty in this patent was a casting apparatus. This was made of two metal plates loosely hinged 'like a portfolio'. The matrix was laid on the lower plate while it was in a horizontal position and metal strips were put round it, on three sides. The thickness of the strips determined the thickness of the casting. The upper plate was clamped down and the box pivoted on an axle so that the open side was uppermost. The molten metal was then poured into the opening and a stereotype was cast.

318 Part of a Matrix of a Page of 'The Times', 1 May 1862

In 1857 the first whole page stereo for a newspaper was successfully cast by the brothers J. and B. Dellagana for *The Times*. By 1866 they were using a curved casting-box producing a cast which fitted the plate cylinder of a rotary printing machine. This provided the curved printing surface necessary for the successful application of the rotary principle to printing with its great potentiality for increased machine speeds.

319 Stereotyping Equipment used at 'The Times' in the Nineteenth Century

The photographs show the most important pieces of equipment used in the process patented by Dellagana in 1861, as practised in *The Times* office. (1) A rolling or 'mangel' press used for moulding from the type forme; (2) A hand guillotine for trimming the dried matrix; (3) A curved casting-box for making plates for use on a rotary printing machine; (4) A machine used to trim the tail or 'tang' off the cast; (5) A hand-powered 'borer' for planing the back of the plate to the radius of the plate cylinder of a rotary printing machine; (6) A beveller to trim the plates. *Plate 9*

319a Stereotyping by the Papier Mâché Process at Poppins Court, c. 1889

The damp flong was laid on the forme and beaten with a flat brush thus being forced between the words and lines, and indented by every letter to become a perfect mould of the whole. The damp flong, still in position on the forme, was then covered with a blanket and dried under pressure in a hot press, when it was removed and detached from the type.

After it had been trimmed and prepared for casting the mould was placed flat in a pivotal casting-box. Gauges (to determine the thickness of the plate to be cast) were then placed on each side and at the foot of the moulded page, the lid of the casting box was closed, the whole was pivoted to the vertical position, and molten lead alloy was poured into the aperture at the top. When cool, the plate was removed for finishing and mounting. *Plate 9*

Greek becomes a Science

320 DOM BERNARD MONTFAUCON, Palaeographia Graeca. *Paris 1708*

What Mabillon (no. 292) did for the study of medieval Latin documents, this other great member of the congregation of St. Maur achieved in the field of medieval Greek studies. His monumental work, published a year after Mabillon's death, also created a new discipline, that of Byzantine palaeography; his results have had to be modified only in so far as photography has facilitated, and the discovery of papyri has widened, modern research.

Does the External World Exist?

321 GEORGE BERKELEY, Principles of Human Knowledge. *Dublin 1710*

From Descartes and Locke (nos. 262, 297), Berkeley derived his stringent empiricism, but apart from this was independent of all influence. In this work his principle that an object does not exist without a mind to perceive it was first laid down. The extension of this theory, that a mind must be the spring of the universe, is the central point of Berkeley's metaphysics. His intuitive methods have made his theories liable to misconception, but the fineness of his thought is instanced by the fact that the difficulties in his scheme have proved to be the points on which later philosophical thinking has turned.

Poet and Scholar

322 HORACE, Opera. Edited by Richard Bentley. *London 1711*

The *Odes* of Horace have been, with their subtle simplicity, terse yet infinitely expressive, a constant source of inspiration. All through the years they have been taught in schools, quoted in parliaments, even read in boardrooms. The edition of Bentley (1662–1742), the greatest classical scholar Britain has produced, is one of his major triumphs. Bold yet sensitive, deeply learned and at the same time understanding, it combines, as did Bentley himself, temerity, authority, and subtlety. It is one of the works of classical scholarship which has an enduring and international reputation.

Nature or Nurture?

323 JACOB BERNOULLI, Ars conjectandi. *Basel 1713*

This entry has to cover an erudite family of Protestant refugees from Antwerp who settled in Basel in 1622, and in three generations produced eight mathematicians of whom the following were outstanding. Jacob I (1654–1705) developed the calculus and gave it new applications after Leibniz and Newton (nos. 324, 306). He also wrote this profound treatise on the theory of probability. Johann I (1667–1748) extended the subject still further and wrote learnedly on optics, tides, sailing-ships, and mechanical displacements. Nicolaus (1662–1715) earned the highest degree in law at the age of 20, emigrated to Russia, and was given a state funeral by Catherine the Great. Daniel (1700–82) won the French Academy prize ten times, established the theory of kinetic gases and foreshadowed jet-propulsion. Of their 120 traceable descendants the majority have been distinguished.

A New Philosophy

324 GOTTFRIED WILHELM VON LEIBNIZ, Monadologie. *1714*

The most complete statement of the philosophy of one of the major systematic thinkers of modern times. Probably derived from Giordano Bruno, his system of philosophy was developed in close connexion with both physics and mathematics. His influence in metaphysics and logic as well as mathematics has persisted until our own day, when Russell and Whitehead's attempt to develop a system of mathematical logic as a basis of all scientific thought was inspired by him. Leibniz also conceived the idea of a universal language and of a universal encyclopedia in which all human knowledge should be systematized.

Desert Islands

325 DANIEL DEFOE, The Life and Strange Surprising Adventures of Robinson Crusoe. *London 1719–20*

The romance of Crusoe's adventures, the figure of civilized man fending for himself on a desert island, has made an imperishable impression on the mind of man throughout the civilized world. Man Friday anticipates Rousseau's 'noble savage' (no. 350). The countless imitations are ample confirmation of the impact of the book. Much of modern science fiction is basically Crusoe's island changed to a planet. This is the first of three volumes.

A Monument of Italian Scholarship

326 LODOVICO ANTONIO MURATORI, Rerum Italicarum scriptores. *Milan 1723–51*

Muratori, successively librarian of the Biblioteca Ambrosiana (1695) and to the Duke of Modena (1700), was the first to apply the critical methods of Mabillon (no. 292) to the entire corpus of medieval sources of a whole country. His collection of chronicles, law codes, letters, and poems made him the founding-father of the history of medieval Italy; all his editions are still fundamental, and a large number of them have not yet been superseded.

Measuring the Climate

327 GABRIEL DANIEL FAHRENHEIT, Experiments concerning the Degrees of Heat. *London 1724.*

Fahrenheit introduced the thermometric scale which bears his name. Immersing the thermometer in a solution of ice-water and salt he established freezing-point at 32° and the boiling-point of water at sea-level at 212°. This Fahrenheit scale with an interval of 180° between freezing and boiling-points of water has been adopted for general use in Britain and the United States to this day, as owing to its small degrees it permits very accurate readings for meteorological research. Nevertheless, it is now being generally superseded by the centigrade system. Fahrenheit improved the accuracy of the thermometer by substituting mercury for alcohol, and invented a new barometer and a hygrometer.

A New Counterpoint

328 JOHANN JOSEPH FUX, Gradus ad parnassum. *Vienna 1725*

Fux formulated rules of counterpoint that stood for nearly 200 years. The book has been frequently translated and reprinted—the latest edition in 1944. Mozart and Haydn were among the first of countless musicians nurtured on it. Debussy's humorous tribute in his *Children's Corner* suite will be recalled.

The History of Civilizations

329 GIAMBATTISTA VICO, Principi di una scienza nova intorna alla natura delle nazioni. *Naples 1725*

Vico's idea of the cyclical pattern of history, the rise and fall of civilizations in a continuous process from barbarism to civilization, was revived in our own day by Spengler (no. 596) and partly by Toynbee (no. 607). The importance of myth, tradition, and language for our understanding of primitive people is here first recognized, and Vico's explanation of the mutual hostility of social classes brought him near the Marxists. This fundamental contribution to historical philosophy and method was forgotten until the German romantics took it up, and through them it greatly influenced modern historical research.

Plant Nutrition

330 STEPHEN HALES, Vegetable Staticks or An Account of some Statical Experiments on the Sap in Vegetables. *London 1727–32*

Hales first showed that plants inspire and give off air. He studied the movement of sap in plants, discovering what is now known as root pressure. By the use of a manometer or pressure gauge, Hales traced blood-pressure, and its velocity in various animals. He is now regarded as one of the founders of modern experimental physiology.

An Improved Encyclopedia

331 EPHRAIM CHAMBERS, Cyclopedia, or an Universal Dictionary of Arts and Sciences. 2 volumes. *London 1728*

Following Harris (no. 305), Chambers concentrated on the natural sciences. A good French scholar, he adapted Moréri and Bayle (nos. 289, 300) to the common-sense climate of the English Enlightenment. Thanks to his editorial accomplishments—for instance, he introduced cross-references—the *Cyclopedia* was revised, translated, and imitated throughout the eighteenth century: the *Encyclopédie* (no. 343) was originally planned as a translation of Chambers's book. Dr. Johnson told Boswell that he formed his style partly on Chambers's 'Proposals' for this book.

Modern Dentistry Emerges

332 PIERRE FAUCHARD, Le Chirurgien Dentiste. *Paris 1728*

Fauchard made many inventions and other contributions to the technique of dentistry, but his chief merit is to have placed dentistry on a scientific basis and to have codified all that was best in its practice.

The Seed of Methodism

333 WILLIAM LAW, A Serious call to a Devout and Holy Life. *London 1729*

Law's *Serious Call* is one of the greatest of English devotional works. Law (1686–1761) foreshadowed the rising of Methodism and where he sowed, John Wesley reaped. Dr. Johnson (no. 344) attributed to the *Serious Call* his first earnest attention to religion. Wesley wrote 'it will be hardly excelled, if it be equalled, in the English language, either for beauty of expression or for justice and depth of thought'.

The 'Discovery' of the Alps

333a [ALBRECHT VON HALLER], Versuch Schweizerischer Gedichten. *Berne 1732*

Haller, a Swiss patrician, was one of the leading eighteenth-century anatomists, physiologists, and botanists; he wished Linné (no. 336) to become his successor as professor in Göttingen. His poetry, didactic and descriptive, places him only among the minor poets of his age; but *Die Alpen* created a new feeling for nature. Haller was the first to appreciate the grandeur of the Alps, hitherto regarded with fear and antipathy, and —anticipating Rousseau (no. 350)—to extol the simple life of the mountain peasants, hitherto an object of pity or derision.

Zedler's Lexicon

334 Großes vollständiges Universal-Lexicon aller Wissenschaften und Künste. *Johann Heinrich Zedler, Halle and Leipzig 1732–54*

Usually quoted by the publisher's name as *Zedler's Lexicon*, these huge folios constitute a major achievement of scholarship and lexicography. For the first time a staff of editors was employed each of whom was responsible for a special subject and its consistent treatment.

It was the first encyclopedia to include biographies of living persons and is therefore still useful as a storehouse of information on minor eighteenth-century people and institutions long since excluded from current reference books.

The Improvement of Agriculture

335 JETHRO TULL, Horse-hoeing husbandry. *London 1733*

Modern scientific agriculture in Britain begins with the work of Tull. He invented the seed-drill and the horse-hoe and found a method of pulverizing the soil for cultivation without manure. He introduced the system of sowing seeds in parallel rows between which the horse-hoe was used for cleaning the soil. His invention first made possible the elimination of much manual labour on the farms and laid the foundation for mechanizing and rationalizing the growing of crops. His book was translated into French and had a considerable influence in France, Voltaire being one of Tull's enthusiastic followers.

Classification of the Natural World

336 CAROLUS LINNAEUS, Systema naturae. *Leiden 1735*

The starting-point of modern systematic botany. Linné established the principles of class, order, genus, and species for all plants and animals. He further divided all living things into genera and species, a binomial system which has remained in use until today. His artificial system of classification, based on the number of stamens and pistils in the flower, was eventually superseded by a more natural system. At a time of great confusion in botanical nomenclature when there was a tremendous extension of botanical knowledge, his principle was of the greatest benefit to botanical science.

A Great Religious Polemic

337 JOSEPH BUTLER, The Analogy of Religion, Natural and Revealed. *London 1736*

This great polemic against deism draws an analogy between the observed principles of nature and the revealed principles of religion. Butler held that objections to the one were objections to the other and that a divine, moral government of the universe was an inescapable conclusion of scientific reasoning.

'Esse est Percipi'

338 DAVID HUME, A Treatise of Human Nature. *London 1739–40*

Hume (1711–76) was concerned to improve and correct the tenets of Locke and Berkeley (nos. 297, 321). Where the former postulated a material substance and the latter a spiritual, Hume held that the continued existence of objects distinct from perception is illusion. Hitherto a distinction had been made between reason and the combined product of sensation and experience, Hume declared that our 'rational' judgements are simply associations by custom. In the second and third books he examines the passions and morals. He rejects the view that the distinction between right and wrong is one of reason; the subject decides such issues by reference to itself. However, a moral sense is demanded as the supreme end, and by it the happiness of self and others can be combined. These opinions made an immediate impact abroad, and to some extent foreshadowed the speculations of Bentham and the Mills (nos. 378, 531).

Principle of Equilibrium

339 JEAN LE ROND D'ALEMBERT, Traité de dynamique. *Paris 1743*

The first major work of d'Alembert this is a landmark in the history of mechanics. D'Alembert's principle, still known as such, states that the 'internal forces of inertia must be equal and opposite to the forces that produce the acceleration'. With Diderot he edited the *Encyclopédie* (no. 343).

A Standard Natural History

340 GEORGE LOUIS LECLERC COMTE DE BUFFON, Histoire naturelle, générale et particulière. *Paris 1744–85*

This work presented for the first time a complete survey of natural history in a popular form, collecting together facts from many sources. It went through many editions and translations and remained very popular throughout the nineteenth century. Daubenton, Lacepède, and others collaborated with Buffon, and the book, which appeared in 44 volumes, was extensively illustrated.

Analytical Mathematics

341 LEONHARD EULER, Introductio in Analysin infinitorum. *Lausanne 1748*

Euler wrote a number of works of great importance to the development of pure mathematics. The present book established analytical mathematics as an independent science and reduced analytical operations to a much simpler basis. Many of his principles are still used in teaching mathematics.

The Spirit of Law

342 CHARLES, MARQUIS DE MONTESQUIEU, De l'esprit des lois. *Geneva 1748*

Montesquieu is known for the destructive criticism of French legal and political institutions contained in the *Lettres persanes* (1721) and for the constructive criticism of *De l'esprit des lois*, in which he compared the various kinds of constitution, with special reference to the defects of the French monarchical system. He put forward a liberal and benevolent form of monarchy subject to safeguards of individual liberty. His theories deeply influenced the political thinking which led to the French and the American Revolutions.

The French 'Encyclopédie'

343 Encyclopédie ou dictionnaire raisonné des sciences, des arts et des métiers, par une société des gens de lettres. *Paris 1751–65*

A monument and signpost in the history of European thought; the acme of French Enlightenment; a herald of the French Revolution; and a permanent source for all aspects of eighteenth-century civilization. Originally intended as a mere translation of Chambers (no. 331), it became a vehicle for the boldest expression of the spirit of the age. The editor-in-chief, Denis Diderot (1713–84), enlisted the co-operation of the most brilliant philosophers: d'Alembert (no. 339), Voltaire (nos. 345, 347), Montesquieu (no. 342), Holbach (no. 357), Condillac, and Turgot among them.

The King's English

344 SAMUEL JOHNSON, Dictionary of the English Language. *London 1755*

This is the most amazing, enduring, and endearing one-man performance in the field of lexicography. Johnson's lucid and often idiosyncratic definitions have kept their freshness, and the *Dictionary* may still be consulted for instruction or pleasure. Johnson's endeavours to 'fix' the English language once and for all, however, were nullified by Webster (no. 482) and shown to be delusive by the *Oxford English Dictionary* (no. 559).

The Birth of Cultural History

345 FRANÇOIS MARIE AROUET DE VOLTAIRE, Essai sur l'histoire générale et sur les mœurs et l'esprit des nations. *Paris 1756*

This book, begun in 1753 and issued in its final form in 1769 (omitting the reference to history in the title), has secured for Voltaire the title of the father of the history of civilization (as distinct from political history) and the creator of a '*philosophie d'histoire*' (a term coined by himself) which removed the barriers between Christian and non-Christian, European and non-European concepts of history. Voltaire, the historian, marks the watershed between Bossuet and Ranke (nos. 291, 477).

The Beginning of Atomic Physics

346 RUGGIERO GIUSEPPE BOSCOVICH, Philosophiae naturalis theoria. *Venice 1758*

This classic work by the great scientist on atomic physics is now recognized as fundamental in physical science. In Boscovich's view all matter is made up of atoms which are mere centres of attractive and repulsive force acting at a distance. No actual collision of atoms takes place, all action between bodies being action at a distance only. It is a notable example of the transference of ideas that as Boscovich has influenced modern atomic physics, so he was deeply influenced by Lucretius (no. 218).

'Le meilleur des mondes possibles'

347 FRANÇOIS MARIE AROUET DE VOLTAIRE, Candide, ou l'optimisme. *[Geneva] 1759*

Ostensibly a high-spirited novelette, in fact this is perhaps Voltaire's major contribution to philosophical thought. Candide and his engaging mentor Dr. Pangloss have caught the imagination of succeeding generations, ridiculing their follies and shaking them out of their complacency. His prose style is inimitable. It was published anonymously and Voltaire deliberately muddied the trail to avoid proscription of the book. Its bibliography is therefore obscure. It was reprinted or pirated many times in the early years; the Cramer edition, formerly accepted as the first, is now dethroned in favour of the one shown, which may have been printed in London.

The Measurement of Light

348 JOHANN HEINRICH LAMBERT, Photometria. *Augsburg 1760*

Following ideas first advanced by Bouguer, Lambert laid the foundations for the exact scientific measurement of the strength of light. He invented the photometer here described and propounded the law of the absorption of light named after him. His discoveries are of fundamental importance in astronomy, photography, and visual research generally. Lambert also first suggested the use of perspective as a means of making maps, and left important works in mathematics, cosmology, and rationalist philosophy.

The Founder of Pathological Anatomy

349 GIOVANNI BATTISTA MORGAGNI, De sedibus et causis morborum per anatomen indigatus. *Venice 1761*

At the age of 79 Morgagni completed this immense work reporting about 700 cases and post-mortems. Correlating the clinical record with the post-mortem findings, he based his diagnosis and treatment on a knowledge of the anatomical conditions of diseases. The description of many pathological conditions is due to him. Combining the task of pathologist and anatomist, he made possible great improvements in diagnosis and prognosis.

Social Contract and the French Revolution

350 JEAN-JACQUES ROUSSEAU, Principes du droit politique [i.e. Du contrat social]. *Amsterdam 1762*

Rousseau (1712–78) was fundamentally at odds with the established beliefs of his time. In the Age of Reason he advocated the greater force of intuition: against artificial refinement, he urged a return to the natural state. So, defying the absolute monarchy of France, he published his exposition of the social contract, never more clearly or powerfully stated, that government is dependent upon the mandate of the people. It had a profound influence on French political thought, and was perhaps more directly the cause of the Revolution than any other single factor. This is probably the second of two printings in 1762.

The Invention of the Chronometer

351 [JOHN HARRISON], An Account of the Proceedings in Order to discover the Longitude. *London 1763*

This anonymous paper won the prize of £20,000 offered by the Board of Longitude for an accurate chronometer and thus revolutionized the navigation system. Harrison was the inventor of a number of other improvements in clock construction.

Penal Reform

352 CESARE BECCARIA, Dei delitti e delle pene. *[London] 1764*

Beccaria was the first writer to plead for humane views on the treatment of criminals. Opposing capital punishment, torture, and the use of force, he maintained that education and cure of the criminal rather than revenge should be the aim of society in its treatment of the offender. The book had an immense immediate success, six editions being published within eighteen months. Many translations were also published, including a French one with an anonymous commentary by Voltaire. Its success led to the introduction of many reforms in the penal codes of the principal European nations.

The Nobility of Ancient Art

353 JOHANN JOACHIM WINCKELMANN, Geschichte der Kunst des Altertums. *Dresden 1764*

In his masterpiece Winckelmann set out both the history of Greek art and the principles on which it seemed to him to be based. To him all the conditions, political, social, and intellectual, of life in ancient Greece seemed to foster the highest creative activity. The end of art is beauty, and the true artist depicts a 'noble simplicity and calm greatness, in which natural proportions are maintained, without breaking the harmony of the general outline'. The enthusiasm and the impressive style of Winckelmann's work give it an enduring value; it formed a starting-point for Lessing's *Laokoön* (no. 355a), and exercised a deep influence on the aesthetic theory of the age. It was superseded only when genuine works of Greek art became known. Winckelmann's weakness lay in basing his theories almost exclusively on late Hellenic and Roman copies which he mistook for originals.

The Practice of English Law

354 SIR WILLIAM BLACKSTONE, Commentaries on the Laws of England. *London 1765*

The four volumes of the *Commentaries*, completed in 1769, formed the standard treatise on common law for nearly 100 years. They were translated into French, German, Italian, and Russian, and remain a hallowed textbook for students. Blackstone's judgments are still quoted and revered in English and Commonwealth courts and in the United States of America.

The First Gothic Novel

355 [HORACE WALPOLE], The Castle of Otranto, a Story. Translated by William Marshal, Gent. From the Original Italian of Onuphrio Muralto, Canon of the Church of St. Nicholas at Otranto. *London 1765*

'*The Castle of Otranto* is remarkable not only for the wild interest of the story, but as the first modern attempt to found a tale of amusing fiction upon the basis of the ancient romances of chivalry' wrote Sir Walter Scott. The elaborate subterfuge on the title-page promulgated an atmosphere of fabrication which Chatterton thought to justify the Rowley Poems, influenced Ireland, the Shakespeare forger, and others including the whole school of Gothic novelists. Its influence on Poe is manifest and has survived in such novels as *Dracula* and in modern detective stories and horror films.

This is the presentation copy to William Cole. Walpole's letter to him, 9 March 1765, explains that the story was inspired by a dream and that its setting was Strawberry Hill. Cole transcribed Walpole's letter on the fly-leaves.

The Limits of the Arts

355a GOTTHOLD LESSING, Laokoön oder über die Grenzen der Malerei und Poesie. *Berlin 1766*

Lessing (1729–81), in the words of Macaulay, 'beyond all dispute, the first critic of Europe', was one of the principle figures in the *Aufklärung*, the emancipation of German literature from the narrow classicism of the French school. *Laokoön*, which takes its name from the famous statue discovered in Rome in the sixteenth century, discusses the differences in the sculptor's treatment of Laocoön wrestling with the serpents, and in Virgil's famous description of the same scene, and from there goes on to discuss the limits and limitations of all the arts. It is the first work to consider what the arts are for, and its theme has become the theme of all criticism.

Scientific Agriculture Begins

356 ARTHUR YOUNG, A Six Weeks Tour through the Southern Counties of England and Wales. *London 1768*

Young published a series of tours in England and France and these, together with his reports on the agriculture of various counties issued when he became the first secretary to the Board of Agriculture, provide us with much information about the ideas of this great reformer of English agriculture. He wanted to establish larger farm units and security of tenure, increase the fertility of soil by using fertilizers, improve crop production, stock breeding, and the road system—in short, he introduced the ideas of modern scientific agriculture and farm management. His books were translated into Russian, French, and German, and their influence went far beyond the frontiers of England.

Eighteenth-century Free-thought

357 N. MIRABAD (i.e. Baron D'Holbach), Système de la nature. *London [Amsterdam] 1770*

D'Holbach, a nobleman from the Rhenish Palatinate, was one of the leading figures of the French Enlightenment. His uncompromisingly atheistic *Système de la nature* became the principal free-thought textbook of the late eighteenth century. It was published pseudonymously, and very few knew that it was by the cultivated and courtly Baron. An English translation appeared in 1795.

The First Modern Treatise on Language

358 JOHANN GOTTFRIED HERDER, Abhandlung über den Ursprung der Sprache. *Berlin 1772*

Herder departed from the current medieval view that language is a divine gift. By observation and comparison of ancient and modern language he reached the conclusion that language was a human invention. He thus originated the scientific study of language.

The Discovery of Oxygen Foreshadowed

359 JOSEPH PRIESTLEY, Observations on Different Kinds of Air. *London 1772*

This paper announced the discovery of hydrochloric acid and nitric oxide and the use of the latter in measuring the purity of air—which led through the work of Cavendish, Fontana, and others to exact eudiometry. Priestley also describes experiments proving that growing plants can restore air which has been vitiated by combustion, respiration, or putrefaction, and proposes the saturation of water with carbonic acid under pressure leading to the creation of the mineral-water industry. Priestley greatly improved experimental methods for the investigation of gases, and in 1774 discovered oxygen—independently of Rey, Scheele, and Lavoisier (no. 379).

Scots Wha' Hae!

360 Encyclopaedia Britannica, or a Dictionary of Arts and Sciences. *London 1773*.

The most famous of all encyclopedias in the English language was sponsored by 'a society of gentlemen in Scotland' and produced by the antiquarian William Smellie, the engraver Andrew Bell, and the printer Colin Macfarquhar, all of Edinburgh. It was the British counterblast to the French *Encyclopédie* (no. 343), and appeared first in numbers each priced 6*d*., or 8*d*. on better paper (1768–71). The triumphal progress started with the second edition (10 vols., 1777–84) and continued for 150 years until the ownership was transferred to the United States.

The Foundation of Anthropology

361 JOHANN FRIEDRICH BLUMENBACH, De generis humani varietate nativa. *Göttingen 1776*

With this work Blumenbach founded the science of anthropology. Having studied comparative anatomy, he was the first to realize its importance in the study of man's history, and this led him to make very important craniological observations. His classification of races by measurement and their division into five—Caucasian or white, Mongolian or yellow, Malayan or brown, Negro or black, and American or red—has remained fundamental until our day with comparatively little modification.

The Declaration of Independence

362 In Congress, 4 July, 1776, A Declaration. *John Dunlap, Philadelphia 1776*

The Continental Congress resolved on 2 July 1776, 'that these United Colonies are, and of right ought to be, free and independent states'. On 4 July they accepted, with some modifications, Thomas Jefferson's 'Rough Draft' of why secession from the British Empire was lawful because 'a decent respect to the opinions of mankind required that they should declare the causes which impel them to the separation'. Of the original broadside *Declaration* only fifteen copies survive. It was set up and printed the same night by Dunlap under the watchful eye of the Committee of Five appointed by Congress for the purpose. Shown with it is its first newspaper appearance, 10 July, the form in which 'We, the people' first read it.

The Age of 'Laissez-faire'

363 ADAM SMITH, The Wealth of Nations. *A. Strahan, London 1776*

Although Adam Smith did not create the study of political economy, *The Wealth of Nations*, coming at a point when 'natural liberty' was being widely debated, had a decisive influence both on the study of national economy and on the freeing of economic policy from the artificial restraint of the mercantilist system (*see* no. 278). Smith's statement that labour is the source of a nation's commodities and that the variations in 'stock' values are due to the interaction of wages, profits, and rent, formulated the doctrine of the classic school of economic thought, and round it all modern economic discussion has revolved.

The End of the Ancient World

364 EDWARD GIBBON, The History of the Decline and Fall of the Roman Empire. *A. Strahan and T. Cadell, London 1776–88*

From the moment when the publisher, William Strahan, read the manuscript and immediately doubled the printing order, this masterpiece of literary style and historical penetration has remained, with Macaulay (no. 515), one of the most popular historical works. Although Gibbon's main thesis—that the fall of Rome was due to the victory of Christianity—is untenable, his comprehensive picture of the Roman and Byzantine world from the death of Marcus Aurelius (180) to the fall of Constantinople (1453) has made his place secure also among scholars.

A New Continent

365 CAPTAIN JAMES COOK, A Voyage towards the South Pole and Round the World. *London 1777*

An account of Cook's second great voyage, lasting three years, in which he visited New Zealand, discovered some unknown islands in the Pacific, satisfactorily disproved the existence of a great Antarctic continent, and showed that he had conquered the spectre of scurvy by losing only one man out of 118.

Cook also charted the east coast of Australia —hitherto unknown—and on his third voyage, seeking a North-west passage, he discovered Hawaii.

Prison Reform

366 JOHN HOWARD, The State of Prisons. *London 1777*

From the casual experience of visiting Bedford jail, came Howard's determination to improve prison conditions. When he died of prison fever in 1790 he was famous in every European country. *The State of Prisons*, which passed through edition after edition, served to reinforce his constant endeavours to improve the appalling conditions of eighteenth-century prisons.

Two copies are shown, one open (lent by the Howard League for Penal Reform), the other (lent by Eton College) to show a fine painting of Howard beneath the vellum, by Edwards of Halifax. *Plate 28*

The Discovery of 'Mesmerism'

367 FRANZ ANTON MESMER, Mémoire sur la découverte du magnétisme animal. *Geneva and Paris 1779*

Mesmer's name is perpetuated in 'mesmerism'. Experimenting with the use of magnetism in medical treatment he found that there was a healing magnetic power in his own hands and that he could obtain results in treating nervous disorders without a magnet. He called this faculty 'animal' magnetism. Though attacked as a charlatan and never himself grasping the full significance of his treatment, there is no doubt that his discovery of the suggestibility on the part of the patient was the key to the healing he accomplished and that it was an essential element in the development of modern hypnosis and psychotherapy.

Pure Reason

368 IMMANUEL KANT, Kritik der reinen Vernunft. *Riga 1781*

The influence of Kant (1724–1804) is felt, more than that of any other philosopher, in the critical method of modern philosophers. No other thinker has been able to hold with such firmness the balance between speculative and empirical ideas, the consideration of which is predominant in modern philosophy. His penetrating analysis of the elements involved in synthesis, and the subjective process by which these elements are realized in the individual consciousness, demonstrated the operation of 'pure reason', and the simplicity and cogency of his arguments achieved immediate fame. His methods fascinated Coleridge; they were amplified by Fichte (no. 386); they dominated Western philosophical thought throughout the nineteenth century, as they do today.

The First Aerial Voyage

369 FAUJAS DE SAINT-FOND, Description des expériences de la machine aérostatique de MM. Montgolfier. *Paris 1783*

Despite the centuries of fruitless effort to fly like the birds, it was a balloon—a 'cloud enclosed in a bag'—that first took men for a voyage in the air. Faujas de Saint-Fond here describes this epoch-making event when, on 21 November 1783, Pilâtre de Rozier (pilot) and the Marquis d'Arlandes took off from the Château de la Muette in the Bois de Boulogne, in their gaily decorated Montgolfier hot-air balloon, and sailed across Paris for twenty-five minutes. This 5½-mile journey introduced the first air age. *Plate 29*

The Discovery of a New Planet

370 SIR FREDERICK WILLIAM HERSCHEL, Motion of the Solar System in Space. *London 1783*

Herschel's most widely known discovery is that of a new planet in 1781, now named Uranus. His most important scientific discovery is probably the proof—arrived at by observation of pairs of stars in close contiguity—that the laws of gravity and other mechanical laws applicable in the solar system also apply in the more remote systems of the universe. He made many of his own instruments, notably the famous reflecting telescope at Slough of 40-ft. focal length and a 4-ft. aperture.

The Sunday School Movement

371 [ROBERT RAIKES], The Gloucester Journal. *Gloucester, 3 November 1783*

Raikes inherited proprietorship of the *Journal* from his father. He inserted a paragraph in this issue as a piece of local news on the Sunday schools he had started in his neighbourhood. Inquiries poured in from all over the kingdom. Wesley notes the spread of the movement in 1784 and in 1786 it was said that 200,000 children were enrolled. In 1789 the movement spread to the U.S.A.

Figaro

372 PIERRE AUGUSTIN CARON DE BEAUMARCHAIS, La Folle Journée ou le Mariage de Figaro. *Kehl 1784*

1784 represented a peak in the life of Beaumarchais. Sixty-seven performances of *Figaro* were given in that year; public interest was whetted by its satirical references to the aristocracy, and it was this that first won it fame. Although greeted with enthusiasm by society it in fact contributed largely to its destruction. It is, however, the music of Mozart which has immortalized it, and kept it as the perfect type of comedy. To Beaumarchais, a controversial figure, whose other principal achievement was his edition of the complete works of Voltaire, its transformation would probably be surprising, but no one can doubt its immortality.

This is not the first edition, which appeared earlier in the same year, but the one printed by Beaumarchais himself at Kehl, where the works of Voltaire were also printed (Baskerville's types were purchased for this purpose).

'The Boast of Scotland'

373 ROBERT BURNS, Poems Chiefly in the Scottish Dialect. *Kilmarnock 1786*

There has never been a more truly national poet than Burns. Himself of humble origin he spoke the language of the people and his songs are part of the air breathed by Scots the world over. It has been said of the *Lyrical Ballads* (no. 433) that no clue can be gained from them that 'men eat or drink, marry or are given in marriage'. None could say that of Burns. He may have gone to the other extreme, but his lyrics are as full of life as he was himself. They are 'the links, the watch-words, the masonic symbols of Scottish life'.

The Indo-European Family of Languages

374 Sir William Jones, On the Hindus. *London 1786*

This was a paper read to the Bengal Asiatic Society and published in their Transactions. Jones, from 1783 judge of the supreme court of the East India Company in Calcutta, was one of the originators of Sanskrit studies and the first to recognize the relationship between Sanskrit, Greek, Latin, and Gothic. He was thus the founder of comparative philology. His discovery was carried further by Rask, Bopp, and Grimm (nos. 443, 449, 456). (*See also* 358.)

Theory of Acoustics

375 Ernst Florens Friedrich Chladni, Neue Entdeckungen über die Theorie des Klanges. *Leipzig 1787*

This is the first book in which the theory of acoustics was scientifically expounded. Chladni, a professor of physics in Breslau, made experiments with sand scattered on metal plates, the edges of which were then bowed vertically and the resulting figures made in the sand were recorded. These still are known as Chladni figures, and the laws of acoustics which he based on them have never been challenged.

A Classical Companion

376 John Lemprière, Bibliotheca classica. *Reading 1788*

'Lemprière's Classical Dictionary' is the first of a new kind of manual: the rendering of a body of knowledge not easily accessible in any other form into a system of alphabetical articles for the use of those who lack the time or the learning to seek out the sources; the 'Oxford Companion' series is a distinguished descendant. Lemprière (*c.* 1765–1824) was born in Jersey and was a schoolmaster for most of his life. His dictionary of classical mythology, always readable and lively if inaccurate, has been frequently re-edited; it has special fame as a source of inspiration to Keats.

The American Constitution Interpreted

377 Alexander Hamilton, James Madison (and) John Jay, The Federalist. *New York 1788*

Three of America's leading statesmen here explain and defend the new constitution, attempting to win ratification for it in the important but hostile state of New York. It has become one of America's most important contributions to political theory. Exhibited is George Washington's copy as well as a scrapbook containing the original pseudonymous newspaper appearances of these essays.

Utilitarianism

378 Jeremy Bentham, Principles of Morals and Legislation. *London 1789*

His fame as the inventor of 'utilitarian' philosophy has latterly made the doctrine of Bentham somewhat unfashionable; it seems facile. But that it should be so is a measure of his influence, for the facts which are now considered too obvious to need demonstration were not seen at all until Bentham pointed them out. 'The greatest happiness of the greatest number' is not the be-all and end-all of Benthamism (the phrase came earlier, from Priestley or Beccaria); it lies rather in the unflinching application of common sense to the nature of society, an application which has provided the basis for modern political science.

A Revolution in Chemistry

379 Antoine de Lavoisier, Traité de chimie. *Paris 1789*

The chemical revolution was begun by the criticism of alchemical views and the phlogiston theory by such as Boyle (no. 274) and Rey, and was completed by Lavoisier. Lavoisier's use of the chemical balance demonstrated the weight of matter at every chemical change, and a rational system of elements was established. He defined element and compound, explained burning as a chemical combination with oxygen, and his ideas on the conservation of matter enabled him to develop methods of chemical analysis. Lavoisier was a victim of the French Revolution, but he said: 'La révolution en chimie est faite.'

The Consequences of Revolution

380 Edmund Burke, Reflections on the Revolution in France. *London 1790*

It is strange that Burke, who for all his influence enjoyed less of the practical business of government than most of his contemporaries, should have written, in defence of a working régime and against a liberating revolution, one of the most brilliant of polemics. Though he spoke for the prevailing reaction of horror, his argument was not without faults, as trenchantly set forth in *The Rights of Man* (no. 382). But Burke's words on the French popular leaders are still valid today: 'Alas, they little know how many a weary step is to be taken before they can form themselves into a mass which has a true political personality.'

Discovery of Animal Electricity

381 LUIGI GALVANI, De viribus electricitatis in motu musculari. *Bologna 1791*

Galvani noticed that dissected frogs' legs twitched whenever an electric charge occurred near them. He called this force 'animal electricity'. He sent the paper to Volta (no. 432) who repeated the experiments which led directly to his discovery of the Voltaic pile, the source of direct current generation. This copy is inscribed by Galvani to Volta.

The Rights of Man

382 THOMAS PAINE, The Rights of Man. *London 1791*

The Rights of Man was written in answer to Burke's sharp reaction to the French Revolution (no. 380). In it, with a force and clarity which have made the book ever memorable, Paine laid down those principles of fundamental human rights which must stand, no matter what excesses were committed to achieve them. Paine's deep and bitter knowledge of practical politics enabled him to see where Burke's vision was clouded with horror, and his work has remained the textbook of all radical thought and the clearest exposition of the elementary principles of democracy.

Women's Rights

383 MARY WOLLSTONECRAFT, A Vindication of the Rights of Women. *London 1792*

Like her husband William Godwin (no. 384), Mary Wollstonecraft endured all the unpopularity of a pioneer ahead of the times, without living to see her predictions fulfilled. *A Vindication* was a courageous attack on the conventions of the period, which was to be remembered years later (*see* no. 586) when the struggle which she began was brought to a successful conclusion.

Rational Man

384 WILLIAM GODWIN, An Enquiry concerning Political Justice. *London 1793*

This is one of the earliest and clearest theoretical expositions of socialist and anarchist doctrine. Godwin believed that the motives of all human action were subject to reason, that reason taught benevolence, and that therefore all rational creatures could live in harmony without laws and institutions. Neglected at the time, his doctrines first found a practical exponent in the philanthropic industrial experiments of Robert Owen (no. 446).

Can Man Become Perfect?

385 MARIE JEAN ANTOINE NICOLAS MARQUIS DE CONDORCET, Esquisse d'un tableau historique des progrès de l'esprit humain. *Paris 1794*

This prophetic statement on the development of mankind has remained the inspiration for liberal rationalists throughout the nineteenth and twentieth centuries. Condorcet believed in the perfectibility of man. Mankind is destined for an indefinite progress in the future—the gospel of the nineteenth century. He predicted growing equality between classes and nations, the intellectual, physical, and moral improvement of man, and popular education as the source of all true progress.

The Foundations of Knowledge

386 JOHANN GOTTLIEB FICHTE, Über den Begriff der Wissenschaftslehre. *Weimar 1794*

Fichte was a devoted disciple of Kant (no. 368), but his own theories, developed during his professorship at Jena 1794–9, went beyond Kant in completing and enlarging his work, by demonstrating that all the necessary conditions of knowledge can be derived from a single principle, and consequently a complete system of knowledge can be achieved. In the *Wissenschaftslehre* the way is prepared for the later Hegelian dialectic, and it provided a basis for all nineteenth-century German philosophical speculation.

Practical Proof of the Existence of God

387 WILLIAM PALEY, Evidences of Christianity. *London 1794*

Until this century 'Paley's Evidences' was the first theological treatise for all students. It is the epitome of eighteenth-century theological reasoning; rational, empirical, it seeks to demonstrate the existence of God by reference to physical phenomena, particularly the human body, and in doing so controverts the theory of the adaptation of an organism to its circumstances by use. Without an understanding of Paley's position, the opposition to the theory of evolution is incomprehensible; the *Evidences* is a testimony to a whole climate of thought, which is still alive.

Theory of the Earth

388 CHARLES HUTTON, The Theory of the Earth. *Edinburgh 1795*

Modern geology and meteorology begin with this work. Hutton developed the view that the formation of the earth is one continuing process which can be studied entirely from terrestrial materials without cosmological or supernatural ideas intervening. He investigated the changes of the atmosphere, and in his theory of rains found that rainfall is controlled by the humidity of the air and different aerial currents in the higher atmosphere.

The New Philology

389 FRIEDRICH AUGUST WOLF, Prolegomena in Homerum. *Halle 1795*

When Wolf was elected to a chair at the Prussian University at Halle in 1783, a critical point in the history of education had been reached. The literary impulse of the Renaissance was almost spent, and the new ideas, derived from Locke and Rousseau, sought to free scholarship from its dry triviality at the expense of discipline and scientific inquiry. Wolf, by force of will and the aid of Frederick the Great's ministers, founded the new 'knowledge of human nature as exhibited in antiquity'. The *Prolegomena* were written in a great hurry to meet the needs of a lecture course, and they have all the merits of lectures: command of method, the gift of inspiration, breadth of view. It is not a theory, but a collection of great ideas, which have inspired and given purpose to education ever since.

The Origins of Brockhaus

390 [FRIEDRICH ARNOLD BROCKHAUS], Conversationslexikon mit vorzüglicher Rücksicht auf die gegenwärtigen Zeiten. *Leipzig 1796–1808*

Dr. R. G. Löbel's *Conversationslexicon* had been issued at a loss by several successive publishers before 1808 when Friedrich Arnold Brockhaus, with the sure instinct of the great publisher, recognized its potentialities, bought it, and developed it into one of the most consistently successful dictionaries. During 150 years, sixteen editions (each frequently reprinted) have appeared of the German 'Brockhaus', and licensed adaptations as well as rival imitations have appeared in Russia, Italy, France, Spain, England, and the United States.

The Beginnings of Sociology

391 SIR FREDERICK MORTON EDEN, The State of the Poor. *London 1797*

This book represents the first real attempt at a survey of working-class conditions, diets, and ways of living. Based on reports sent in by correspondents all over the country, it presents an invaluable picture of the condition of agricultural workers, miners, and rural paupers in the early years of the French wars.

The Discovery of Vaccination

392 EDWARD JENNER, An Inquiry into the Causes and Effects of Variolae Vaccinae, a Disease Known by the Name of . . . Cowpox. *London 1798*

Epidemics of smallpox had raged throughout Europe and America for many years. Jenner, a country practitioner in Gloucestershire, noticed that some villagers having cowpox remained immune from smallpox and that others having had a mild form of smallpox were immune from a second attack. He conceived the idea of injecting cowpox lymph taken from one patient into another who had not yet been immunized. The success of this method was the beginning of vaccination, one of the greatest practical advances in preventive medicine.

Population and Subsistence

393 THOMAS MALTHUS, An Essay on the Principle of Population. *London 1798*

'Malthus's law', that population increases at a greater rate than the means of subsistence, was one of the first and is still one of the most widely debated of modern economic theories. The work aroused a storm of controversy since Malthus held that checks on the growth of population would be necessary, a theory which is still not finally extinguished. Malthus has exercised a strong influence, not merely in economics, but in the whole realm of social theory.

Exploration of Africa

394 MUNGO PARK, Travels in the Interior of Africa. *London 1799*

Park was the first European of modern times to reach the Niger. He explored it in two journeys in 1795 and 1805, suffering great hardship. When attacked by natives he was drowned in 1805, after exploring the river as far as Boussa. Park stimulated the many others who followed him by the publication of this book in 1799. It became a classic of travel literature, being translated into most European languages. His scientific observations on the botany and meteorology and on the social and domestic life of the Negroes of the region have remained of lasting value.

'The Second Edition of Newton's Principia'

395 PIERRE SIMON LAPLACE, Traité de mécanique céleste. *Paris 1799–1825*

In this codification of the work of his predecessors, the further consequences of the theories of Newton, Euler, d'Alembert, and Lagrange (nos. 295, 341, 339) were brilliantly expounded. Laplace developed an analytical theory of tides, deduced the mass of the moon, improved the calculation of cosmic orbits, and predicted that Saturn's rings would be found to rotate. Most notably of all, he propounded the modern Nebular Hypothesis, independently adumbrated by Kant.

THE HAND PRESS

396 Rolling or Copper-plate Press, Eighteenth or early Nineteenth Century

In the rolling press, used for printing from incised or etched plates, power is applied by passing the plate and paper, covered by thick blankets, between oaken rollers held in a rigid frame. The upper roller, turned by a capstan, carries the plate through the press. The use of a cylinder makes it possible to print an area limited only by the width of the rollers. Modern rolling presses have steel cylinders and gearing between the capstan and the impression roller. *Plate 10*

397 A Lithographic Handpress, c. 1875

The press shown here is still in regular use as a transfer press. An exact replica of it by the same maker is illustrated and described in Richmond's *Grammar of Lithography* first published in 1878. Pressure is regulated to the thickness of the stone by the screw in the crosshead which determines the height of the scraper in the pressure box. Pressure is applied by depressing the lever: this operates an eccentric which has the effect of raising the cylinder underneath the framing thus bringing the stone and tympan to the scraper. By turning the handle, friction between the cylinder and the bed-bands forces the stone under the scraper. *Plate 10*

398 Stanhope Press, about 1800

The Stanhope Press was the first hand-press to combine an iron frame, compound lever action, and a platen which covered the whole forme. It was designed by Charles, 3rd Earl Stanhope (1753–1816), whose interest in the improvement of printing also led him to experiment with stereotyping and logotypes. According to John Johnson (*Typographia*, 1824) the first press was made by Robert Walker, Stanhope's engineer, in 1800, and used by William Bulmer. Stanhope deliberately refrained from patenting his design, so that the printing trade might have free use of it. The power of the conventional screw was increased towards the end of the pull by the action of the compound levers. This at first caused the staple to break, and the press was redesigned in 1807 with the curved and flanged staples seen in most surviving examples. *Plate 11*

399 Ruthven Press, 1813

John Ruthven, an Edinburgh printer, patented in 1813 an iron press in which the bed carrying the type remained stationary while the platen was moved over it on a wheeled carriage. Springs kept the platen raised until the moment of impression, when power was applied through a series of levers worked by depressing a bar at the side of the press. All descriptions of the press agree that it had merits, but, for one reason or another, it found no favour with the trade. *Plate 11*

400 Columbian Press, 1817

The Columbian press derived its power from a system of levers which converted the lateral movement of the bar to the vertical movement of the iron beam from which the platen was suspended. A cast-iron eagle, the most conspicuous feature, acted as an adjustable counterweight. George Clymer of Philadelphia, the inventor, produced many improved experimental wooden and iron presses from 1800 onwards. He brought his final design, the Columbian, to England in 1817, and here it was more successful than in his native United States. Johnson (*Typographia*, 1824) speaks highly of its power, and Hansard (*Typographia*, 1825) refers to the only substantial improvement which appears to have been made in the design: the moving of the hinge of the bar from the further to the near cheek of the press.

401 Albion Press, c. 1822

The Albion Press (the name is evidently a counter to that of the Columbian) was invented by R. W. Cope in or before 1822. Its power was derived from a knuckle-joint working within the hollow piston from which the platen was suspended. Pulling the bar brought an inclined slab of steel (the chill) towards a vertical position, forcing down the platen. The Albion was simple in construction (and therefore durable and cheap), more compact than the Columbian, and easy to work. Presses working on similar principles were designed and used in America (Washington Press) and Germany (Hagar Press). Both Albion and Columbian presses were used commercially well into the twentieth century and several of the English private presses, among them Kelmscott, Doves, and Ashendene, used Albion presses.

THE APPLICATION OF MECHANICAL POWER

It is assumed that the printers of the late eighteenth and early nineteenth centuries were aware of the changes in manufacturing methods which were taking place during the Industrial Revolution; for they printed accounts of all that was happening. It is likely that some of them considered how mechanical invention might be applied to their own operations, and how steam-power could be used to make their work easier, more speedy, and more profitable.

Nevertheless, printers were slow to adopt the new ideas. The reasons for this have still to be studied, but it was then an old craft industry of conservative mind which had not hitherto been subjected to demands beyond the capacity of its workers and their equipment. It may have been thought that the crafts of the compositor and pressman were too complicated for the machine designer. But when the industry was overtaken by a continuously multiplying demand for books and newspapers from a rapidly increasing population which was fast becoming more prosperous and more literate, change was inevitable.

The need for higher operational speeds was felt most acutely in the offices of the daily newspapers, where, of necessity, production was limited to a few of the early hours of each morning. The problem increased in urgency with a steep rise in circulation which, in the case of *The Times*, was phenomenal. It was the newspaper offices, and *The Times* in particular, which took the initiative in mechanization and gave it the needed impetus throughout most of the century.

The machines shown here, and the enlarged prints on the walls, have been selected to illustrate that evolution. This part of the Exhibition is historical, and its arrangement a broadly logical sequence. It has two main divisions: one illustrates the slow development of mechanical composition, the other the evolution of mechanical printing. A smaller section covers stereotyping, a process on which successful rotary printing depended.

MECHANICAL PLATENS AND PRINTING MACHINES

The wooden hand-press, used by printers for 350 years, was essentially a machine, for the movement of its carriage and platen were effected by simple mechanisms set in motion by hand. This was also true of Stanhope's iron press of 1800, which made no fundamental change in design, but improved output because those mechanisms were more efficient and powerful so that a forme might be printed at one pull of the bar, instead of two as formerly. The next step was to apply power drive. As early as 1790 William Nicholson made sketchy but prophetic proposals for printing with cylinders, which he never carried out. Practical experimentation and invention began in the first years of the nineteenth century and led to the development of three groups of printing machines: they were the mechanical platen, the flat-bed and cylinder machine, and the rotary machine.

The mechanical platen, in the form inherited from the hand-press, had a limited success and eventually died out. (It is regretted that the ubiquitous and invaluable jobbing platen machine can have no place in the present Exhibition.) The flat-bed and cylinder machine, although restricted in size and capacity because of the mechanical limitations placed upon it by a heavy reciprocating carriage, was the object of much ingenious design and soon formed the largest group. The rotary machine, possessing all the advantages of a continuous rotative movement, offered the greatest promise to the engineers but was slow to reach maturity. The chief reason for this was the difficulty of securing rectangular-shaped type on a roller-like surface, and success was delayed until curved stereotypes could be made from type formes and attached to printing cylinders. But the evolution of the newspaper rotary was not complete until it printed the paper on both sides, fed from a continuous reel, and delivered its product folded.

402 Nicholson's Proposals for Printing Machines, 1790

It would not be true to say that any of the developments in printing machinery originated with William Nicholson, but he made an uncanny forecast of the direction development was to take. The two drawings shown are taken from Savage's *Dictionary of the Art of Printing*, 1841, which reproduced Nicholson's patent in full.

In the first drawing, which has the outline of a hand-press, *A* is the impression cylinder in gear with and driving the carriage *HI* to and fro. *B* is the inking cylinder, with distributing rollers: these take their ink supply from the 'ink block' (duct) at *O* as this advances with the carriage.

In the second drawing, which shows three cylinders vertically arranged, *B* is an inking cylinder with distributors and an ink duct; *A* is a cylinder 'having the letter imposed upon its surface'; *E* is the impression cylinder.

From the patent specification

403 Koenig's First Experiments: the 'Suhl Press', c. 1803

We owe the invention of the printing machine to Frederick Koenig who was born in Thuringia in 1774 and became a printer. His first idea was to improve the method of inking, which, at that time, was done by dabbing the type with leather-covered 'balls', and his experiments were directed to that end. Koenig went in 1803 to Suhl in Saxony to experiment on a printing machine in collaboration with a mechanic named Kummer, and there produced a design which has come to be called the 'Suhl Press'. It was to be a power-driven press in which he proposed to use rollers, covered with leather like the ink-balls, and to position them at right angles to the travel of the carriage, so that they inked the type forme as it passed to and from the platen. Whether the construction of a machine of this kind was completed is uncertain.

Photograph of a model

404 The First Power-driven Printing Machine, 1810

In 1806 Koenig came to London where he entered into partnership with Thomas Bensley, a prominent printer, and two others. He was joined by his fellow countryman Andreas Bauer, a skilled engineer, and continued his experiments. In 1810 he was granted his first British patent for a machine which, in the following year, was at work in Bensley's office where it printed sheet H of the *Annual Register* for that year.

The machine was a development of the Suhl Press and was driven by steam-power. The inking system was, like that proposed for the Suhl, a vertical arrangement of rollers, but much improved, and two inkers now covered the forme. The machine was fully automatic, requiring only the manual laying-on and taking-off of sheets.

But it was a failure, and contemporary critics said this was due to the retention of the screw to actuate the platen. The real mistake was to have persevered with the unpromising platen principle at all, as the inventor was to admit by adopting the impression cylinder in the design of his next machine.

Technical drawings

405 The First Cylinder Printing Machine, 1812

In 1811 Koenig took out a patent for another machine which he built a year later. The 'pressing cylinder' was divided into three sections and each section was fitted with a frisket to hold the paper against the cylinder during printing. At each third of a revolution the cylinder was stopped while another sheet was laid on the machine, and to allow the reciprocating carriage to return, the cylinder being recessed at intervals for this purpose. There were two 'inking cylinders' which revolved constantly in opposite directions and were made to rock so that they were alternately lowered to ink the type and raised to clear the forme on its return. The output was 800 impressions an hour.

Koenig had secured the right to make multiple machines to this design, and when the machine just described was shown in Bensley's office Mr. John Walter ordered two of the double machines for Printing House Square.

Photograph of a model

406 Bacon and Donkin's Prismatic Rotary Machine, 1813

Although it did not succeed, this machine was important for two reasons: it was the first machine to be made on the rotary principle and it was provided with a very advanced inking system. The inventors used ordinary type which they arranged on four sides of a prism, opposite an impression cylinder of similar shape. The ink ductor had a steel plate and metal roller, and thumb-screws, regulating the pressure of the plate against the roller, controlled the flow of ink, as on a modern ink fountain. Moreover, for the first time an elastic composition of glue and treacle was used to cover the inking rollers. One of these machines was installed at the Cambridge University Press.

An engraving

407 The First Machine made for 'The Times', 1814

The first double machine ordered by Mr. John Walter had two cylinders but only one type forme: output was doubled by printing on both journeys of the reciprocating carriage. The friskets were now discarded and this machine was fitted with endless tapes to secure the sheet of paper during printing. Output was raised to 1,100 impressions an hour.

The machine was erected at Printing House Square in secret, and the first issue of *The Times* which it printed was that dated 29 November 1814. *Plate 12*

A model

408 Cowper's Rotary, 1816

Edward Cowper, the brother-in-law of Applegath, with whom he was to be associated as an engineering adviser for many years, recognized, like Nicholson, the advantages of a curved printing surface mounted on a continuously revolving cylinder. The difficulty was to provide this surface. Cowper, who would have been aware of the Bacon and Donkin project, must have realized that single types, however shaped or arranged, had very serious disadvantages, and that the solid stereotype plate offered much better prospects of success if they could be curved.

The only method of casting stereotypes known at that time was the plaster process, which produced a flat plate. Cowper's patent described how these plates were to be heated and then passed between two rollers to curve them. There was, of course, the risk of breaking the plates during the operation, but the method worked; it was used for printing £1 notes at the Bank of England, where these machines were installed for the purpose.

Engraving from the patent specification

409 The First Perfecting Machine, 1816

All the machines hitherto described printed on one side of the sheet only: this machine, built by Koenig and Bauer, printed on both sides, and was called by its makers a 'completing machine'. This was a combination of two printing units having two type formes, two (widely separated) cylinders, and two inking systems. The paper was put on tapes, which were briefly halted and then put in motion, carrying the sheet round the first cylinder and forward, through a register-checking device, to the second printing cylinder. The direction taken by the tapes had the effect of bringing the second side of the sheet face to face with the forme at the second printing cylinder, where it was printed.

The cylinders were in continuous motion, and in order that they should clear the formes on the return journey of the carriage, the radius of each was reduced in the non-printing area. The machine printed 900–1,000 sheets an hour, printed on both sides.

Photograph of a model

410 The First Two-revolution Machine, 1817

The 'two-revolution machine' is so called because it makes an impression at every second turn of the cylinder.

This machine was built by Koenig and Bauer in 1818 and installed in the printing office of Richard Taylor in London. Its cylinder turned in fixed bearings and was in continuous rotation. Two-thirds of its surface was recessed to allow clearance for the forme to pass under it to the inking end of the bed. It printed 900–1,000 double demy sheets an hour.

Photograph of a model

411 Rutt's Patent Printing Machine, 1819

This small machine was put in motion by hand labour. As with Koenig's first cylinder machine, Rutt's cylinder made one-third of a revolution and then halted to allow the carriage to return. The racks on the carriage turned the cylinder. The inking rollers were independently driven through bevel gears.

An engraving

412 Applegath and Cowper's Perfecting Machine, c. 1820

After Koenig returned to Germany in 1818 Augustus Applegath and Edward Cowper, working on behalf of *The Times*, made many improvements in the machinery there.

They also introduced machines of their own. In 1818 Cowper invented the ink table fixed to the type carriage and mounted his rollers horizontally, thus superseding Koenig's vertical arrangement. He also introduced 'carrying drums' in perfecting machines, to transfer and turn the sheet between the two printing cylinders. Other improvements were specified in a patent granted to Applegath in 1823 which included the device of placing ink distributing rollers diagonally to give them end motion to effect their purpose better. (They were called 'wavers'.) In the perfecting machine the inking systems were repositioned at each end. This made the machine more compact and shortened the travel of the bed, thus increasing speed and output.

A woodcut

413 The Napier Gripper, c. 1824

The 'Nay-peer' perfector, designed by David Napier but not patented, was notable for several innovations. It was the first machine to be fitted with grippers; the gap between the cylinders (common to all earlier perfectors) was closed, and the cylinders built in gear with one another. The sheet transfer from one cylinder to the other was direct, and made by the simultaneous opening and closing of the two sets of grippers; after printing, the sheets were delivered mechanically.

The cylinders, which were in continuous motion, were alternately lowered for printing and raised to clear the returning forme, by a rocking frame. A wooden rider over the inkers had a worm at either end to give it an endways movement, to improve distribution: there were no 'wavers'.

An engraving

414 Applegath and Cowper's machine for 'The Times', 1828

The increasing circulation of this newspaper obliged John Walter II to enlarge the capacity of his machinery and he commissioned Applegath and Cowper to build a new one. They then built this four-feeder, to print four sheets at a time, on one side of the paper only. The two engineers had undertaken to print 3,600 sheets an hour but the machine ran at 4,200 an hour for more than twenty years.

This machine had four cylinders and four feeding stations, but only one forme of type: this travelled the full length of the machine and was inked at each end and in the middle during each journey. The cylinders were made to rise and fall alternately, one of each group printing at one traverse of the carriage, the other pair printing on the return.

A woodcut

415 Napier's Double-feeder Power Platen, 1830

The platen principle was later revived, and it has been recorded that all the best work was printed on such machines before the introduction of the Wharfedale. David Napier's machine was the most successful of the group.

The platen, which was placed in the centre of the machine, was raised and lowered by knuckle joints at each side of the frame. The ink tables and type beds were operated through a slide working in the grooves of a revolving iron drum situated under the machine. Sheets were fed to tympans and friskets. By this time composition rollers were in general use and a standard inking system had been established.

A wood engraving

416 Rowland Hill's Rotary Machine, 1835

This experimental machine was invented by Sir Rowland Hill who first proposed the penny post. It revived the proposals for printing from movable types arranged round a cylinder, first made by William Nicholson forty-five years earlier. Both proposals called for tapered type bodies. But, whereas Nicholson would have used type made in the normal way and scraped it down to the size required, Rowland Hill's patent specified casting in a special mould.

The principal innovation was the proposal to print from a continuous web of paper, but this intention was frustrated by government insistence that, for the purpose of the stamp duty then payable, newspapers must be printed in single sheets.

It is most probable, however, that the tapered type would have created technical difficulties in casting, composing, and printing which could not have been overcome.

Provision was made in the specification for the automatic damping of the web on the machine before printing, it is believed for the first time. The traditional pre-damping of paper, whether intended for hand press, or printing machine, continued for many years.

417 The 'Main' Machine, c. 1840

A problem that engaged the designers of flatbed presses was to harmonize the rotation of the impression cylinder with the reciprocal movement of the bed. The Main press, named after the machine-minder who invented it, was also known as the 'Tumbler' from the movement of its impression cylinder.

When the sheet had been printed, and the bed was ready to return, the cylinder was raised slightly and reversed with the carriage in the opposite direction, the racks on the cylinder and carriage remaining in gear, and therefore in harmony, continuously.

A wood engraving

418 Printing from Stereotypes cast in a Curve, 1845

A method of making stereotypes from layers of paper pasted together had been patented in France by Genoux as early as 1829. Moulds made from this material (flong) were thin and flexible, and the first to realize that they could be used for casting curved plates were Worms and Philippe, who took out a French patent for the method in 1845.

The engraving accompanying their specification shows a web-fed perfecting rotary, and also a curved casting-box with a papier-mâché mould in position. The inventors encountered difficulties in casting their plates and this impeded the development of their machine.

An engraving from the patent specification

419 Applegath's Vertical Rotary, 1848

Applegath has recorded how, in 1846, he learned that 'the demand for *The Times* was limited by the want of a quicker machine. . .'. He then 'determined upon changing the reciprocating motion of the forme into a circular one'. The machine then built had a large vertical type cylinder, more than 5 ft. in diameter, in continuous rotation and, in contact with it, eight impression cylinders, each 13 in. in diameter and revolving on its own vertical axis. Part of the circumference of the type cylinders was used as an ink table. Inking rollers were grouped between the impression cylinders.

Ordinary type was used, arranged in columns and secured in galleys which were mounted on the surface of the printing cylinder. They thus formed a number of facets with wedge-shaped gaps between, which were filled with wedge-shaped column rules. The middle column rule of each page was fixed. The printing surface was not, therefore, a cylinder but a polygon, and the impression cylinder was adjusted to this contour with paper overlays.

The laying-on boards (feeding stations) were approached from a raised platform. The paper was laid to feeding drums and carried vertically downwards; it was then stopped, suspended for a moment, and finally guided into horizontal tapes which conveyed it round the impression cylinder for printing. The machine averaged 12,000 impressions an hour, printed on one side of the paper.

This was an ingenious machine of impressive appearance, which served its purpose well for twenty years, but it could have done little to advance the idea of rotary printing.

A wood engraving

420 Hoe's 'Lightning' Type-revolving Machine, 1848

Eleven years before Applegath's vertical rotary was built, David Napier had been granted a patent for a sheet-fed multi-cylinder machine 'having the type fixed upon one cylinder. . .'. It was a horizontal machine, and the drawing accompanying the specification shows ten impression cylinders.

The same idea was taken up by Robert Hoe of New York who made many horizontal machines on this principle, his first having four cylinders and his later ones six, eight, and ten cylinders. In its general conception the Hoe machine was similar to Applegath's but the horizontal arrangement was much more convenient. The sheets, printed on one side, were delivered by flyers.

The machines were compact and well-built and appealed to the newspaper proprietors. *The Times* ordered two in 1857 which eventually superseded the Applegath machine. The Hoe 'Lightning' was later adapted to take stereotype plates.

421 Nelson's Rotary Machine, 1851

One of the earliest machines embodying the whole principle of rotary printing appears to have been invented by Thomas Nelson of Edinburgh. The machine shown here was exhibited at the Great Exhibition in 1851 and is the earliest rotary machine known to survive in Britain.

The machine was fed from a web and printed the first side of the paper at the two lower cylinders; then it perforated the paper at the two middle cylinders, printed the reverse side at the two upper cylinders, and finally separated the web into sheets, along the perforations, at the small rollers. *Plate 12*

422 The First Wharfedale Machine, 1858

In the Wharfedale, much the best known of the stop-cylinder machines, the cylinder has a gear-wheel at each side, one free and the other fixed, which run in mesh with a rack on each side of the machine bed. When the cylinder has made its printing-revolution it is halted to allow the carriage to return. This is provided for by flattening the radius on the under side of the cylinder for a few inches and by reducing the teeth of the fixed gear-wheel. The free gear-wheel reverses with the carriage, and at the end of this revolution engages a pawl in the cylinder which is thus set in motion again.

The photograph is of the first machine, built in 1858, with David Payne, the inventor, behind the cylinder. It was never patented. In 1865 David Payne patented improvements to the machine which included the rack-and-wheel bed-motion, and also the cylinder push-back mechanism, which ensured perfect 'register' (the precise positioning of the impression on the paper). *Plate 13*

A photograph

423 The Ingle Stop-Cylinder, 1858

This machine was invented by Henry Ingle, a London engineer, whose patent was for 'imparting the to-and-fro motion to the table . . . from a quadrant. . . . It was one of the earliest of the stop-cylinder machines and was of simple construction. It was fast and particularly suitable for light work. *Plate 13*

424 The Anglo-French Machine, c. 1865

This machine, made by Hopkinson and Cope in England, and Marinoni in France, was modelled on the Napier Gripper and strongly influenced by French design. It was much stouter in construction than its prototype, which it soon displaced. The inking system was also much improved.

The sheet was fed to brass lays, and the front of the laying-on board rose while the sheet was laid on, and dropped to allow the grippers to take the sheet. Provision was made for interleaving at the second (outer) cylinder to prevent set-off. The interleaves were fed from a separate laying-on board placed over the second cylinder, and were taken in by a drop-bar arrangement and carried by independent tapes to meet the sheet (already printed on one side) as it was taken by the second cylinder grippers.

A wood engraving

425 William Bullock's Rotary, 1865

This American machine, made for the *Philadelphian Inquirer*, has been described as 'the first really automatic printing machine'. It was web-fed, and printed on both sides of the paper from curved stereos, cast from moulds prepared from flong. Before printing, the paper was damped and cut into sheets. In their passage through the machine the sheets were transferred by grippers: no tapes were used.

This machine was much smaller and cheaper than the Hoe ten-feeder and had a capacity of 10,000 full-size eight-page newspapers an hour.

A wood engraving

426 The First Newspaper Machine with a Folder, 1869

The later models of William Bullock's machines were improved by the addition of an automatic folding machine, invented by Walter Scott of New York.

A drawing

427 The Walter Rotary Machine, 1868

The leadership of *The Times* in the evolution of printing machinery over a period of fifty years culminated in the development, by their own engineers, of a rotary machine which was named after the proprietor of the day, John Walter III. It was a completely automatic web-fed perfector, printing from curved stereotype plates. The paper was damped on its way to the printing cylinders and there was a device for cleaning the second cylinder blanket to reduce the effects of set-off. A folder was fitted to this machine which had an output of 12,000 eight-page newspapers an hour.

A wood engraving

428 Hoe's 'Double Supplement' Reel-fed Rotary, 1878

The expansion of the newspaper trade encouraged investment in the construction of ever-larger rotary machines: the Hoe 'Double Supplement' was one of these. The machine had two elements, built at right-angles to each other, one having a double-width cylinder (i.e. its width was equal to four full-size pages instead of two). Two reels, of different widths, fed the machine. After printing (on both sides) the wider web was slit, and the total of three 'ribbons' which resulted were brought together, one above the other, by turner bars, and led over a triangular former which made the centre fold. A knife separated the folded web into copies, and a blade-bearing cylinder gave each completed copy a final cross-fold, for convenience in handling and packing.

The 'Double Supplement' machine printed papers of from 4 to 12 pages at 24,000 copies an hour and sixteen-page papers at half this speed. In later Hoe rotaries the units were brought into a straight line, and the cylinders of equal length were used.

A wood engraving

429 The Miehle Two-revolution Machine, 1887

For several years the manufacturers of two-revolution machines had been modifying their designs to gain increases in speed and output. The problem was to control the momentum of the reciprocating carriage (with the type forme on it) at the instant of reversal. Their solution was to reduce the weight of the bed, but this adversely affected both impression and register.

Robert Miehle, a young Chicago pressman (or machine-minder) approached the problem in a different way and in so doing made an important contribution to printing machine design. The machine he patented and perfected had a bed movement with an enlarged star wheel and rack so powerful that it effectively controlled the forward momentum of a bed of massive construction and such great strength that it immediately took the lead among others of its class. The Miehle machine, in several models, continues to be marketed and sold all over the world.

The cylinder revolves continuously, is raised

after the impression in order to clear the forme during its second revolution, and is then brought down on impression again by the action of a cam and eccentrics.

A photograph

430 A Late Nineteenth-century Wharfedale, c. 1895

The stop-cylinder machine remained basically unchanged, but was steadily improved in detail. It was strengthened for heavy half-tone work, or streamlined for faster speeds; it was fitted with flyers or other sheet-delivery mechanisms; it was given geared inking; and so on. At the end of the century the Wharfedale was still the principal machine used by British book-printers, and by the printers of newspapers and periodicals of smaller circulations.

A Photograph

Discovery of Infra-red Rays

431 WILLIAM HERSCHEL, Three Papers on Radiant Heat, the Infra-red Rays, &c. *London 1800*

By means of delicate experiments at one end of the spectrum with a thermometer Herschel, an astronomer, made a major contribution to physics. He was the first to discover the existence of light rays invisible to the human eye, and his discovery of the infra-red rays had a speedy sequel in the discovery of the more familiar ultra-violet.

The Invention of the Electric Battery

432 ALEXANDER VOLTA, On the Electricity excited by the Mere Contact of Conducting Substances of Different Kinds. In a Letter . . . to the Rt. Hon. Sir Joseph Banks, Bart., K.B., P.R.S. *London 1800*

Pursuing the investigations of Galvani (no. 381) Volta took the practical step that produced the first continuous and controllable electric current. The voltaic pile revolutionized the theory and practice of electricity so that within 100 years of his invention more progress was made than in the 2,400 years between the tentative experiences of Thales and the publication of Volta's letter. The pile consisted of a series of copper and zinc disks separated by pieces of cloth, paper, or paste-board soaked in a saline or acid fluid. Suitable connexion to an electroscope showed that the pile produced a regular flow of what Volta, with a gracious gesture, called the galvanic fluid.

Plate 30

A Manifesto of the Romantic Movement

433 WILLIAM WORDSWORTH and SAMUEL TAYLOR COLERIDGE, Lyrical Ballads. *London 1800*

Wordsworth's famous preface on his theory of poetry first appeared in this, the second edition. Misconception was caused by Coleridge's trenchant criticisms of it in 1814. It is not the incidental remarks on diction that are important but the revolt against eighteenth-century artificiality. Its outline of the supreme function of poetry expressed in such phrases as that poetry 'takes its origin from emotion recollected in tranquillity' set a new tone.

'The Prince of Mathematicians'

434 KARL FRIEDRICH GAUSS, Disquisitiones arithmeticae. *Leipzig 1801*

The headline is from A. T. Bell's *Men of Mathematics* who also writes of it 'A new direction was given to the higher arithmetic with the publication of the *Disquisitiones*, and the theory of numbers . . . assumed coherence and rose to the dignity of a mathematical science on a par with algebra, analysis and geometry. The book has been called "a book of seven seals". It is hard reading, even for experts, but the treasures it contains . . . are now available to all . . . [thanks to] Dirichlet, who first broke the seven seals.' Although only 24 when this book was published it was Gauss's farewell to pure mathematics.

The Most Celebrated of Modern Educators

435 JOHANN HEINRICH PESTALOZZI, Wie Gertrud ihre Kinder lehrt. *Bern and Zürich 1801*

Pestalozzi's method was to draw out the child's mind rather than to stuff it with information, to regard the pupil as more important than the subject, to deal with 'the whole man' and to use psychological methods of approach. In all this he was the sole pioneer.

The Last Natural Philosopher

436 THOMAS YOUNG, On the Theory of Light and Colours. *London 1802*

He was the last of the natural philosophers who could know all that was to be known. He was the author of the wave theory of light, he expounded the mechanism of vision, stated the laws of blood circulation, introduced the modern conceptions of 'energy' and 'work done', gave a sound theory of tides, and helped to decipher the hieroglyphics of the Rosetta Stone.

The Abolition of Slavery

437 William Wilberforce, A Letter on the Abolition of the Slavery Trade. *London 1807*

As Wilberforce lay dying in 1833 news was brought to him of the second reading of the Bill abolishing slavery in all the dominions of the English Crown. The Bill was passed one month after he died. Perhaps no man has been able to see a personal campaign, carried on by word of mouth and by means of the printing-press, for one of the fundamental Rights of Man, so triumphantly successful.

The Atomic Theory

438 John Dalton, A New System of Chemical Philosophy. Part I. *Manchester 1808*

Dalton stated (*a*) that every element is composed of homogeneous particles, the weight of which is constant, and (*b*) that elements combine with one another to form chemical compounds in invariable proportions. Aston's isotope theories (no. 599) have modified (*a*) but Dalton's was the first precise and scientific statement of a theory as old as Democritus. Further volumes of this great work appeared in 1810 and 1827.

The Father of Aerial Navigation

439 George Cayley. On Aerial Navigation. *London 1809*

The modern aeroplane concept was invented by a Yorkshire baronet named Sir George Cayley, who also built and had flown the first gliders of history—both models and full-sized machines. All modern flying derives directly from this remarkable man. His long triple paper shown here as it first appeared in Nicholson's *Journal of Philosophy, &c.*, for 1809–10, laid the foundations upon which the modern science of aerodynamics is based. Cayley was rightly called—even in his own day—'the father of aerial navigation'.

The Beginnings of Evolutionary Theory

440 J. B. P. A. Lamarck, Philosophie zoologique. *Paris 1809*

Lamarck's best-known work and a classic in the literature of the evolutionary theory. It propounds the theory that species were not perpetually unalterable and that the more complex might have been developed from simpler forms. His ideas were furthered by Oscar Hertwig, Samuel Butler, and Bernard Shaw.

Invention of the Torpedo

441 Robert Fulton, Torpedo War and Submarine Explosions. *New York 1810*

In 1805 Fulton first demonstrated the military importance of his underwater torpedo. Although he failed in his efforts to convince the British and the French of its capabilities, he continued to refine and improve his invention in an effort to interest the United States Government. This pamphlet is his argument, and represents the first detailed explanation of the weapon that was to revolutionize naval warfare a century later.

The Founder of Homeopathy

442 Christian Friedrich Samuel Hahnemann, Organon der rationellen Heilkunde. *Dresden 1810*

The significance of Hahnemann's work for us is less in the use of minute doses of drugs than in his approach to organic disorders. He emphasized the importance of treating the patient as a whole rather than the symptoms, and thus foreshadowed the psychosomatic standpoint of modern medicine.

Nordic Philology

443 Rasmus Christian Rask, Bejledning til der Islandske eller gamler Nordiske Sprog. *Copenhagen 1811*

The first of an important series of publications which made Rask one of the founders of the modern science of language. The interest that his writings aroused in the ancient Scandinavian tongues directed attention to their literature. In 1818 Rask edited the first complete texts of the Eddas of Snorri (no. 279) and Saemund with versions in modern Swedish.

The Separation of History from Mythology

444 Barthold Georg Niebuhr, Römische Geschichte bis 241 v. Chr. *Berlin 1811–12, 1832*

Niebuhr (1776–1831), originally a banker like Grote (no. 507) and temporarily a civil servant like Macaulay (no. 515), is the founder of modern scientific history. His critical examination of the sources and his emphasis on institutions rather than individuals finally separated history from mythology. The *Roman History* was at once translated into English and imitated by Michelet (no. 511) in his *Histoire romaine* (1831). Niebuhr is the father of modern German scholarship and, alas! of its heavy-handed unreadability. Nevertheless, 'all historians', in the words of Mommsen 'so far as they are worthy of the name, are his pupils'.

Hansard

445 T. C. HANSARD, Parliamentary Debates. *London 1812*

The earliest accurate reports of the proceedings of Parliament are among the achievements of the many-sided genius of William Cobbett (no. 485). The first series (which included the previous year) came out in 1804; in 1808, T. C. Hansard (1776–1833), author of *Typographia*, the most reliable survey of printing of its day, became the printer of the *Debates*, inheriting his father's interest in parliamentary affairs (Luke Hansard was printer to the House from 1774 to 1828). In 1812 he bought the *Debates* from Cobbett, and from 1818, when Cobbett's name disappeared from the title-page, 'Hansard' has been the name by which the record of Parliament has been known. Protected by privilege from the threat of libel, it has served as a model to most of the parliamentary records of the world.

Industrial Philanthropy

446 ROBERT OWEN, A New View of Society. *London 1813–14*

The first statement of socialist doctrine came not from a theorist but from one who based it on practical experiment. Robert Owen was a successful owner of cotton mills in Manchester into which he introduced reforms to improve labouring conditions which were enormously successful. His success led him to generalize on his experience, extending it to include education and industrial co-operation, and his example was instrumental in the passing of the Factory Act of 1819. The deflation of the post-war period caused a reaction which turned Owen into an impractical dreamer, but his early work lives on wherever socialist principles are practised.

To the Pacific Overland

447 MERIWEATHER LEWIS and WILLIAM CLARK, History of the Expedition under the Command of Captains Lewis and Clark . . . to the Pacific Ocean. Performed during the Years 1804–5–6. *Philadelphia 1814*

These explorers traced the Mississippi River to its source, portaged over the Rockies, and descended to the Pacific coast. They returned overland to St. Louis, thus stimulating a tremendous interest in the resources of the vast and unknown Louisiana territory. They vindicated Thomas Jefferson's decision to purchase the area in 1803, thus committing the United States to a trans-Mississippi expansion.

Fiction Rivals History

448 [WALTER SCOTT], Waverley; or 'tis Sixty Years Since. *Edinburgh 1814*

The first of the 'Waverley novels' was published anonymously, but admirers of Scott's balladry and verse epics divined the author. It was the birth of the historical novel, and at one swoop Scott had established a new literary form. History had previously been a dry occupation for the learned: only a few antiquarians, like John Aubrey, had felt the 'romance' of history. Now Scott opened up a new field for the human imagination, the retrospective, and so successful has it been that historians must now (*see* Macaulay, no. 515) compete with it for attention.

Foundation of Comparative Grammar

449 FRANZ BOPP, Über das Conjugationssystem der Sanskritsprache in Vergleichung mit jenen der griechischen, lateinischen, persischen und germanischen Sprachen. *Frankfurt 1816*

Following up the discoveries of Jones and Rask on the relationship of the Indo-European languages (nos. 374, 443), the first publication of the young Berlin professor (1791–1867) established the science of comparative grammar 'à peu près comme Christophe Colomb a découvert l'Amérique en cherchant la route des Indes' (Meillet). Bopp later added Lithuanian, Slav, Armenian, Celtic, and Albanian to this group of cognate languages; to which Tokharic and Hittite have only recently been added.

The Father of Historical Geology

450 WILLIAM SMITH, Strata Identified by Organized Fossils. *London 1816–19*

He was the first to relate systematically fossil remains to the order of rock stratification and thus instituted a method since universally adopted. This notion was first dimly perceived by Empedocles in the fifth century B.C. but was never followed up.

The Founder of Comparative Anatomy

451 GEORGES LÉOPOLD DAGOBERT CUVIER, Le Règne animal distribué d'après son organisation. *Paris 1817*

A carnivore has sharp teeth, strong jaws, a digestive system able to absorb its food, and so on. This is a commonplace to us but Cuvier was the first to apply such analyses and comparisons to the entire animal kingdom, dividing them into classes, as Linné (no. 336) had divided the plants. Cuvier also saw that this homogeneity of the individual should enable any competent naturalist to reconstruct a complete animal from any significant part of its anatomy. The importance of this for modern anthropology (no. 492) is clear.

Chemistry of the Sun

452 JOSEPH VON FRAUNHOFER, Bestimmung des Brechungs- und Farbenzerstreuungsvermögens. *Munich 1817*

Fraunhofer charted over 300 dark lines in the solar spectrum and similar phenomena in planetary spectra. These are still known as Fraunhofer lines. They revolutionized solar chemistry and eventually led directly to the establishment of spectrum analysis by Kirchhoff in 1860 (*see* nos. 535, 593, 594, 599).

The Distribution of Wealth

453 DAVID RICARDO, Principles of Political Economy and Taxation. *London 1817*

In this, one of the great works on economics, Ricardo, who had made a fortune on the London Stock Exchange, investigated the causes determining the distribution of wealth, and laid down his famous theories of taxation and rent. Following Adam Smith (no. 363) he explored the practical facts of the movement and influence of wealth in a national economy. His thought contains some of the fundamental concepts of modern economics.

The Philosophy of Pessimism

454 ARTHUR SCHOPENHAUER, Die Welt als Wille und Vorstellung. *Leipzig [1818]*

Schopenhauer held that Kant's 'thing-in-itself' is the cosmic will—the only reality. But the cosmic will is evil. The good life consists in breaking down individual will by practising chastity, voluntary poverty, fasting, and self-denial. The result is nothingness and the aim of the saint is non-existence.

His ideas greatly impressed and influenced Nietzsche and Wagner (nos. 554, 520). He rejected the idealistic view that change and progress are synonymous. His pessimistic attitude on this question has proved more acceptable to the modern mind than the obstinate optimism of the Victorians.

The Invention of the Stethoscope

455 R. T. H. LAENNEC, De l'auscultation. *Paris 1819*

The stethoscope, now the most familiar instrument used by the physician, was invented by Laennec. Originally simply a roll of stiff paper applied to the chest of the patient in order to amplify the sounds of the heart's action, Laennec soon replaced it with a tube of cedar wood. The publication of this book caused a revolution in the study of afflictions of the heart and lungs.

The History of Language

456 JACOB GRIMM, Deutsche Grammatik. *Berlin 1819–37*

Jacob Grimm, author-collector, with his brother Wilhelm, of the 'Fairy Tales', traced in his *German Grammar* the historical development of the Indo-European languages, whose relationship Jones and Bopp had discovered (nos. 374, 449). Building on Rask's observation of 'consonant shifts' (no. 443), he established 'Grimm's law'. This is based on hitherto unnoticed relationship in the use of consonants in the transition of Greek and Latin works into German. He also separated language from literature, and gave all languages, even dialects, a common importance from the philologist's standpoint.

The Discovery of Electro-Magnetism

457 JOHANN CHRISTIAN OERSTED, Experimenta circa effectum conflictus electrici. *Copenhagen 1820*

In a class demonstration in 1819 Oersted was surprised to see a compass needle deflected by an adjacent electric current. Further investigation convinced him of the identity of electricity and magnetism. An immediate result was the construction of an electric telegraph by Gauss (no. 434) and Weber. The researches of Faraday (no. 487), Maxwell (no. 542), Hertz (no. 564), and countless others stem from this discovery.

The Value of Organization

458 GEORG WILHELM FRIEDRICH HEGEL, Grundlinien der Philosophie des Rechts. *Berlin 1821*

Hegel was the successor of Fichte (no. 386) in the chair of philosophy at Berlin. His first publication, his *Rechtsphilosophie*, was the beginning of a complete system of morals and philosophy in which the concept of a sociology dominated by the idea of the State first appeared. It turned away from the apparent chaos of the democratic advocates of individual rights in favour of an overwhelming sense that liberty cannot exist apart from order, and that the vital connexion of all parts of the body politic is the source of all good. This theory has been misused by totalitarian propagandists (nos. 512, 547, 601), but despite its weaknesses, Hegel's thesis still has its value.

The Gothic Revival

459 AUGUSTUS CHARLES PUGIN, Specimens of Gothic Architecture. *London 1821–3*

As an architect Pugin had very little practice, but as the reviver of a scientific study of medieval architecture and as the mentor of other architects (notably his son Augustus Welby Pugin), and thus as the prime mover in the neo-Gothic movement, his influence is of the first importance. Whereas before Gothic architecture had been a fashionable craze, amusing in itself, but unworthy of serious study, Pugin demonstrated that the absence of known architectural theory in medieval times covered a formidable architectural competence. A whole century's architecture was influenced by this exposition, to be seen in monuments as diverse as the Mont St. Michel, the Nicolauskirche in Hamburg, Milan Cathedral, and St. Pancras Station.

MECHANICAL TYPECASTING

460 Brandt Typecasting Machine, 1838

This, the earliest successful machine for the purpose, was invented by David Bruce junior of New York in 1838. He sold his patent to his uncle, who employed a locksmith, L. Brandt, to build the machine. Brandt came to Europe, and by 1845 was selling the design in Germany as his own.

It embodies Bruce's earlier invention of a pump to blow molten metal into the mould (*c.* 1834) and was the forerunner of the 'pivotal' class of machines commonly used during the past hundred years in America and Great Britain to make type in moderate quantity to be set by hand. In these machines the mould is on the end of an arm which is moved by the action of a cam so as to present the jet of the mould to the valve of the metal-pot and release the casting afterwards.

In 1846 Brandt sold a licence to exploit his pretended invention in Sweden to the typefounder L. J. Hjerta; and it is from him that this specimen has descended. *Plate 14*

461 Wicks Rotary Type-casting Machine, c. 1881

This type-casting machine, which was invented by Frederick Wicks in 1878, had a hundred moulds, and was claimed to be capable of delivering 60,000 finished types per hour. It was designed to furnish type in the very large quantities needed to supply the cold-type composing machines in newspaper offices. A stream of molten metal was forced into moulds mounted on a chain which were presented in rapid succession before the nozzle of a metal pot. It was used at *The Times*. This type-caster came too late: it was quickly superseded by hot-metal machines which both cast and composed type. *Plate 15*

MECHANICAL COMPOSITION

The search for a way of speeding type composition by mechanical means produced a wide range of machines and devices over a long period, from Church's patent of 1822 to Mergenthaler's Linotype of 1890. A great deal of money went into this development, for the promised reward was great, and it is surprising that success eluded so many for so long. The mistake of the earlier designers was to begin where Gutenberg had left off 400 years before—with type.

The assembly of single type from a magazine, by operating a keyboard, was easily contrived; but the breaking up of the continuous line of type which came from the early machines to the lengths required, had to be done by hand. Justification (the spacing out of the lines to a predetermined length) was even more difficult. Moreover, with machines of this kind, it was still necessary to distribute the type after printing.

These machines for 'cold type composition', as it is described by the present generation of printers, were offered to the trade in great variety; for composing, line-justifying, or distributing; or for a combination of composing with one or both of the other operations. One of the last to appear was the Paige composing, line-justifying, and distributing machine, an American mammoth weighing three tons, which was developed between 1878 and 1894 at a cost of more than a million dollars.

About 1877 a young German mechanic in Baltimore helped with the construction of an experimental machine which was part of a plan to avoid the expense of type composition by the use of a lithographic technique: he was Ottmar Mergenthaler, and was to give his name to the company which developed and manufactured the first hot-metal composing machine—the Linotype. Over several years he and his associates tried and abandoned many alternative proposals before they produced their first successful machine in 1890.

Mergenthaler singled out the matrix as the element in the chain of type casting and composing operations most amenable to mechanical assembly. The matrices were assembled and justified in a machine, and when they had been used to cast a solid bar or 'slug' of type, were immediately distributed for further circulation, in a continuing cycle of operations.

But all this would have come to nothing without another outstanding invention, the punchcutting machine completed by Linn Boyd Benton, a Milwaukee typefounder, in 1884. For the Linotype, by its nature, made an unprecedented demand on matrices, and this, in turn, called for punches in numbers which could not have been provided by all the punchcutters in the world. Indeed, the Linotype, and the other composing systems which followed it, would have failed completely without a method of mechanical punchcutting such as Benton's.

Soon afterwards, in 1897, Tolbert Lanston of Washington succeeded with hot-metal composition in another way. He arranged his matrices in a grid, and by a system of mathematical coordinates selected the one to be presented to the mould (fed with hot metal from below) so as to cast single types in justified lines. Lanston's caster was controlled by a paper ribbon previously perforated on a separate keyboard.

462 Church Composing Machine, c. 1822

A representation of the earliest patented composing machine. It was part of an invention by Dr. William Church, of Vermont, U.S.A., covered by his British patent of 1822 for an improved printing-press, a casting machine, and a composing machine. While there is no evidence that a composing machine was built, the design included features which were embodied in later inventions. The type was stored in inclined channels, from which it was released by the operation of a keyboard. The released type fell into a horizontal race where it was assembled by rocking arms into a continuous line. Like other early composing machines, Church's did not provide for justification of the lines, leaving that to be done by hand. Power was provided by a clockwork mechanism.

Believed to be a photograph of a model

463 Young and Delcambre Composing Machine, 1840

The first composing machine known to have been used in a printing office was invented by James Young and Adrien Delcambre assisted by Henry Bessemer. It was not a great advance on Church's design. Type was held in long, narrow boxes from which it was released by a keyboard so that it slid down an inclined channel to a point where it was assembled into a line. The problem of making the type arrive in the right order, although solved by Church, had to be solved over again by Bessemer. He curved the channels to make them of equal length. The machine was used to set the *Family Herald* (founded 1842), and an engraving of it was used in the title-piece of that journal. The use of the Young and Delcambre machine was opposed by the London Union of Compositors, particularly because female labour was employed to operate it.

A contemporary wood engraving

464 Hattersley Composing Machine, 1857

Robert Hattersley of Manchester invented a machine which was one of the longer-lived of those which followed that of Young and Delcambre. Type was contained in a horizontal magazine and released down vertical channels leading to an assembly point. The machine incorporated two notable improvements: its keyboard was more compact than those of its predecessors, and the assembled type was delivered so that the compositor could easily space the matter before removing it from the machine to the composing stick. It was claimed that a good operator could compose 7,500 letters an hour. It required no power. Some of these machines were still in use as late as 1915. Hattersley also invented a trigger-action distributing stick for use with the machine.

A wood engraving

465 Mackie Composing Machine, 1867

The use of a continuously perforated paper strip, applied to the loom by Bouchon in 1725, was first proposed for type composition by D. Mackenzie in his British patent of 1848, and put to practical use in the machine invented by a Warrington journalist, Dr. Alexander Mackie, in 1867. The paper ribbon was first perforated on a separate keyboard (foreshadowing Lanston's Monotype) and afterwards fed into the composing machine. The type was contained in pockets placed at the periphery of a revolving horizontal disk and, as it was released, passed into a channel where it was justified by hand. The machine, known as 'the pickpocket', was used at the *Warrington Guardian*.

A pen-and-ink drawing

466 Kastenbein Composing Machine, 1869

Another simple keyboard type-setting machine was invented by Charles Kastenbein in 1869. It was improved and put to practical use at *The Times* printing office. The type was held in vertical tubes and when ejected by the operation of a keyboard fell into a type-race from which it was taken by a second operator who justified the lines. A distributing machine was provided with this apparatus. Later, *The Times* took to using new type cast in Wicks Rotary Typecaster to fill this machine and melted it down after use. This is the first recorded adoption of the principle of 'no distribution'.

A wood engraving

467 The Thorne Composing and Distributing Machine, 1880

The main features of this machine, patented in U.S.A. in 1880, were the two vertical cylinders, placed one above the other, for the interconnected operations of composing and distributing type. Each cylinder had ninety longitudinal channels, arranged radially, for the accommodation of type, the lower one, which was stationary, being the magazine. Operation of the keyboard ejected the lowest types from the channels of the magazine on to a circulating disk and from thence they were carried to a belt which delivered them to a galley where justification was carried out by hand.

Because the system required that the back of the type of each character and space should have a different combination of nicks, the founts used on the machine had to be specially adapted for it. The upper cylinder was charged by filling its channels with dead matter for distribution, these being wide enough to accommodate any letter in the fount. The channels in thel ower cylinder, however, were cut with wards so that they admitted only the characters whose nicks fitted them. In operation, the upper cylinder revolved in steps, halting when its channels were in alignment with those of the stationary lower cylinder. As each type reached the channel with wards complementary to its own nicks, it dropped down to replenish the magazine. Machines of this kind were installed in the offices of the *Manchester Guardian* and the *Bradford Observer*.

A drawing

468 Wicks Composing Machine, c. 1883

The Wicks Composer was another two-man machine, one man operating the long keyboard and the other spacing out the assembled type. It was invented by Frederick Wicks, who also invented the Wicks Rotary Type-caster. The machine held type in inclined channels and released it by operation of the keyboard. A number of the most frequently occurring combinations of characters could be set by the simultaneous depression of two or more keys. Wicks composing machines, supplied daily with new type from the Wicks foundry, were used for the *Morning Post* until 1910, when they were replaced by Linotypes.

A photograph

469 Linotype Composing Machine (Square-base), 1890

The Linotype, which was invented by Ottmar Mergenthaler (1854–99), stores a large number of single matrices in a magazine. These are released from a keyboard, assembled in words which are separated by double-wedge spaces used to justify the completed line as it is brought to the orifice of a mould, and there cast in a type-high bar or 'slug'. A V-shaped gap is cut out of the upper part of the matrix, and the inside walls of the gap are toothed. After casting, the line of matrices is raised to a distributor-bar formed with seven wards, along which they move suspended by their teeth. The wards are interrupted on a system which has the effect of releasing each matrix as it reaches its own channel in the magazine.

It has been said that Mergenthaler found many of the devices he incorporated in his machine already waiting for him: the keyboard, the magazine, the guide-plate with curving channels, the mould, the type metal, the system of wards and combinations, and, of course, the matrix.

But the idea of the circulating matrix was his, and he brought together all the parts needed for his purpose and persevered until he made them work smoothly as a machine. The double-wedge self-justifying space, however, was not his, for this essential element in his design had already been patented by Schuckers. And without Benton's punchcutting machine, which was already available to meet the incalculable requirement of matrices, his machine would have died almost as soon as it was born. *Plate 17*

470 The Paige Compositor, 1894

This, the largest, most complicated, and most versatile of cold-type composing machines was invented by James W. Paige of Rochester, New York, who experimented with it from 1872 to 1887 before a complete machine was constructed. When the operator had completed a line he at once proceeded with the next, while the machine automatically measured and justified the first and pushed it on to a galley, leaded or solid as desired. Distribution went on at the same time. A second machine was built in 1894 when all further work ceased. The Paige had already been overtaken by the hot-metal Linotype.

A photograph

471 'Monotype' Composing Machine: The Keyboard, 1897

The 'Monotype' system, the only survivor of a small group of composing mechanisms incorporating perforated paper controllers, was developed by Tolbert Lanston of Washington between 1885 and 1897. It is in two parts and composes single types in justified lines. The keyboard makes perforations in a continuous roll of paper and these control the character-selecting mechanism on the caster. It also measures the width of the characters as they are set and calculates the space required between words to justify the line.

Plate 18

472 'Monotype' Composing Machine: The Caster, 1897

'Monotype' matrices are arranged in a grid and secured in a steel case located over a mould in the casting machine. The perforated paper ribbon prepared on the keyboard causes a supply of compressed air to be directed to a series of stops which determine the position of the case over the mould so that the selected characters are cast as single types in a justified line. The last perforation made for each line by the keyboard signals the width of the space required between words to expand successive lines to a uniform length. As the paper ribbon is fed into the caster in reverse, this is the first signal to be received, and so justification is achieved.

The machine shown here was the first to be sent to England, and was received in 1897. It was known as the 'limited fount' machine because it carried only 132 matrices. *Plate 19*

473 Pulsometer Composing Machine, 1902

This, the last cold-type composing machine, was a British invention and differed from most earlier machines in that the type reservoirs were placed horizontally instead of vertically. Depression of a key raised the foremost piece of type in the reservoir until it projected over the edge of a guide plate, the piece of type behind being pressed forward by a weighted follower. The type dropped down a channel to a curved trough in front of the operator, and was pushed forward until a line was composed. Justification was by hand. *Plate 16*

474 Pulsometer Distributing Machine, c. 1904

Type set by the Pulsometer compositor was distributed by a separate machine, which also was operated by a keyboard. The galley of type was inclined at an angle, sloping towards the keyboard, and its lowest line was received in a raised trough. The operator read the type and pressed keys corresponding with the thickness of the type which was then diverted through a series of bridge pieces to the mouths of the appropriate channels. When it was full, the channel could be taken out and the contents fed into the corresponding channel of the composing machine.

Plate 16

475 Grant-Legros Punchcutting Machine, c. 1910

Essentially this is the mechanical punchcutter invented by the American, Linn Boyd Benton, and covered by his British patent of 1885, but it embodies modifications by several engineers and is distinguished by those of L. A. Legros and J. C. Grant, who made the machine exhibited for their own use.

Machines of this kind cut steel punches by means of diminutive routers and milling cutters driven by power and directed by an operator manipulating a vertical bar hung in a universal joint near its upper end. The lower end of the bar is made to follow the contours of a pattern letter in relief on a table beneath it. The ratio of the pattern to the face cut on the punch is variable by adjustment of the machine, so that letters of different sizes can be made from one pattern.

The modifications by Legros and Grant were aimed mainly at making it easier to read the micrometer adjustment for the depth of cut and to fix the pattern precisely in the right position.

Plate 15

Carnot's Cycle

476 NICOLAS-LEONARD SADI CARNOT, Réflexions sur la puissance motrice du feu et sur les machines propres à développer cette puissance. *Paris 1824*

Carnot was one of the most brilliant scientists in history and worked in nearly all branches ot mathematical and physical science, while also devoting time to music and athletics.

Working with engines, he found the true nature of heat and the best methods of determining its mechanical equivalent. The most original feature of his method was the invention of the cycle of operations now called by his name, one of the basic laws of thermodynamics. His work was little noticed until in 1848 Lord Kelvin drew attention to it, and together with Joule was able to apply and further develop Carnot's discoveries. His work on the principle of the conservation of energy anticipated Helmholtz (no. 510).

The Beginnings of Modern Critical History

477 LEOPOLD RANKE, Zur Kritik neuerer Geschichtschreiber. *Leipzig and Berlin 1824*

Ranke first applied to modern history the critical principles Niebuhr (no. 444) had established for ancient history and thereby set up novel standards of scholarship which have since become universally accepted: the rigorous examination of contemporary writers, the reliance on primary sources, and the conviction that all history is universal history.

The Apogee of Medieval Scholarship

478 Monumenta Germaniae historica. *Hanover 1826 (still in progress)*

The collection of the sources of medieval German history planned by the statesman Baron vom Stein (1819) and under the editorship of Georg Heinrich Pertz (from 1823 to 1873) and his successors became a model for research and editorship. The critical methods developed by the 'Monumentists' finally served as the standard of technical perfection everywhere—even in England.

The Discovery of the Mammalian Ovum

479 KARL ERNST VON BAER, De ovi mammalium et hominis genesi. *Leipzig 1827*

De Graaf (1641–73) and Haller (1708–77) (no. 333a) had investigated the processes of ovulation, but it was left for Baer to plot the course of fertilization from its later stages back to the ovary and there to identify the minute cell which was the ovum.

In a second great work, *Über Entwicklungsgeschichte der Tiere*, 1828–34, he enlarged the field of investigation, and became the founder of modern embryology. *Plate 31*

A Landmark in Electrical Science

480 GEORG SIMON OHM, Die Galvanische Kette mathematisch bearbeitet. *Berlin 1827*

'Ohm's law', which was propounded in this pamphlet, gives the same equation for the propagation of electricity as Fourier had already advanced for the propagation of heat. From this law Ohm's name has passed into technical electrical terminology. The copy shown belonged to John Tyndall, the great nineteenth-century popularizer of science.

Brownian Movement

481 ROBERT BROWN, A Brief Account of Microscopical Observations ... in 1827 ... on the General Existence of Active Molecules in Organic and Inorganic Bodies. *London 1828*

Brown observed under a microscope the irregular movement of minute particles in liquid now known as the 'Brownian movement'. This movement was explained by Ramsay in 1879 as being due to bombardment of molecules, which was experimentally proved by Perrin in 1908 who was also able to calculate the weight of the molecule of water. The principle involved was further developed by Einstein (nos. 595, 602). This paper also made a contribution to the theory of colloids.

The English of America

482 NOAH WEBSTER, An American Dictionary of the English Language. *New York 1828*

Webster (1758–1843) was an indefatigable producer of dictionaries. An ardent American nationalist, he aimed at severing linguistic ties with England. As his *Dictionary* became, and has remained, the standard American dictionary, he has in fact succeeded in breaking the fetters imposed upon the English language by Dr. Johnson (no. 344) to the ultimate benefit of the living languages of both countries.

Reading for the Blind

483 Louis Braille, Procédé pour écrire au moyen de points. *Paris 1829*

Edmund C. Johnson, Tangible Typography: or, how the blind read. *London 1853*

The first efforts to educate the sightless and make them happy and useful members of society were made in the eighteenth century. In 1785 Haüy founded the first school for the blind. He and others experimented with raised characters for teaching them to read but none succeeded until Braille perfected a system of embossed dots first adumbrated by Barbier. This was completely successful and is now in almost universal use. It is significant that both Braille and Moon, who devised a system for teaching older people, were themselves blind.

The only known copy of the Braille original work is in the possession of the Association Valentin Haüy in Paris and cannot be borrowed because of its extreme fragility. An enlargement of it is shown on the wall above this show-case.

Johnson's book shows all the known systems for teaching the blind to read, among them the earliest known specimen of Braille in England.

The Struggle for Reform

484 The Black Book. *London 1830*

This massive compilation of all the electoral abuses under the old system was one of the most influential documents in the struggle which led to the passing of the first Reform Act (1832). It is above all a practical document, and the emphasis on the need to have a practical as well as an equitable representation of the people lies at the root of parliamentary democracy.

The Land

485 William Cobbett, Rural Rides. *London 1830*

In 1821 a committee proposed certain remedies to alleviate agricultural depression after the war. Cobbett (1762–1835) disagreed with them, and 'made up his mind to see for himself, and to enforce by actual observation of rural conditions, the statements he had made in answer to the arguments of the landlords before the Agricultural Committee'. The rides he made, and the vividness and force with which he described what he saw, have made his work a classic; in his accounts of the poverty caused by widespread enclosure he struck the first blow in the long struggle for improving the condition of labourers on the land.

Positivism

486 Auguste Comte, Cours de philosophie positive. *Paris 1830–42*

The remarkable achievement of Comte, all argument about the validity of his theories aside, is the construction of a system which embraces all human thought and knowledge. The course of knowledge is seen as the development from a theological to a metaphysical state, in both of which the cause of phenomena is sought outside the objects in which they appear and from thence to the positive state, in which all phenomena are explicable in terms of interrelation with other phenomena. Comte's attempt to link up all science, to relate its development to the progress of society, and to combine it with a system of improvement with humanity in place of an external supreme being, is still one of the major documents of secular philosophy.

Faraday's Researches

487 Michael Faraday, Experimental Researches in Electricity. *London 1831*

When Faraday was 41 he published the first—and when he was 64 the last—of his original scientific papers on electro-magnetism. They are the foundations of a large part of modern electrical engineering. Faraday himself said of them 'it does surprise even my partiality, that [the different parts] should have the degree of consistency and apparent general accuracy which they seem to me to present', and, of the second, 'I regret the presence of those papers which partake of a controversial character'.

The Philosophy of War

488 Karl von Clausewitz, Vom Kriege. *Berlin 1832–4*

Clausewitz, in his lectures at the Prussian Military Academy (from 1816), used the lessons learned from the French revolutionary and Napoleonic wars for a systematic inquiry into the interdependence of politics and warfare and the principles governing either and both. The universal applicability of Clausewitz's theories (published posthumously by his widow) won immediate recognition. But Clausewitz's basic conception—that military decisions must always be subordinate to political considerations—found its greatest disciples in Lincoln, Bismarck, Lloyd George, and Churchill, whereas its disregard by Ludendorff and Hitler helped to bring about Germany's downfall in two world wars.

The Mirror of Man's Intellect

489 Johann Wolfgang von Goethe, Faust. *Leipzig 1834*

The first complete edition of Goethe's *magnum opus* on which he had been at work since 1774. George Henry Lewes wrote that 'it has every element: wit, pathos, wisdom, farce, mystery, melody, reverence, doubt, magic and irony. . . . In *Faust* we see as in a mirror the eternal problem of our intellectual existence.'

The Ugly Duckling

490 Hans Andersen, Eventyr. *Copenhagen 1835(–7)*

The tales of Hans Christian Andersen are the most famous of their kind in the world. They revived a forgotten literary form, the fairy tale of fantastic and imaginary people and things, to come into being; even more important, they are the source of modern imaginative literature designed for children. Andersen swiftly found fame all over the world, a fame which he is never likely to lose.

Biblical Criticism

491 David Friedrich Strauss, Das Leben Jesu kritisch bearbeitet. *Tübingen 1835*

This pioneer study of the Gospels 'in which all miracle was to be regarded as unhistorical, and all vital contradiction as decisive against credibility', was written by Strauss when he was 27. It let loose 'a battery of criticism unparalleled in the literary annals of Germany'—and cost Strauss his lectureship at Tübingen. It was translated into English by George Eliot in 1846 (her first publication), and had a great influence on later Biblical criticism.

The Philosophy of Speech

491a Karl Wilhelm von Humboldt, Über die Verschiedenheit des menschlichen Sprachbaues . . . *Berlin 1836*

Humboldt (1767–1835) was distinguished in his own time as a critic and as a diplomatist who did much to form the final coalition against Napoleon. His fame today rests on his work as a philologist, and in particular on his posthumous tract on the differences in linguistic structure. In this he laid down the principle that the character and structure of a language correspond with the character and lives of its speakers. This forms the basis of the study of the morphology of speech, by which languages are distinguished and classified according to the differences in these 'inner forms'; it is an essential part of modern linguistic theory.

Adam and Eve were Black

492 James Cowles Prichard, Researches into the Physical History of Man. *London 1836–47*

Prichard's vast researches were directed to 'the physical diversities which characterise different races of men'. He concluded that the human race was originally dark skinned and that the white man developed under the influence of civilization. His conclusion that 'all human races are of one species and one family' was added to the second edition of the *Researches*, 1836. Unfortunately this pronouncement with the elaborate reasoning leading up to it escaped Darwin's notice (no. 530). It is, however, the third edition, which we show, that was to contain all that was then known about the various races of mankind and thus to form a synthesis upon which modern ethnological research has been based.

The Dramatized Revolution

493 Thomas Carlyle, The French Revolution. *London 1837*

Whereas Michelet (no. 511) hailed the French Revolution as the birth of a new age, Carlyle saw it as the twilight of the gods. He wrote a secular 'tract for the times' in a series of unforgettable scenes and imaginative portraits in which he gave forceful expression to his Scottish puritanism and idealism. Not the work of an historian but of a poet, the book has never had the approval of scholars, but has, outside France, moulded the popular conception of the French Revolution, down to the present day.

The Penny Post

494 (*a*) Rowland Hill, Post Office Reform, its Importance and Practicability. *London 1837* (*b*) Third Report from the Select Committee on Postage. . . . *Ordered by the House of Commons to be printed 13 August 1838*

Neither Rowland Hill's privately printed pamphlet nor the publication of a revised edition, both in 1837, moved the British Government to adopt his scheme for a penny post.

Between February 1835 and January 1838 an investigating committee of three members issued ten reports on Post Office reform. Hill's pamphlet caused the appointment of a new and larger committee. Hill gave lengthy evidence before this committee, who timidly recommended a twopenny post. The Government adopted their report with the signal exception that they reduced the figure to one penny and the great revolution was accomplished. The report is opened at the beginning of Hill's evidence.

The Tolpuddle Martyrs

495 GEORGE LOVELESS, Victims of Whiggery, a Statement of the Persecution experienced by the Dorchester Labourers. *London [1837]*

George and James Loveless established a 'Friendly Society of Agricultural Labourers' in Tolpuddle and with four others were transported to Botany Bay for seven years for 'administering an unlawful oath'. Agitation by the Owenites (no. 446) and others was kept alive by the 'London Dorchester Committee' who fostered the above publication. The sentence was remitted and the men were brought home in 1838. They had struck a blow from which the opposition to trades unionism never recovered. The pamphlet is now exceedingly rare and a first edition of it has proved unprocurable.

The Cell as the Basis of Life

496 THEODOR SCHWANN, Mikroskopische Untersuchungen über die Uebereinstimmung in der Struktur und dem Wachstum der Thiere und Pflanzen. *Berlin 1839*

Schwann adopted the cell theory which Schleiden had propounded but misapplied in 1838. He expanded it into a general theory as the basis of all vital phenomena. He anticipated Pasteur's fermentation theories (no. 539), and discovered and named pepsin.

The Ice Age

497 JEAN LOUIS RODOLPHE AGASSIZ, Études sur les glaciers. *Neuchâtel 1840*

Together with Charpentier, Agassiz made extensive observations on the glaciers near Chamonix and the great moraines of the Rhône Valley, investigating the action of glaciers on the formation of land masses. He concluded that the whole of north-west Switzerland had been covered by ice in a former geological period and that the moraines and the formation of rocks were due to glacial movements. These observations were the beginning of modern glacial geology.

The Policy of Nationalism

498 FRIEDRICH LIST, Das nationale System der politischen Oekonomie. *Stuttgart 1841.*

Believing the nation to be a real entity standing between the individual and the human race, List was the great opponent of Adam Smith's mercantilist system (no. 363). The mystique of List's ideas is clearly seen in the emergence of protectionism and in the passionate nationalism of young nations. There would appear to be a distant connexion between the *Zollverein*, so energetically fostered by List, and the Common Market.

Tract XC

499 JOHN HENRY NEWMAN, Remarks in certain passages in the Thirty-nine Articles. *[London 1841]*

Perhaps the most controversial of the *Tracts for the Times* ('On the privileges of the Church and against Popery and Dissent') issued by the leaders of the Oxford Movement. The argument of this tract is to the effect that the XXXIX articles are capable of being interpreted in a sense compatible with the theology of the Roman Catholic Church. This alarmed many of the leaders of the Church of England, and led all but two of the Heads of houses at Oxford to condemn it.

The Foundation of Modern Sanitation

500 ERNEST CHADWICK, Report to Her Majesty's Principal Secretary of State for the Home Department from the Poor Law Commissioners, on an Inquiry into the Sanitary Condition of the Labouring Population. *London 1842*

Chadwick's epoch-making reports as chief executive officer of the newly formed Poor Law Commission. Young, in *Early Victorian England*, says of the report that it is 'a step from which descends by regular stages the Health Board of 1848, the Local Government Board of 1870, the existing Ministry of Health'. Engels quotes extensively from this report in his book *The Position of the Working Classes in England.*

The Chemistry of Living Things

501 JUSTUS LIEBIG, Die organische Chimie in ihrer Anwendung zur Physiologie. *Braunschweig 1842*

This and the companion volume on agriculture entitle him to be regarded as the founder of modern organic and inorganic chemistry. His analyses of innumerable compounds led to syntheses in the laboratory and, for example, to the great artificial fertilizer industry. He founded bio-chemistry by his researches into the raw materials of which organisms are built.

The Founder of Existentialism

502 SÖREN AABYE KIERKEGAARD. Enten-Eller. *Copenhagen 1843*

This is the first work, written before he was 29, of one whose admission to the front rank of modern thinkers has been delayed by his writing in Danish. The book is a bundle of papers, essays, and notes seemingly ill assorted, but in fact dialectically arranged. Kierkegaard, who had been educated in the Hegelian school (no. 458), later reacted against it. Passing through phases of aestheticism he proceeded through a vague religiosity to a Christianity of a very specific kind. He opposed the Hegelian dialectic with one of his own which profoundly involved each man as 'existing' before God.

Art and Socialism

503 JOHN RUSKIN, Modern Painters. *London 1843–60*

These five treatises, published over seventeen years, the first when Ruskin was only 24, contain some of the most extensive and penetrating studies of the purpose and nature of art ever written in English. In his insight into imagination, his passionate concern with beauty, and its spread into all branches of human life, he was in advance of his time, but he lived to see his doctrines widely accepted. Possessed of the means to do so, he did his best to put his beliefs into practice, and the wider spread of non-materialistic views owes much to him.

The Creator of the Kindergarten

504 FRIEDRICH WILHELM AUGUST FROEBEL, Mutter- und Kose-Lieder. Dichtung und Bilder zur edlen Pflege des Kindheitslebens . . . *Blankenburg bei Rudolstadt [1844]*

Froebel, having spent two years at Pestalozzi's establishment at Yverdun in Switzerland (no. 435), further developed the ideas of this great educational reformer. He conceived the function of education as the development of the faculties of children by arousing their co-operation; their voluntary activity must be the mainspring of their education. Froebel created the first 'kindergarten' which has become a universal institution. Here play was used to promote educational objects, to guide the children's development, and to bring them to 'unity with themselves'.

The Invention of Photography

505 (*a*) WILLIAM HENRY FOX TALBOT, The Pencil of Nature. *London 1844[–6]*

(*b*) LOUIS JACQUES MANDÉ DAGUERRE, Historique et description des procédés du daguerréotype. *Paris 1839*

Priority of discovery will be argued till doomsday by the respective supporters of Niepce, Daguerre, and Fox Talbot. The Englishman was unquestionably the inventor of the negative/positive process which has completely superseded the French invention. Fox Talbot's book, originally issued in parts, and obstinately and erroneously given the date of the first part when published as a book, contains a full account of his process, which he patented, and twenty-four actual photographs taken by means of it. The copy shown comes from Lacock Abbey where the process was perfected.

England's 'Two Nations'

506 BENJAMIN DISRAELI, Earl of Beaconsfield, Sybil or the Two Nations. *London 1845*

Industrialism and the egoistic pursuit of wealth by the new middle classes had destroyed the harmony of British political life. Disraeli, after personal visits to the factory districts, gave for the first time, an accurate statement of the facts of life there. In this novel he explains the political and economic aspects of his 'New England' movement and expounds the view of a nation divided into rich and poor, the 'two nations'. Disraeli's brilliant exposition of the situation and his prophetic criticism aroused the conscience of the country and started a movement of social reform —Tory democracy—the impetus of which is not yet exhausted.

The Glory that was Greece

507 GEORGE GROTE, History of Greece. *London 1846–56*

Grote, a friend of Bentham and Mill (nos. 378, 531) and co-founder of London University, retired from banking in 1843 to devote himself to the history of Greece. The work was received with universal acclamation, translated into French and German, and shaped the European conception of classical Hellas throughout the nineteenth century. Grote's idealistic over-estimation of democracy and his neglect of social and economic factors eventually killed the book. It still remains a monument of Victorian scholarship, and the source of the ideal of 'the noble and the good' which coloured the Victorian tradition of political and educational thought.

Founder of Modern Biblical Criticism

508 FERDINAND CHRISTIAN BAUR, Kritische Untersuchungen über die kanonischen Evangelisten. *Tübingen 1847*

The founder of the Tübingen school of modern New Testament criticism was also a philosopher, consistently following Hegel (no. 458). Thus he applied dialectic to dogma. It would be untrue, however, to say that Baur imposed Hegelian dogma upon Christian dogma. His reconstruction of early Christian history was buttressed by a fresh, detailed, and thorough study of the documents. Many of Baur's dates and conclusions have been reversed, but his philosophical approach was highly esteemed and dominated New Testament criticism throughout the nineteenth century until superseded by new historical and philological methods The copy shown is lent by Tübingen University, with which the name of Baur is indissolubly associated.

The Stone Age

509 BOUCHER DE PERTHES, Antiquités celtiques et antédiluviennes. *Paris 1847–64*

Boucher could not reconcile his discovery of flint implements at Abbeville with the accepted Mosaic cosmogony based on Ussher's calculations. He was ridiculed by the orthodox, but his postulate of much more remote human antiquity is now accepted.

The Conservation of Energy

510 HERMANN VON HELMHOLTZ, Über die Erhaltung der Kraft. *Berlin 1847*

This work contains the first comprehensive statement of the law of the conservation of energy—all kinds of energy, heat, light, electricity, and all chemical phenomena, are capable of transformation from one to the other, but are indestructible. Tartaglia, Carnot (nos. 196, 476), Mayer, and Joule made contributions to this theory, but Helmholtz proved it mathematically as capable of universal application. His work led to the construction of efficient heat engines and eventually to the liquefaction of all known gases. Helmholtz invented the ophthalmoscope in 1851 and made many important contributions to physiology, mathematics, and electricity.

The Idealized Revolution

511 JULES MICHELET, Histoire de la Révolution Française. *Paris 1847–53*

History was, to Michelet, 'resurrection of the past', and he succeeded in providing France and the world with the most colourful and fervent justification of the French Revolution. It is a sustained panegyric of radical democracy with 'only one hero—the people'. As with Carlyle (no. 493), the reader forgets the author's bias and inaccuracies while carried away by the grandiose flow of the story. In his immense *Histoire de France* he wrote the first modern history of that country.

Workers of the World Unite!

512 [KARL MARX and FRIEDRICH ENGELS], Manifest der kommunistischen Partei. *London 1848*

This brilliant exposé of the more practical recommendations of Marxism advocates ten immediate reforms at least half of which are neither Marxist nor revolutionary and are orthodox modern political practices. It concludes with the now famous exhortation, the workers having 'nothing to lose but their chains. They have the whole world to gain.' There were three printings dated 1848, one of which seems really to belong to 1856. The authors' names were first disclosed in an English translation in *The Red Republican*, in 1850.

The First Baedeker

513 KARL BÄDEKER, Rheinreise von Basel bis Düsseldorf. Sechste verbesserte und vermehrte Auflage der Klein'schen Rheinreise bearbeitet von K. Bädeker. *Coblenz 1849*

The first of the famous series of travel guides now known and copied all over the world. They have done much to encourage travel and to familiarize millions of people with foreign lands. Karl Bädeker bought up J. A. Klein's *Rheinreise* after the author's death, but it was not until the sixth edition that he felt justified in putting his own name on the title-page. The familiar red cover was adopted in the fifties.

The Covered Wagon

514 FRANCIS PARKMAN, The California and Oregon Trail. Being Sketches of Prairie and Rocky Mountain Life. *New York and London 1849*

Parkman's most popular work, *The Oregon Trail*, became a classic in the author's own lifetime. It was serialized in the *Knickerbocker Magazine* between February 1847 and February 1849. One of the few really good descriptive accounts of the rigours of overland travel and the habits of the plains Indians, this book became the 'bible' of western migrants and adventurers. It is the acknowledged masterpiece of America's most readable historian.

The Whig Interpretation of History

515 THOMAS BABINGTON MACAULAY, History of England from the Accession of James II. *London 1849–61*

The first historical work deliberately designed to outsell the best-selling novel of the day, Macaulay's book immediately fulfilled its author's aspiration: each volume sold about 150,000 copies within a month of its publication. Macaulay has remained the supreme advocate of the Whig interpretation of history, and the translation of his *History* into almost every literary language has perpetuated his ideas almost to this day. No historical work in English since Gibbon (no. 364) has had a comparable success.

A Landmark in Scholarship

516 KARL LACHMANN, Lucretius: de rerum natura. *Berlin 1850*

The great edition of Lucretius, published at the end of his life, was perhaps the finest achievement of Lachmann (1793–1851). He was already famous as a philologist, both in classical languages and in the development of German. His brilliant assessment of the different values of the manuscripts of Lucretius set a new standard in the analysis of corrupt texts in concentrating conjecture on the actual readings. It was indeed 'a landmark in textual criticism': the first edition to be based on a truly scientific method.

How the Earth Rotates

517 JEAN B. L. FOUCAULT, Sur divers signes sensibles du mouvement diurne de la terre. *Paris 1851*

Although the rotation of the earth had been accepted since Copernicus (no. 201), Foucault first demonstrated it by experiment. He performed his celebrated pendulum experiment in the Panthéon in 1851, and again in the following year he performed another experiment with the help of the gyroscope, his own invention. This latter instrument has been used in modern navigation as a stabilizer, and led to the possibility of the automatic pilot in aviation.

The First International Exhibition

518 Exhibition of the Works of Industry of All Nations, 1851. Report of the Juries. *London 1852*

This quintessence of Victorianism was inspired by Prince Albert without whose unflagging enthusiasm it would not have materialized. It was the first international exhibition and its effect on world commerce was incalculable. Many new inventions were introduced and it is fitting that we should show one of the fifty or so copies illustrated by Talbotypes (no. 505), for it was also the first considerable public display of photography and photographic apparatus.

The Novel as Propaganda

519 HARRIET BEECHER STOWE, Uncle Tom's Cabin; or Life among the Lowly. 2 volumes. *Boston and Cleveland 1852*

Inspired by a deep hatred of slavery, Harriet Beecher Stowe wrote the most influential novel of propaganda in American literature. The work appeared first as a serial in the *National Era*, a Washington abolitionist newspaper, but its shocking, melodramatic story of slaves and their owners made its greatest effect when published as a book in 1852. Its impact was felt in all parts of the nation, and equally strongly in Europe where it influenced public opinion in the approaching American Civil War.

Children of all classes devoured it, and Eva became a rival in popularity to Little Nell. Swinburne described Mrs. Stowe as the 'rampant Maenad of Massachusetts'.

A New Theory of Opera

520 RICHARD WAGNER, Drei Operndichtungen nebst einer Mitteilung. *Leipzig 1852*

Wagner's philosophy is fustian, his literary style is appalling, and his 'poetry' is often preposterous. His adoption as a kind of posthumous member of the Nazi Party is sufficient condemnation of his politics. But as a musician he was among the masters. A vast knowledge of the subject formed the basis for a revolutionary technique of opera which welded music and words into a synthesis never before attempted. The prefatory essay to these three libretti is a closely reasoned statement of his theories.

Hitler's French Mentor

521 JOSEPH-ARTHUR COMTE DE GOBINEAU, Essai sur l'inégalité des races humaines. 4 volumes. *Paris 1853–5*

Gobineau championed the theory that 'race' is permanent and unchangeable, and proclaimed the Nordic or, as he called them, 'Aryan' peoples to be the élite, destined to rule the rest of mankind. Although he considered the Germans a poor mixture of Celts and Slavs, his theories were adopted with special fervour in Germany because they seemed to provide a biological foundation for racism, anti-semitism, and pan-Germanism, culminating in national socialism (*see* no. 601).

The Invention of Quaternions

522 SIR WILLIAM ROWAN HAMILTON, Lectures on Quaternions. *Dublin 1853*

Quaternions were invented by Hamilton. They are an extension of ordinary complex numbers and are widely used in the solution of algebraic equations of the second and higher degrees. This was, in fact, a new algebra, a discovery comparable in importance to non-Euclidean geometry.

The Gospel of Materialism

523 FRIEDRICH KARL LUDWIG BÜCHNER, Kraft und Stoff. *Tübingen 1855*

Büchner leaves one in no doubt as to the extent of his materialistic philosophy. Mind, soul, thought are by-products of an animal organism in the same way as motion is the product of the steam-engine. The outcry over this book compelled him to resign his professorship, but he had many disciples, Dühring and Haeckel among them, and is still venerated by 'free-thinkers' all over the world.

Suez Canal Projected

524 FERDINAND DE LESSEPS, Percement de l'Isthme de Suez. *Paris 1855*

On 30 November 1854 de Lesseps received a concession from the Egyptian Viceroy which authorized the construction of a canal across the Isthmus of Suez. The indifference of the Sultan and the declared opposition of the British were serious obstacles which de Lesseps had to overcome, with other obstacles nearer home. The first step was to outline his project in full in this book. Construction was begun in 1859, and the canal was formally opened to traffic ten years later.

The Great American Poet

525 WALT WHITMAN, Leaves of Grass. *Brooklyn 1855*

'I dwelt on Birth and Life, clothing my ideas in pictures, days, transactions of my time . . . saturating them with the vehemence of price and audacity of freedom necessary to loosen the mind of still-to-be form'd America from the folds, the superstitions, and all the long, tenacious, and shifting anti-democratic authorities of the Asiatic and European past—my enclosing purport being to express, above all artificial regulation and aid, the eternal Bodily Character of One's-Self.' This is Whitman's own later comment on *Leaves of Grass*.

Christianity and Exploration in Africa

526 DAVID LIVINGSTONE, Missionary Travels. *London 1857*

Livingstone was the greatest of African explorers. During his thirty years of travel he covered about a third of the continent from the Cape to the equator and from the Atlantic to the Indian Ocean. He was a keen scientific observer and by living with the African peoples penetrated the essential nature of African life. His example inspired many other explorers and missionaries, to further the conquest of Africa by the European nations. The practical application of the ideas of Wilberforce (no. 437) was due to his efforts. The copy shown is inscribed by the author, and is one of a few copies for presentation, with a coloured frontispiece not included in the published edition. *Plate 32*

Neanderthal Man

527 JOHANN CARL FÜHLROT, Menschliche Überreste aus einer Felsengrotte des Düsselthals. *Bonn 1857 and 1859*

Human remains handed by quarry workers in the Neander Valley to Fühlrot, an Elberfeld archaeologist, were described in these two papers presented jointly with Schaafhausen to a Rhineland natural history society. Described more fully and publicly in Müller's *Archiv* in 1858 they evoked Virchow's (no. 529) pronouncement that the skull was that of an idiot. Huxley took the discovery as a corner-stone in *Man's Place in Nature*, 1863, and thus the human race was brought within the scope of evolutionary theory.

The Lady with the Lamp

528 [Florence Nightingale], Notes on Matters affecting the Health, Efficiency, and Hospital Administration of the British Army. *London 1858*

This terrible indictment of almost criminal inefficiency is at once the least known and most efficacious of her writings. Printed and privately circulated at her own expense, the threat of its publication brought the War Office to heel, and a Royal Commission recommended the drastic revision of health services which ultimately produced the modern hospital. The copy shown comes from St. Thomas's Hospital where Miss Nightingale founded the first training school for nurses.

'Omnis cellula e cellula'

529 Rudolf Virchow, Die Cellularpathologie. *Berlin 1858*

Mainly concerned with basing pathology on the cell theory of Schwann (no. 496) and Schleiden, Virchow considerably extended its range and importance. His immortal aphorism, quoted above, meant that cell development is not discontinuous as had been thought and that there are no specific disease cells, but only disorders of healthy cells. His classic investigations of specific disorders are too numerous to mention here.

The Theory of Evolution

530 (*a*) Charles Darwin and Alfred Russell Wallace, On the Tendency of Species to form Varieties. . . . *London 1858*
(*b*) Charles Darwin. On the Origin of Species. *London 1859*

Darwin was one of the great generalizers—Newton (no. 295) and Einstein (no. 595) are others—who have profoundly affected the mind of man. The scientific-cum-theological dogma of the immutability of species had been proof against sceptics from Lucretius to Lyell. They guessed at what Darwin was the first to prove. From being an *a priori* anticipation the theory of evolution became with Darwin an interpretation of nature and eventually a causal theory affecting every department of scientific research. This is what is essential in Darwin's contribution. The modifications due to the rediscovery of Mendel's investigations by Bateson (nos. 545, 565), Weissman's germ-plasm hypothesis, and the virtual elimination of 'natural selection' as the basic cause of evolutionary change do not affect Darwin's eminence as a pioneer. The joint paper by Darwin and Wallace —one of two recorded surviving copies—was communicated to the Linnaean Society at the suggestion of J. D. Hooker, Darwin's mentor, to resolve the situation caused by the discovery that Wallace had been thinking along the same lines as Darwin, though without his wealth of observational material.

Liberty

531 John Stuart Mill, On Liberty. *London 1859*

Mill was a disciple of Bentham (no. 378), from whom he developed his own utilitarian theories, which remained his constant study to the end of his life. His famous tract on liberty represents a central point in the history of Utilitarianism, and is the extension of that doctrine to the liberty of the individual. Hitherto liberty had always been considered relative, in relation to tyranny or oppression: Mill extended tyranny to include a custom-ridden majority, and declared that 'the sole end for which mankind is warranted in interfering with liberty of action is self-protection'.

Victorian Uplift

532 Samuel Smiles, Self-help. *London 1859*

Some 20,000 copies of this book were sold in the year of publication. *Self-Help*, along with Martin Tupper's *Proverbial Philosophy* and 'Eliza Cookery' and Charles Dickens, enjoyed enormous popularity with the moral and sentimental Victorian public. It is the low-brow equivalent of *Heroes and Hero Worship* and corresponds in its spirit to, say, Wilhelmina Stitch.

The Apogee of Cultural History

533 Jacob Burckhardt, Die Cultur der Renaissance in Italien. *Leipzig 1860*

'The most penetrating and subtle treatise on the history of civilization' (in Lord Acton's words) portrays and interprets the growth of modern individualism in thirteenth- to fifteenth-century Italy, and for almost a century it determined the general conception of the Renaissance. Burckhardt's *Constantine the Great* (1853) reinterpreted Gibbon (no. 364), and his *Greek Cultural History* (1898–1902) destroyed the idealized picture presented by Grote (no. 507).

'Septem contra Christum'

534 Essays and Reviews. *London 1860*

This volume of essays by seven liberal Anglicans, Archbishop Temple, Mark Pattison, and Jowett among them, panicked the bishops into a prosecution, which finally led the Judicial Committee of the Privy Council to pronounce against the necessity for a clergyman to believe in 'the eternity of future punishment'. Lord Westbury, who presided, was said to have 'dismissed Hell with costs', and 'taken away from orthodox members of the Church of England their last hope of everlasting damnation'. Although little read now, its influence, enormous at the time, has persisted to this day.

Spectrum Analysis

535 GUSTAV KIRCHHOFF, Untersuchungen über das Sonnenspectrum. *Berlin 1860*

Kirchhoff's investigations followed up those of Fraunhofer (no. 452) and his successors with the triumphal declaration that every glowing vapour emits characteristic rays by which its chemical constitution may be infallibly recognized. Thus the new science of spectrum analysis was born. It was further developed by Bunsen.

Matriarchal Society

536 JOHANN JACOB BACHOFEN, Das Mutterrecht. *Stuttgart 1861*

This Swiss scholar discovered not only in Oriental societies but also in classical antiquity traces of a conception of society based not on patriarchal, but on matriarchal power. This state of society of 'the mother-right' is described by Herodotus, found in Sparta and reflected strongly in the Oedipus myth. Bachofen's discovery helped to lead to a complete change of views in sociological study and law.

'Antiseptics'

537 IGNAZ PHILIPP SEMMELWEISS. Die Aetiologie, des Begriff des und die Prophylaxis des Kinderbettfiebers. *Budapest, Vienna, and Leipzig 1861*

This is one of the most epoch-making books in the entire history of medicine. Concerned at the tragic prevalence of puerperal fever in his Vienna hospital, Semmelweiss diagnosed it as a septicaemia caused by vaginal examination made with unclean hands. He recommended 'brushing up' with chloride of lime which is the basis of aseptic —wrongly called antiseptic—practice. He was fiercely opposed and persecuted and he died a victim of brooding insanity.

The Red Cross

538 HENRI DUNANT, Un Souvenir de Solférino. *Geneva 1862*

This eyewitness account of the appalling suffering and lack of medical care at the battle of Solferino was directly responsible for the Geneva Convention of 1864 and the founding of the International Red Cross Society. Dunant received the Nobel Peace Prize in 1901, but lost all his money in speculation and died a poor man in 1910.

Discovery of Bacteria

539 LOUIS PASTEUR, Les Corpuscules organisés. *Paris 1862*

Pasteur was originally a physical chemist, but his researches on the nature of fermentation led him to the discovery of bacteria and yeast, and thence to the 'germ theory' of disease from which has developed all modern bacteriology, immunology, and the science of public health. The very ancient idea of spontaneous generation, or the origin of living beings from inanimate matter, was shown by him to be as untrue for bacteria as for the higher organisms.

The Gettysburg Address

540 ABRAHAM LINCOLN, The Gettysburg Solemnities. . . . Published at the Washington Chronicle Office *[1863]*

The occasion was the dedication of the cemetery at Gettysburg on 19 November 1863. Edward Everett's 'oration' on this occasion, also reported here, lasted two hours, every word of which is now forgotten. Lincoln's 'speech' comprised ten sentences and lasted less than five minutes. It is immortal, one of the supreme utterances of democratic freedom. The copy of the first printing, exhibited, is one of three recorded.

A Christian Historian

541 ERNEST RENAN, Vie de Jésus. *Paris 1863*

Ernest Renan, Breton by birth, philologist, historian, and Christian, was a writer and lecturer whose melodious style was combined with an historical sense of the force of physical circumstance in the best tradition of French historiography which derived from Michelet (no. 511). This *Vie de Jesus* is perhaps the most famous of all his books, in which he produced a work at once historically valid, eminently readable and theologically profound. It was, nevertheless, widely attacked as heretical, if not blasphemous.

Light as a Form of Electricity

542 JAMES CLERK MAXWELL, A Dynamical Theory of the Electromagnetic Field. *London 1864*

Faraday (no. 487) discovered that electricity could influence a light beam. Maxwell's twenty equations proclaimed the electromagnetic nature of light which brought both electricity and light within the scope of dynamics, the wave theory of electricity which led to wireless, and the corpuscular theory of electricity which foreshadowed the electron. The further implications of this discovery were worked out by Einstein (no. 602).

Alice in Wonderland

543 LEWIS CARROLL [i.e. Charles Lutwidge Dodgson], Alice's Adventures in Wonderland. *London 1865*

Alice's Adventures in Wonderland and its no less famous sequel *Through the Looking Glass*, although ostensibly written for children, are unique among 'juveniles' in appealing equally if not more strongly to adults. Written by an Oxford don, a clergyman, and a professional mathematician, they abound in characters—the Red Queen, the White Knight, the Mad Hatter, Humpty Dumpty—who are part of everybody's mental furniture. And the philosophic profundity of scores, if not hundreds, of these characters' observations, long household words wherever English is spoken, gains mightily from the delicious fantasy of their setting.

The first edition (1865) of *Alice* was withdrawn by the author because of the poor printing of Sir John Tenniel's almost equally famous illustrations; and less than twenty copies are known to survive. This is a proof copy bound up by one of the compositors at the Oxford University Press for his young daughter.

Discovering the Source of the Nile

544 SIR SAMUEL WHITE BAKER, Albert Nyanza, Great Basin of the Nile. 2 volumes. *London 1866*

A classic account of the exploration of East Africa in the search for the source of the White Nile. Baker discovered the great lake which he named Albert Nyanza and proved that the Nile flows through it. This book, together with some of his others, was the first to bring to Europe a picture of Africa as it really was, in contrast to the legends and myths—some of which persist in relation to these regions. His writings had much influence on British expansion in Africa with its great political and economic consequences.

The New Science of Genetics

545 GREGOR JOHANN MENDEL, Versuche über Pflanzen-Hybriden. *Brünn [1865] 1866*

Cross-breeding of sweet peas in the garden of his monastery enabled Mendel, a monk and science master at a local secondary school, to observe and record the hitherto unsuspected laws of heredity. His tabulations and the introduction of the terms 'dominant' and 'recessive' revolutionized the science of biology. Further research along these lines has extended beyond pure science with its studies of genes and chromosomes to everyday life where 'results obtained in the flowerpot, the milk bottle and the breeding pan' are now on an exact scientific basis.

What is the English Constitution?

546 WALTER BAGEHOT, The English Constitution. *London 1867.*

This classic account of the English constitution led to a wider and better understanding of its working. Bagehot wrote about it not so much from the legal point of view as from his own practical experience of the life of society and his personal contacts with politicians. He showed how the close co-operation between executive government and legislature established by the cabinet system is the effective part of the English constitution and the real centre of power—or was so at least until very recent times. Bagehot's book had a wide influence, and was translated into French, Italian, and German.

The New Religion

547 KARL MARX, Das Kapital. Vol. 1. *Hamburg 1867*

The first volume of this work was the only one either completed by Marx or published during his lifetime. The 3 volumes are the infallible source of appeal on questions of Marxian orthodoxy. Heresy is judged and condemned according to their dogmas and not in the light of reason. It is all here from the theories of value and surplus-value, through the dictatorship of the proletariat to the neo-Hegelian dialectic of materialism.

American Free-thought

548 ROBERT G. INGERSOLL, An Oration on the Gods. *Peoria, Illinois, 1872*

Ingersoll, Civil War Colonel and 'the leading American orator of his generation', undoubtedly reached a wider audience through the printed and spoken word than did almost any other free-thought propagandist. 'His ethical indictment of orthodox religion . . . was the deepest source of his influence . . . and was never really answered by the clerics and others who affected to dismiss it' (J. M. Robertson). Many of his pamphlets were reprinted in England. This is his first published work.

Christian Science

549 MARY BAKER EDDY, Science and Health. *Boston 1875*

This work, first printed in a thousand copies, has had a remarkable influence upon American religious history. Its editions are to be measured in hundreds. Mrs. Eddy held the dualism of mind and matter to be an error. Science is the wisdom of the Eternal Mind reached through Jesus Christ —hence 'Christian Science'. The doctrine that traces physical effect to a mental cause and asserts that the power of prayer and belief will deliver one from sickness has had an influence out of all proportion to the actual membership of her following. This is a presentation copy inscribed by the author.

The Invention of the Telephone

550 ALEXANDER GRAHAM BELL, Researches in Telephony, *New York 1876*

The first intelligible sentences exchanged over the telephone, were from one room to another in the same house. They were 'Do you understand what I say?' 'Yes; I understand you perfectly'. In the same month, March 1876, Bell took out his first patent which, though often contested, was uniformly upheld by the courts. Bell was born in Edinburgh. He became an American citizen in 1874.

The Pathology of Crime

551 CESARE LOMBROSO, L'Uomo Delinquente. *Turin 1878.*

His theory that pathological abnormalities are far commoner in criminals than in normal persons with the conclusion that there is a definite criminal type was for long discredited. It is now accepted in so far as the modern treatment of criminals is increasingly reformatory and remedial rather than punitive. The first edition was published in Milan, in 1876.

The Height of Prussian Chauvinism

552 HEINRICH VON TREITSCHKE, Deutsche Geschichte im neunzehnten Jahrhundert. 5 volumes. *Berlin 1879–94*

Treitschke was the most aggressive representative of the 'Prussian school' of historians who set political partisanship against Ranke's detachment (no. 477). The broad sweep of his vision—embracing every aspect of cultural and economic life, combined with a brilliant style making him the equal of Macaulay and Michelet (nos. 515, 511), —secured Treitschke an enthusiastic reception among the German *bourgeoisie*. His chauvinism, anti-Semitism, hostility to democracy, and hatred of England were welcomed by them.

The Cause of Tuberculosis Discovered

553 ROBERT KOCH, Die Aetiologie der Tuberkulose. *Berlin 1882*

In this short paper Koch announced his isolation of the tubercle bacillus, and the special culture and differential staining methods he had first introduced in 1876. These new methods of identifying and later of photographing microscopic objects were further advanced by Ehrlich (no. 589). Koch's great work on the etiology of surgical infections, 1878, is a medical classic.

The Superman

554 FRIEDRICH NIETZSCHE, Also sprach Zarathustra. Parts I–III. *Chemnitz 1883*. Part IV. *Leipzig 1891*

The culmination of his aristocratic nihilism, his revolt against all convention, religious or social, cast in aphoristic form with epigrammatic wit and force of expression, are best displayed in this pseudo-prophetical work.

Liberal Imperialism

555 JOHN ROBERT SEELEY, The Expansion of England. *London 1883*

To Seeley, Regius Professor of History in Cambridge, history meant chiefly the background of politics and the school of statesmanship. His *Expansion* gained its deserved fame for entirely wrong reasons. Seeley's one ill-guarded remark that the English 'conquered half the world in a fit of absence of mind' became an almost ineradicable slogan. His profound reflections on the magnitude and the moral obligations of empire-building did not prevent the book from becoming the bible of British Imperialists.

D.N.B.

556 The Dictionary of National Biography. *London 1885*

The first editor, Sir Leslie Stephen, made this product of co-operative scholarship a counterpart of the *Oxford English Dictionary* (no. 559)—a work of reference which is an essential of every library in the world, and the pattern upon which similar enterprises have been based elsewhere.

Theological Liberalism

557 ADOLF VON HARNACK, Lehrbuch der Dogmengeschichte. *Freiburg-im-Breisgau 1886–9*

Holding that Christian dogma is of historical and largely of Hellenistic rather than of Divine origin, Harnack believed that Protestants have superseded it with a profounder form of faith. Harnack's influence on education and scholarship is exemplified in his having founded in 1910 the Kaiser Wilhelm Gesellschaft in which all the German research institutes are combined.

The Copernicus of Geometry

558 NICOLAS IVANOVITCH LOBATCHEWSKY, Geometrische Untersuchungen zur Theorie der Parallellinien. *Berlin 1887*

Lobatchewsky was the first to challenge the universality of Euclidean geometry, notably that the axiom on parallel lines was true only if the earth was flat. Riemann in 1854 and Minkowski in 1908 (no. 588) carried these ideas further to a point where Euclidian geometry had to be abandoned, the fourth dimension introduced, and the space–time conception fundamental to relativity was posited. The above edition is listed because the earlier editions of 1829 and 1840 proved unprocurable.

The English of the World

559 JAMES MURRAY, HENRY BRADLEY, W. A. CRAIGIE, C. T. ONIONS (eds.), A New English Dictionary on Historical Principles. 12 volumes. *Oxford 1888–1933*

Conceived at Cambridge and begun at Oxford in 1879, the *Oxford English Dictionary*, as it was known from the beginning and expressly thus named in the 'corrected re-issue', has established itself and its offspring (*The Shorter*, *The Concise*, *The Pocket*, *The Little*, *Oxford Dictionaries*) as the greatest treasure-house of any language in the world for its comprehensiveness as well as its scholarship.

The Salvation Army

560 GENERAL WILLIAM BOOTH, In Darkest England. *London [1890]*

In 1878 Booth founded the Salvation Army, and in 1890, the same year that Stanley published *In Darkest Africa*, he published *In Darkest England and The Way Out*. In this book he analysed the causes of the pauperism and vice of the period, and proposed a remedy by ten expedients. These included land settlement, emigration, rescue work among prostitutes and at the prison-gate, the poor man's bank, and the poor man's lawyer. Money was liberally subscribed, and a large part of the scheme was carried through.

An Anthropological Masterpiece

561 SIR JAMES GEORGE FRAZER, The Golden Bough. Vol. I. *London 1890*

The genesis of this work, in 2 volumes, was to solve the riddle of the King of the Wood in the Arician grove of Diana. Frazer can hardly himself have expected that it would become his life work—an inexhaustible fund of knowledge on magic and comparative religion in 12 volumes.

A Theatrical Revolution

562 HENDRIK IBSEN, Hedda Gabler. *London 1890*

The fact that Ibsen's moral and political notions seem old fashioned to the younger generation is the measure of his influence as a social reformer. His dramatic technique was equally revolutionary and he founded an entirely new school of dramatic art. The copy shown is one of the twelve copies of the first printing in the original Norwegian, made to secure copyright.

Finger-prints and Criminology

563 SIR FRANCIS GALTON, Finger Prints. *London 1892*

Though the use of finger-prints as identification marks is of very ancient origin, Galton was the first to explain their possibilities for identifying criminals. He also wrote *Decipherment of Blurred Finger Prints* (1893) and *Finger Print Directories* (1895). These investigations formed part of the general scheme of 'Eugenics' formulated by Galton.

The Discovery of Wireless

564 HEINRICH RUDOLF HERTZ, Untersuchungen über die Ausbreitung der elektrischen Kraft. *Leipzig 1892*

Investigating Clerk Maxwell's conception of light as an electromagnetic phenomenon (*see* no. 542), Hertz discovered that waves of electricity could be transmitted and received through space. This led directly to Marconi's perfection of wireless telegraphy (no. 570).

The Laws of Heredity

565 WILLIAM BATESON, Materials for the Study of Variation. *London 1894*

Bateson opposed Galton's theory of continuous inheritance and insisted on the truth of the phenomenon of discontinuity in variation. Shortly afterward's Mendel's forgotten paper (no. 545) was discovered proving that Bateson was correct. Bateson became Mendel's most important defender and propagandist and after much controversy eventually succeeded in establishing the new theory of heredity.

The American Frontier Saga

566 F. J. TURNER, The Significance of the Frontier in American History. *Wisconsin 1894*

One of those *simplificateurs terribles*, Turner tried to explain the whole of American history as an urge to push forward 'the frontier'. Rejected by historians, the term has become an integral part of American folk-lore and journalistic mythology. Its latest issue is the slogan of the 'new frontier' adopted by the Kennedy administration.

The Electron Theory

567 HENDRIK ANTOON LORENTZ, Versuch einer Theorie der electrischen und optischen Erscheinungen in bewegten Körpern. *Leiden 1895*

Concerned to extend the electromagnetic theories of Maxwell (no. 542), Lorentz made the fundamentally new assumption that the behaviour of light and matter was explicable on the assumption of atoms of electricity, now called electrons. Later his hypothesis that a moving object is shortened in the direction of its movement was adopted by Einstein (no. 595).

Discovery of X-Rays

568 WILHELM CONRAD RÖNTGEN, Eine neue Art von Strahlen. *Würzburg 1895*

The discovery of X-rays—'a new type of radiation'—by the fifty-five-year-old Röntgen, professor of physics at Würzburg, in 1895, marks the real starting-point of modern physical research. Such was the impact of this discovery on the world of science that in the next twelve months more than a hundred papers treating of these new effects appeared in the journals, over the names of scientists both amateur and professional. Becquerel (no. 580) was directed to the discovery of radioactivity by Röntgen's discovery; and X-ray analysis in the hands of such as Aston, Moseley, the Braggs (no. 593), and Perutz and his colleagues has revolutionized modern science.

The Inspiration of Zionism

569 THEODOR HERZL, Der Judenstaat. *Vienna 1896*

The publication of this book, which was quickly re-issued in many translations and reprints, aroused the interest of the Jewish people and of the world in general to the vital question of their future. The idea of a territorial segregation of the Jews and their search for a national home was not new, but it was crystallized in this work, to which Herzl had been inspired when contemplating the difficulties caused by both anti-semitism and by the assimilation of the Jews. He treated the problem entirely from the economic and political angle, and suggested the formation of a 'Jewish Company' in London to plan and organize a Jewish State either in South America or in Palestine. In spite of much opposition, the idea took hold and eventually in 1948 the Jewish State of Israel was created.

Marconi Patents Wireless Telegraphy

570 GUGLIELMO MARCONI, Provisional Specification. Improvements in Transmitting Electrical Impulses and Signals. *London, 2 June 1896*

Marconi's first successful experiments were made in Bologna. He came to London and was granted a patent in July 1897. In the same month the Wireless Telegraph Company was formed after exhaustive tests by the G.P.O. These culminated in the successful transatlantic communication of 1901.

The First Practical Cinematograph

571 AUGUSTE and LOUIS LUMIÈRE, Notice sur le cinématographe. *Lyons 1897*

Whatever may be claimed for other early experimenters in cinematography it is certain that Lumière was the first to produce a practical machine with commercial possibilities. This brochure was his first public announcement of his invention, and several of the films listed in it were shown at the memorial exhibition in Paris in 1937 and found to be as good as new. It is worth noting that the reason for complete lack of flicker in these early films was the fact that Lumière used the same machine for both taking and projecting his films. *Plate 32*

Farthest North

572 FRIDTJOF NANSEN, Fram over polhavet. *Kristiania 1897*

On 17 August 1896 the first completely successful modern polar exploration came to an end; Nansen (1861–1930) had returned to his native Norway after reaching the highest latitude (86° 14′) so far attained by man. The account which he wrote was an instant success, and translated into many other languages. It remains the classic story of Polar exploration.

Town and Country Planning

573 EBENEZER HOWARD, To-Morrow: a Peaceful Path to Reform. *London 1898*

Distressed by the overcrowding in large cities Howard wrote this impassioned plea for taking the city into the country-side. In 1903 he persuaded a group of financiers that this was a business proposition, and the first garden city in the world was begun at Letchworth. He was a poor man all his life but was knighted in 1927.

The Father of Tropical Medicine

574 SIR PATRICK MANSON, Tropical Diseases. *London 1898*

The standard textbook on tropical diseases, still valid in its revised form. In 1894 Manson had announced his discovery that at one stage of its existence the mosquito is the host of the malarial parasite and therefore an active agent in spreading the disease. This discovery, developed further by Sir Ronald Ross, made possible the great progress in opening up Africa, particularly as Manson—in association with Joseph Chamberlain—reorganized the whole of the tropical medical service and in 1899 founded the London School of Tropical Medicine.

Conditioned Reflexes

575 IVAN PETROVICH PAVLOV, Die Arbeit der Verdauungsdrüsen. Aus dem Russischen von Dr. A. Walther. *Wiesbaden 1898*

World famous experiments on dogs by which salivary reactions were produced by a kind of Barmecide feast, first called 'psychical secretions' and later 'conditioned reflexes'. The first full statement of Pavlov's experiments in English was in *Conditioned Reflexes*, 1927.

Good and Bad Design

576 WILLIAM MORRIS, Some Hints on Pattern-designing. *London 1899*

Perhaps Morris's most lasting achievement was the establishment of the 'useful arts' as arts in opposition to 'mere' craftsmanship. In this work he asserted that good design should be extended to objects for *use* as well as works of art, and, both here and in his own works—books, textiles, furniture—he amply vindicated his claim.

The Meaning of Dreams

577 SIGMUND FREUD, Die Traumdeutung. *Leipzig and Vienna 1900*

Ernest Jones, Freud's biographer and friend, wrote of this book: 'It is without any doubt Freud's greatest work, and one which contains the germ of all his later work.' Its conclusions were completely new and totally unexpected. It contains all the basic features of psychoanalytic theory and practice—the erotic nature of dreams, the 'Oedipus complex', and, above all, the theory of the unconscious and the libido. The new field of study thus opened by this one man is still largely unexplored and its implications have revolutionized our thinking in many fields.

The Quantum Theory

578 MAX PLANCK, Zur Theorie des Gesetzes der Energieverteilung im Normalspectrum. *Leipzig 1900*

He postulated that energy is not continuous but is released in small, discrete, indivisible units which he called quanta; and discovered a constant for them—Planck's quantum. Its ramifications are incalculable—the formulation of a general law of radiation and the behaviour of bodies at low temperatures are among them. Overshadowing all this, however, is Einstein's development of the theory in relation to photoelectricity, an indispensable factor in relativity (no. 595).

The Foundation Stone of Bolshevism

579 VLADIMIR ILYITCH LENIN (Ulyanov), Что делать . . . (What is to be done?) *Stuttgart 1902*

The point of departure from the Social-Democrats, or Mensheviks, is here laid down. Denunciation of 'spontaneity', 'opportunism', and 'democracy' are explicit. The need for a monolithic party ready to assume dictatorial powers—the complete basis of the seizure of power in 1917 is contained in *What is to be done?* Stuttgart publication is explained by its being the headquarters of Lenin and his fellow political exiles at the time.

The Discovery of Radioactivity

580 HENRI BECQUEREL, Recherches sur une propriété nouvelle de la matière radio-activité de la Matière. *Paris 1903*

Inspired by Poincaré's exhibition in 1896 of radiographs sent him by Röntgen (no. 568), Becquerel deliberately sought to investigate other phosphorescent phenomena. Accidental fogging of photographic plates in his dark room was traced to the presences of uranium ore and this led to the theory of radioactivity. He suggested to the Curies (no. 581) that pitchblende might repay investigation and thus set them on the trail that led to radium.

The Discovery of Radium

581 MARIE SKLODOWSKA CURIE, Thèses présentées à la Faculté des Sciences de Paris pour obtenir le grade de Docteur ès Sciences. *Paris 1903*

Becquerel (no. 580), following the discovery or Röntgen (no. 568), had discovered the fact or radioactivity in 1896. Madame Curie read a paper on the subject to the Académie des Sciences, and in 1903, in two modestly entitled theses, she announced the final laborious isolation of radium.

Cathode Rays

582 JOSEPH JOHN THOMSON, Conduction or Electricity through Gases. *Cambridge 1903*

Thomson's contributions to atomic physics are innumerable. Perhaps the most epoch-making was his declaration that cathode rays are particles of negative electricity, for this meant the virtual abandonment of the age-old belief in the indestructibility of matter.

Broadcasting Foreshadowed

583 JOHN AMBROSE FLEMING, Improvements in Instruments for Detecting and Measuring Alternating Electric Currents. *London 1904*

This is the invention of the thermionic valve which was used as a detector for wireless telegraphy and, as adapted by Lee Forest in 1907, for wireless telephony. It eventually made broadcasting feasible.

The First Powered Flights

584 WILBUR and ORVILLE WRIGHT, 'The Experiments of the Brothers Wright', Journal of the Aeronautical Society. *London 1904*

After mastering the flight of gliders in a brilliant progression of theory, test, and accomplishment, the brothers Wilbur and Orville Wright made and flew the world's first practical powered aeroplanes, starting with four short flights on the morning of 17 December 1903. This volume is the 1904 *Journal* of what is now the Royal Aeronautical Society, in which the brothers set out simply and accurately what they had attained. It is the first proper account ever to appear in England of what happened on that momentous day at the Kill Devil Sandhills (near Kitty Hawk) in North Carolina.

A Classic of Neurology

585 SIR CHARLES SCOTT SHERRINGTON, The Integrative Action of the Nervous System. *New Haven 1906*

Sherrington's investigation of the spinal nerve centres led him to demonstrate that reflex actions are not isolated phenomena, and that the true function of the nervous system is to integrate the organism making it an individual whole not iust a collection of organs and cells. He developed a new method of analysing reflex actions, and his researches laid the foundations for modern physiological and psychological research.

Votes for Women

586 FREDERICK WILLIAM and EMMELINE PETHWICK LAWRENCE (eds.), Votes for Women. Vol. i, no. 1. *October 1907*

Whatever may be the respective merits of the militant and the non-militant women's suffrage movements there can be little doubt that the militants organized by Mrs. Pankhurst made the greater impact on the public mind. This was their official organ, but militancy was embarked upon only in 1908 when it was adopted more as a counsel of despair than for any other reason. Women were first qualified to vote in Britain in the electoral register of 1919.

The Boy Scout Movement

587 ROBERT, LORD BADEN-POWELL, Scouting for Boys. *London 1908*

Baden-Powell founded the Boy Scout movement in 1908 'to promote good citizenship in the rising generation'. Honour, self-control, and practical efficiency are inculcated in a social organization which has since become world-wide. This is the only recorded copy in the original parts.

Plate 32

The Fourth Dimension

588 HERMANN MINKOWSKI, Raum und Zeit. *Leipzig and Berlin 1908*

Two indispensable features for the extension of Einstein's special theory of 1905 into a universal theory in 1916 (no. 595) were here expounded: (*a*) time as a fourth dimension, one second corresponding to the distance travelled by light in that time, and (*b*) the corollary of a space–time continuum. In this new space conception, Euclidean geometry would not work and thus the pioneering of Lobatchewsky (no. 558) and Riemann was perfected.

Beginnings of Antibiotics

589 PAUL EHRLICH and SAHACHIRO HATA, Die experimentelle Chemotherapie der Spirillosen. *Berlin 1910*

This collaboration between a German chemist and a Japanese bacteriologist resulted in the discovery of Salvarsan ('606'), a specific cure for syphilis. This led to their theory of chemotherapy, the discovery of a specific that would kill bacteria without harming the host and to modern antibiotics. Ehrlich also advanced considerably methods of differential staining in microscopy.

Time and Motion Study

590 FREDERICK WINSLOW TAYLOR, The Principles of Scientific Management. *New York 1911*

F. W. Taylor, an American engineer employed by the Bethlehem Steel Company, was the founder of 'scientific management' in industry. He laid down the main lines of approach to the problem of increased efficiency by standardizing processes and machines, time and motion study, and systematizing 'piece-work' or payment by results. All these systems have been welcomed in Russia, but are anathema to trades unionists almost everywhere else.

Futurism

591 F. T. MARINETTI, Manifesto tecnico della letteratura futurista. *11 May 1912*

Long regarded as a tiresome, flippant, and illegitimate intrusion into the field of aesthetics, the heritage of Marinetti's theories is clearly perceptible. Dadaism, surrealism, abstract painting, concrete music, and blacksmith sculpture are some of the fields on which their impact has been unmistakable.

Rational Christianity

592 ERNST TROELTSCH, Die Soziallehren der christlichen Kirchen. *Tübingen 1912*

The dominating thesis of this famous work of Troeltsch (1865–1923) is the demonstration, on Kantian lines, that religion is a necessity of reason. In it, the significance of modern historical consciousness for the understanding of Christian culture, and the problem of relating the living power of the Christian tradition to the needs of the social and religious unrest of his time, were explored with massive erudition and cogent force.

X-ray Crystallography

593 (*a*) MAX VON LAUE. Interferenzerscheinungen bei Röntgenstrahlen. Theoretischer Teil. *Munich 1912*

(*b*) WILLIAM HENRY and WILLIAM LAWRENCE BRAGG, X-rays and Crystal Structures. *London 1915*

Laue had suggested that the regular arrangement of atoms in a crystal would provide a diffraction grating sufficiently fine to produce spectroscopic effects from X-rays (no. 568) and thus prove that these are light waves of very short wavelength. The Braggs tackled the problem from the other end, concentrating on the knowledge of atomic structure which X-ray shadows could provide. This has revolutionized both pure and applied chemistry. The discoveries of Aston and Moseley (nos. 599, 594) were immediate sequels in pure science. The discovery of the chemical basis of life —DNA—by Perutz and others is only the most recent of the sensational results of the Bragg experiments.

Reconstruction of the Atomic Table

594 HENRY GWYN JEFFREYS MOSELEY, The High Frequency Spectra of the Elements. *London 1913–14*

Moseley used the crystal method of analysis (no. 593) for determining the wavelength of X-rays to the spectra of the elements. From his results he deduced that a new atomic number could be attached to each element based on its nuclear charge. This replaced the fallible table based on atomic weights—a discovery as fundamentally important as the discoveries of the periodic table itself and of spectrum analysis. Four new elements were immediately discovered by his methods.

Einstein on Relativity

595 ALBERT EINSTEIN, Grundlage der allgemeinen Relativitätstheorie. *Leipzig 1916*

Einstein was on the track of his theory of gravitation ('general relativity theory') in 1913–14. In this paper the theory first appears fully fledged. Its importance was at once recognized by specialists, but it was not until 1919, when one of its leading predictions was confirmed by the British Eclipse Expeditions, that it attained public notoriety. It has been said that in 1919 not more than a dozen people in the world had mastered the theory, and not one of them could understand any of the popular summaries of it. The copy shown belonged to Eddington and has his notes.

The Decline of the West

596 OSWALD SPENGLER, Der Untergang des Abendlandes. *Munich 1918*

The principal claim of Spengler (1880–1936) in his very popular work was that civilization has a cyclical form. Although repudiated by historians, his parallels between ancient and modern civilizations had great force upon the semi-literate, especially in Germany and America. Spengler's molehill has generated Toynbee's mountain (no. 607).

An Outline for Peace

597 WOODROW WILSON, The Fourteen Points. *Washington 1918*

On 8 January 1918 President Wilson delivered before Congress the speech containing his famous fourteen points. Among them was contained his proposal for the League of Nations as well as proposals committing himself and his country to the maintenance of peace in Europe. The speech, printed first as House Document 765 in the papers of the 65th Congress, became eventually the basis for peace negotiations with the Central Powers.

The Splitting of the Atom

598 ERNEST, LORD RUTHERFORD, Collision of Alpha Particles with Light Atoms. *London 1919*

Rutherford revolutionized the science of radioactivity in countless ways. Photographs of the tracks of alpha particles which Rutherford shot through nitrogen showed hydrogen atoms emerging from the nuclei of the bombarded element. He described this as 'controlled disintegration of the elements'. We know it as nuclear fission with its end-product the H-bomb.

Discovery of Isotopes

599 FRANCIS WILLIAM ASTON, Isotopes. *London 1922*

Aston, a pupil of Thomson (no. 582), developed one of the first efficient spectroscopes which enabled him to discover many isotopes as the constituents of chemical elements. He discovered 212 of the 281 naturally occurring isotopes, and was able to measure with great precision their exact masses which are fundamental to the nuclear theory and the development of nuclear energy—leading directly to Urey's discovery of 'heavy water'.

The New Architecture

600 LE CORBUSIER [i.e. Charles Edouard Jeanneret], Vers une architecture nouvelle. *Paris 1923*

The most influential architectural book of this century. Here Le Corbusier reprinted the articles he had written whilst preparing the Citrohan projects which had first appeared in *L'Esprit nouveau.* In them he revealed the sources of his extra-architectural inspiration; the machine, ocean liners, motor-cars, &c. He introduced a new aesthetic of architecture and coined the phrase 'la maison — machine à habiter'.

Atonal Music

600a ARNOLD SCHÖNBERG, 'Eine neue Zwölfton-Schrift' (An article in 'Musikblätter des Anbruchs'). *Vienna, January 1925*

Schönberg's first conscious rejection of the 'tyranny' of the major-minor key system came in

1908 when he published the *Drei Klavierstücke* without a key signature.

Berg's opera *Wozzeck*, 1925, was the first notable contribution by an avowed pupil, and other pre-war disciples were Webern and Krenek. The revolutionary nature of Schönberg's theories becomes daily more clear, and his influence on young composers is world-wide.

The Nazi Programme

601 ADOLF HITLER, Mein Kampf. *Munich 1925, 1927*

The programme of a political gangster who herein told the timid and incredulous politicians of his own and other nations exactly and in detail what he would do if he had the power.

New Theory of Gravitation

602 ALBERT EINSTEIN, Zur einheitlichen Feldtheorie. *Berlin 1925–9*

In 1865 Clerk Maxwell (no. 542) correlated electricity and light. Einstein's repeated attempts to bring gravitation within the same correlation were successfully completed in this paper. Thus every form of activity within the sphere of physics was united in a common explanation and the theory of relativity was perfected. The first of a series of papers on this subject.

Matter a Form of Energy

603 LOUIS VICTOR, DUC DE BROGLIE, Ondes et mouvements. *Paris 1926*

The theory of *Wave Mechanics* originated by de Broglie considers the electron as merely a wave in the ether. Thus matter is finally and basically a form of energy. The wave nature of the electron was proved experimentally by Davisson and Germer in 1927.

Good-mannered English

604 HENRY WATSON FOWLER, A Dictionary of Modern English Usage. *Oxford 1926*

With no trace of pedantry, with a constant sense that language is a living growth, and with much wit and humour, Fowler compiled this complete guide to good taste in the choice of words.

The Betrayal of Reason

605 JULIEN BENDA, La Trahison des clercs. *Paris 1927*

Benda was throughout his long life a vigorous defender of reason against romanticism, the intellect as opposed to emotion. His most important work was the denunciation of those who put the intellect to the service of racial or party purposes, instead of devoting it to universal spiritual values. It had a deep influence on the thought of all who opposed the totalitarian régimes.

The Discovery of Penicillin

606 SIR ALEXANDER FLEMING, On the Antibacterial Action of Cultures of a Penicillium. *London 1929*

This epoch-making announcement revolutionized modern medicine. Fleming's discovery was later perfected by Florey and Chain with whom he shared the Nobel Prize for medicine in 1945. The original offprint of this paper is excessively rare. This is a reprint made for his wife in 1940.

Cyclical History

607 ARNOLD TOYNBEE, The Study of History. *1934–54.*

Toynbee's enormous work attempts a complete analysis of the cyclical view of history, in which the civilizations (of which Toynbee identifies twenty-six) are the units. It is liable to the same criticism as Spengler (no. 596) with whom Toynbee shares his popularity in Europe and America.

Artificial Radioactivity

608 G. M. GIANNINI and CO. INC., Method for increasing the Efficiency of Nuclear Reactions and Products Thereof. *London 1935*

Specification for controlling nuclear fission and for producing radioactive isotopes. The former led directly to the achievement of the chain reaction and the latter to fundamental advances in medicine. Among the joint inventors were Fermi and Pontecorvo.

Managed Economics

609 JOHN MAYNARD, LORD KEYNES, General Theory of Employment, Interest and Money. *London 1936*

Few would dispute today the main theses of this epoch-making work, or could imagine the furore of disagreement aroused by its first appearance. That national budgets are major instruments in a planned economy, that financial booms and slumps are controllable by governments rather than by *laissez-faire* is now a universally officially accepted doctrine. Roosevelt's 'New Deal' was the first important application of Keynsian doctrines. This copy is lent by King's College, Cambridge, from Lord Keynes's own collection which he bequeathed to them.

The Battle of Britain

610 WINSTON CHURCHILL, A Speech by the Prime Minister in the House of Commons. *20 August 1940*

One of the Prime Minister's historic exhortations which maintained Britain's sole resistance to Nazi aggression. In it he paid tribute to our salvation by the R.A.F. in the immortal words: 'Never in the field of human conflict was so much owed by so many to so few.'

ILLUSTRATION

Pictures and text cut with a knife on wooden planks probably provided the first printing surface in China and Europe. After the invention of moveable type, wood blocks were used with the type to reproduce initials and illustration. Engraved or etched plates, printed on the 'rolling press' were used where finer detail was required. A third process, lithography, was increasingly used during the nineteenth century, particularly for works requiring large coloured plates.

The most revolutionary change in illustration processes was made in the second half of the nineteenth century, when light-sensitive materials were brought into use for the preparation of relief, intaglio, or lithographic printing surfaces, without the intervention of a hand engraver.

PRE-PHOTOGRAPHIC PROCESSES

Wood-engraving

611 Ornamental Initials, 1673

Decorative initial letters cut in boxwood. Their use at Oxford can be traced back to 1673.

Plate 22

612 Arms of the University of Oxford, 1689

This engraved device, whose use at the University Press can be traced as far back as 1689, is engraved on the end-grain of boxwood. So far as is known this is the earliest surviving example of the technique.

613 Woodcut by Papillon, 1759

Cut on boxwood by J. B. M. Papillon (1698–1776) after a design by Bachelier, for an edition of La Fontaine's *Fables* (Paris 1755–9). Papillon is best known for his minute head-pieces and *culs-de-lampe* which decorate many French books of the mid-eighteenth century. He was the author of a *Traité historique et pratique de la gravure sur bois* (Paris 1766).

614 Wood-engraving by Bewick, 1796

Thomas Bewick (1753–1828) may be said to have revolutionized the art of wood-engraving, though his innovations were stylistic rather than technical. His brilliant technique depended for its full effect upon careful presswork and the wove paper which was then newly available. His achievement was to revive wood-engraving as an effective and economical means of illustrating printed texts. His use of white lines increased the range of effects obtainable by engraving and his delicate technique enabled him to make the most of small blocks. The block shown was engraved for Somerville's *The Chase*.

615 Set of Wood Blocks by John Thompson

These engravings by John Thompson for the title-page of James Puckle's *The Club* are examples of the extreme fineness of line and gradations of tone achieved by wood-engravers of the period.

616 Blocks from the First Issue of the 'Illustrated London News', 1842

The *Illustrated London News*, first issued by Herbert Ingram on 14 May 1842, was the first paper to subordinate text to pictures of current events. It was immediately successful, the circulation rising from 41,000 in 1843 to 123,000 by 1854, when it was printed on a rotary machine. At that time wood-engraving was the only means of producing illustrations in such large numbers; and to meet a deadline, a single large illustration was frequently divided among a number of engravers, and bolted together for printing.

617 Blocks Designed by Walter Crane, 1877

These designs for *The Baby's Opera* were drawn by the artist directly on the wood and engraved by Edmund Evans who also printed the earlier editions. *The Baby's Opera*, the most successful of the books by Walter Crane, has been reprinted continuously from the original blocks.

Intaglio

618 French Copperplate Engraving, c. 1700

'Le Batteur d'Or' (the gold beater), engraved by Louis Simmoneau about 1700, for the *Description des arts et métiers* prepared by the Académie des Sciences in Paris. Copper plates, though they were expensive and slow to print, had advantages for reproducing maps, music, and large detailed drawings.

619 Copy Book printed from Copper Plates, 1741

At the end of the sixteenth century it was found that the flowing line of the burin on copper was better suited to the reproduction of current hands than the relief woodcuts used previously.

The Universal Penman, shown here, includes the work of the most distinguished writing masters of the day and was engraved by George Bickham, himself a skilled calligrapher.

620 An Engraved Text, 1773–7

This edition of Horace was printed wholly from copper plates engraved by John Pine. The text was first set in type, and an impression from it on paper was transferred to the copper, which was then engraved, the decorations being added at the same time. The result was a page of great brilliance and precision, but the method was prohibitively expensive.

621 Variants of Line-etching

a punching.
b mezzotint.
c etching.
d stippling.
e aquatint.

Lithography

Lithography was the invention of Aloys Senefelder, a Bavarian. His first experiments with 'stone printing' (printing from smooth Solenhofen limestone etched in relief) were disappointing, and it was not until 1798 that he discovered that relief was not necessary since a water-soluble coating, such as gum, prevented a greasy ink from adhering to the stone. He drew the design in a greasy medium, and after wetting the stone and inking it with a roller he found that the ink adhered only to the design. In this way he made a true lithographic print.

622 The First Lithography in England, 1803

In 1803, Philip Andre, Senefelder's partner, published a collection of prints by Stothard and others under the title *Specimens of Polyautography*. It was the first book lithographed in England.

623 Lithographs of Drawings by Dürer, 1808

ALBRECHT DÜRER, Christlich-mythologische Handzeichnungen. *Munich 1808*

The collection of drawings, redrawn on the stone by Strixner, and produced by Senefelder in partnership with Baron Aretin, was one of the first important works to be produced wholly by lithography.

624 Senefelder's Manual

JOHANN ALOYS SENEFELDER, Vollständiges Lehrbuch der Steindruckerey. *Munich and Vienna, 1818*

Senefelder's book of lithography was not the first to be published; indeed, it was written partly to correct the errors of other manuals. But it is in many ways the most interesting, for it contains Senefelder's own account of the way in which he discovered the principles of lithography, and how the discovery was put to practical use.

625 Ornamental Lithography

OWEN JONES, The Grammar of Ornament. *London 1856*

Lithography was extensively used during the nineteenth century for large-scale works on the visual arts. One of the most ambitious of these, *The Grammar of Ornament*, was a product of the interest in industrial design stimulated by the Great Exhibition of 1851, where Jones was responsible for the colour scheme and the arrangement of some of the courts. As many as fourteen colours were used in the printing of some of the plates, each colour being printed from a separate stone.

626 Pen-drawn Lithographic Stone, Late Nineteenth Century

A typical example of the elaborate pen technique which could be practised on a smooth-grained lithographic stone.

627 Chalk-drawn Lithographic Stone, 1961

Graham Sutherland's portrait of Mme Helena Rubenstein shows the variety of texture obtainable from a coarsely grained stone on which the artist has drawn directly with a lithographic crayon.

PHOTOGRAPHIC PROCESSES

Relief

628 Printing from Zinc etched in Relief, 1850

Firmin Gillot (1820–72) devised a method of producing a relief printing plate from an engraved or lithographed original by making a transfer on zinc, and etching away the parts not protected by the greasy lithographic ink. The *Journal avantscène*, published in Paris, of which a volume is shown, used Gillot's process to supersede wood-engraving.

629 The First Relief Half-tone, 1854

Paul Pretsch (1803–73), who had worked in the photographic department of the Imperial Printing Office, Vienna, came to London in 1854 and took out a patent in the same year for the 'production of copper and other printing plates'. This print by Pretsch and de la Rue, 'Scene in Gaeta after the Explosion', was the first relief half-tone and the first commercial use of half-tone.

630 Relief Half-tone by F. E. Ives, 1881

F. E. Ives (1856–1937) devised a half-tone process which was commercially successful, although no screen was used. Ives subsequently invented a widely used cross-line screen. This portrait of Edward L. Wilson appeared in the *Philadelphia Photographer.*

631 Meisenbach's 'Improved Process of Photoengraving', 1890

George Meisenbach of Munich devised in 1882 the first photographic half-tone process for letterpress printing which was commercially applicable. At first he used a single-line screen, which was turned through 90° during exposure, and later (after 1889), a cross-line screen.

Intaglio

632 The Beginnings of Photogravure, 1826

Joseph Nicéphore Niepce (1765–1833), the inventor of photography, was also interested in lithography, and attempted unsuccessfully during his experiments in 1815 and 1816 to fix a photographic image on a sensitized stone. In 1826 he produced this intaglio reproduction of a copperplate engraving by making a print from the original transparent with oil, and exposing it in sunlight over a pewter plate sensitized by his asphalt process. This reproduction of a 'Portrait of Cardinal D'Amboise' is the first-known image made by a photo-mechanical process.

633 Fitzeau's Photogravure Process, 1841

Louis Hippolyte Fitzeau was among those who experimented with producing a printing surface from a photograph on copper, known as daguerrotype. 'Man and Boy', here exhibited, is the oldest known photo-mechanical print after Niepce, and the first known example of half-tone printing.

634 Gravure using a Half-tone Screen, 1865

Frederick von Egloffstein, who took out an American and a British patent in 1865, was one of the first to offer commercially an intaglio printing surface prepared from a photograph made through a half-tone screen. This print of a diseased bone was produced by his Heliographic Engraving Company of New York.

635 Klič's Photogravure Process

The first English manual of photogravure by the process of Karl Klič was the book by Thomas Huson, *Photo-Aquatint and Photogravure* (London 1897).

636 The 'Illustrated London News', printed by Rotary and Photogravure, 1914

The *Illustrated London News* pioneered the introduction into Great Britain of high-speed rotogravure.

Planographic

637 Lithophotographie, 1852

Using the asphalt process with which Niepce had experimented in 1815, these four authors of this work, Lemercier, Lerebours, Barreswil, and Davanne, obtained images on grained stones which could be printed on ordinary lithographic printing presses. The collection exhibited, published in 1852–3, contains the first reproductions of photographs successfully made by their method.

638 Poitevin's 'Collotype Process', 1862

Alphonse Louis Poitevin of Paris invented the process now known as collotype. In his application for an English patent granted in 1855, Poitevin described how, by coating a plate with chromated gelatine and printing and developing a photographic image on it, a surface could be obtained which, when damped, responded to ink in the same way as a lithographic stone. His perfected process was described in his *Traité de l'impression lithographique* shown here.

639 A Collotype Print, 1865

Du Motay and Maréchal, using chromated gelatine coatings on a copperplate base, produced the earliest known collotype prints made according to Poitevin's methods. The one exhibited is a portrait of George Sand.

NEWSPAPERS

A habit of reading periodical reports of recent events, formed largely in the seventeenth century, made new demands upon the press. Hunger for news has given printers their most powerful incentive to enlarge and speed-up production. The spread of literacy called in the first place for more newspapers. By the end of the eighteenth century multiplication of presses and recruitment of more men were proving an inadequate and expensive means of satisfying the effective demand. Generally speaking, it was in newspaper printing offices that new mechanical techniques were introduced and improved during the nineteenth century to enlarge output and shorten the interval of time between receipt of copy and delivery of printed sheets folded and quired.

640 'The Trewe Encountre', Newsbook, c. September 1513

The full title of the earliest surviving English news pamphlet is *Hereafter ensue the trewe encountre or Batayle lately don betwene Englande and Scotlande. In which batayle the Scottsshe Kynge was slayne.* It is undated but must have been published shortly after the battle of Flodden on 9 September 1513. It gives an eyewitness account of the battle and lists of casualties and of the English who had distinguished themselves on the field. The format and the types are those of a contemporary book. Such news pamphlets appeared in England occasionally during the sixteenth century, and more frequently after the 1590's.

641 'The Continuation of our Weekely Newes', 1623

By 7 September 1622 the publication in London of booklets of news had become sufficiently regular to justify numbering and dating. The chief publishers of news at that time were two booksellers, Nathaniel Butter and Nicholas Bourne. The book format with a title-page and blank verso, customary in news-books in the sixteenth century, was preserved in this series.

642 A Perfect Diurnall of the Passages in Parliament, 1642

During the Civil War, when a government ban on home news was lifted, several news publishers adopted a regular title instead of changing it with every issue to suit the contents. Because of the increased supply of news the wasteful features of book format were abandoned, and the text began below the title on the first page.

643 'Oxford Gazette' No. 1 [15 November] 1665

The first issue of the British official twice-weekly *Gazette*, believed to be the oldest-established periodical now in circulation. In its early days it contained, besides official notices, court and foreign news and advertisements, and it may be considered as the first English newspaper as distinguished from news-books, for it was a single leaf printed on both sides. Its double-column arrangement was the first step towards the multi-column make-up of later journals.

Numbers 1–23 were headed the *Oxford Gazette* and were edited and printed at Oxford, where the Court, including Parliament and the judicature, had moved because of plague in London. The present heading, the *London Gazette*, was adopted as soon as the Court had gone back to Westminster later in the year. *Plate 20*

644 'Daily Courant' No. 1039, 13 August 1705

No. 1 of Britain's first daily newspaper appeared on 11 March 1702. It adopted the format originated by the *Oxford Gazette*. The thrice-weekly publications begun in 1695, when government control of printing ceased and postal services had become frequent enough to circulate them, were eventually killed by daily newspapers. On the other hand, the evening newspapers of the early eighteenth century appeared on only three days of the week.

645 Royal Gazette (New York) 25 July 1778

In size and format the eighteenth-century American daily newspaper resembled its British contemporary. The advertising on pages 1 and 4 was, however, given more display in New York than in London. Insertions not exceeding 15 lines cost a dollar. *Plate 21*

646 'The Times', 29 November 1814

The increased circulation of *The Times* during the Napoleonic Wars, due to early, accurate news and independent comment, forced John Walter II, son of the founder, to consider how production could be substantially increased. It was evident that the hand-press was incapable of satisfying the demand, and Walter recognized the value of Koenig's inventions. The issue of *The Times* for 29 November 1814 was the first to be printed on a power-driven machine.

647 'The Times', 1 May 1862

After installing printing machines in 1814, *The Times* continued to increase its circulation. Further inventions to increase printing speed were continually explored. The successful stereotyping of the paper on 31 March 1859 opened the way for high-speed, reel-fed, rotary printing.

648 'The Times', 3 July 1872

The cheap daily journals founded in London and the provinces after the abolition of stamp duty in 1855 competed with *The Times* by publishing earlier in the day, and to meet this competition it was necessary for this newspaper to increase production speeds. By 1868 *The Times* was being printed on the Walter reel-fed rotary machine and by 1872 was being composed on the Kastenbein composing machine. *The Times* was thus able to preserve its character as a register of events at home and abroad.

649 'Daily Mail', Number 1, 4 May 1896

The Education Act of 1870 led eventually to general literacy and offered greatly increased opportunities to the publishers of newspapers and magazines. When Lord Northcliffe, then Alfred Harmsworth, founded the *Daily Mail* to appeal to the 'white-collar worker', he already had considerable experience in popular journalism. This was the first daily newspaper to achieve a circulation of a million.

COMPOSITION WITHOUT TYPE, PHOTO COMPOSITION, FILMSETTING

These representations of early attempts to find a substitute method for the assembly of type characters are placed here to bridge the gap between this record of the History of Printing and the Mind of Man, and the great exhibitions of modern printing machinery and technology which are to be seen downstairs and at Olympia. They illustrate the first trials and early systems of a succession of innovations which were designed to make letter-assembly quicker, more convenient, and cheaper than type composition, hot or cold.

One of the earliest recorded approaches to the problem was made by a group in America which was interested in a device for printing on strips of paper from raised characters in lithographic ink: the strips were to be arranged in lines, transferred to a lithographic stone, and printed. The young mechanic, Ottmar Mergenthaler, was drawn into this development in 1877, but we know that these experiments took an entirely different direction which, several years later, led to the invention of the Linotype, the first hot-metal composing machine.

The evolution of the various systems intended for 'type-less' composition was slow, but it gradually gained momentum from the advances in photography, etching techniques, mechanics, and electronics. Meanwhile, the parallel improvement in the design and performance of lithographic printing machines, and in plate-making, offered opportunities for the exploitation of the new methods which printers were quick to recognize. All this is now leading to a major revolution in the printing industry.

650 Porzholt Single-Alphabet Machine, 1896

The idea of composing alphabetic characters by photographic means is not new, and several patents have been taken out for filmsetting machines. One of the earliest was granted to E. Porzholt and was one of a group which depended on an illumination or reflection system. Porzholt proposed a single-alphabet machine utilizing character-bearing keybars. In response to a touch of the key the selected keybar, carried in an upright stationary drum, would swing inward to present its character to the optical axis through the centre of the drum. The character was then illuminated and exposed on sensitized plate which advanced after each exposure.

Diagram from the patent specification

651 Friese-Greene First Letter-bar Machine, 1898

The early cinema pioneer, W. Friese-Greene, patented the first multiple letter-bar filmsetting machine in which upright letters were to be arranged side by side in a magazine containing an entire alphabet of translucent letters on a black background. In response to a keyboard the selected bars were released and, by gravity, reached a stop position corresponding to the letter on the key struck. The composed line appeared through a slot where it could be read and illuminated for photography. The letters were larger than required, the type-positive being the result of optical reduction.

Diagram from the patent specification

652 Richards's Single-Alphabet Machine, 1899

This was the first patent to specify transmitted light for image formation. The proposal was for a single-alphabet machine with transparent characters arranged on a sector. Operation of the keyboard caused the sector to oscillate and present the desired letter to the optical axis of the lens system.

Diagram from the patent specification

653 Uhertype Machine, 1925

The Uhertype employed a glass alphabet cylinder which rotated in response to a perforated tape. Characters were reproduced in lines which were exposed end-to-end on a narrow ribbon of light-sensitive film. After processing the ribbon was cut into lines and assembled in galley form. Later mechanisms were added to provide a proof and to register the spacing required to justify each line. Different faces of type were obtained by changing the glass cylinders bearing master alphabets.

Photograph

654 August-Hunter Machine, 1927

The August-Hunter machine incorporated a master film which carried characters of 18-point size. Variation from 5 point to 96 point was obtained by changing the focus of the lens. Pressing a key located the desired letter in front of the lens system and a piece of film or plate received the exposure.

Photograph

655 Orotype Machine, 1935

The Orotype, of Swiss origin, was a development of the 1925 Typary. Raised letters were composed in a manner similar to the setting of matrices in a hot-metal line-composing machine. The keyboard contained 121 keys. The raised letters (patrices) were held in a magazine and depression of the keys caused them to fall into the assembler where the completed lines were justified. These lines were inked, and a print taken on filmor paper.

Photograph

656 Huebner Machine, 1939

In William C. Huebner's machine the characters were arranged around a stationary disk-like plate. A complete optical projection unit, comprising lens, shutter, light, and reflecting mirrors, was provided for each character. By the operation of the keyboard, the projection units were successively electrically activated to photograph the characters required.

Photograph

656a The Rotofoto System

This, the first British filmsetting machine to be placed on the market, was the invention of one of the twentieth-century filmsetting pioneers, George Westover, and was first shown in 1948. It was manufactured by the Coventry Gauge & Tool Company Ltd. The system was designed to handle text composition and straightforward tabular matter in sizes from 5 to 18 point. The equipment consisted of a standard 'Monotype' keyboard, which produced a perforated spool for the control of the next unit, the line projector. The line projector carried a master negative of each of the normal characters, and the product was a photographic record on 35-mm. film of the matter composed. On completion, the exposed film, after processing, was mounted in a proof-projection carrier. This provided proofs in 9 to 12 point from the original film, lines containing errors being re-set and produced on the line projector on separate film. The text, corrections, and additional matter were pasted up in page form as a guide. The final unit, the make-up projector, produced transparencies of the pages in accordance with the guide proofs, enlarging the images on the 35-mm. film to the final required size. A Rotofoto system installed at the then London School of Printing and Graphic Arts was responsible for the setting of a number of publications from 1949 onwards.

PRINTERS' KEEPSAKES

Plate 24

Before the end of the seventeenth century it was customary in some English printing houses to honour visitors by printing their names and the date in ornamental style by way of a memento.

An account of the manner of printing these souvenirs at the Sheldonian Theatre at Oxford in 1682 survives in burlesque verse (Alicia D'Anvers, *Academia*, London 1691). The guest was invited to witness the setting of the type and to bear the cost of beer for the workmen. The name and date were inserted in a framework of flowers and rules, which were evidently kept standing ready for use. The visitor pulled the press: Celia Fiennes, on one of her *Journeys*, was at the Sheldonian Theatre about 1694 and printed her name 'severall tymes'.

The practice became more general during the eighteenth century, and most surviving specimens date from that time. The form of the keepsake becomes conventional and profusely ornamented. Between two borders of flowers a motto is introduced commemorating the origin of printing. The specimens vary as to the facts, and some go on to give their version of the introduction of the art to England.

About 1770 the ornament dwindles and becomes refined. So far as ordinary visitors were concerned, the keepsake was on the decline. In the nineteenth century it was reserved for distinguished persons, and for the most exalted it was done on silk or satin.

Keepsakes printed on frozen rivers are a special and fairly numerous class going back at least as far as 1684.

Bookplates indistinguishable in form from a memento of a visit to a press, except by the added words 'his [or her] book', are not uncommon. The earliest of the kind, pasted in books, appear to have marked legacies and birthday presents. One commemorates the death of a donor in 1631.

INDEX TO THE EARLS COURT EXHIBITS

GENERAL INDEX

MEMBERS OF THE PRINTING TRADES, AUTHORS, AND SUBJECTS

PLATES

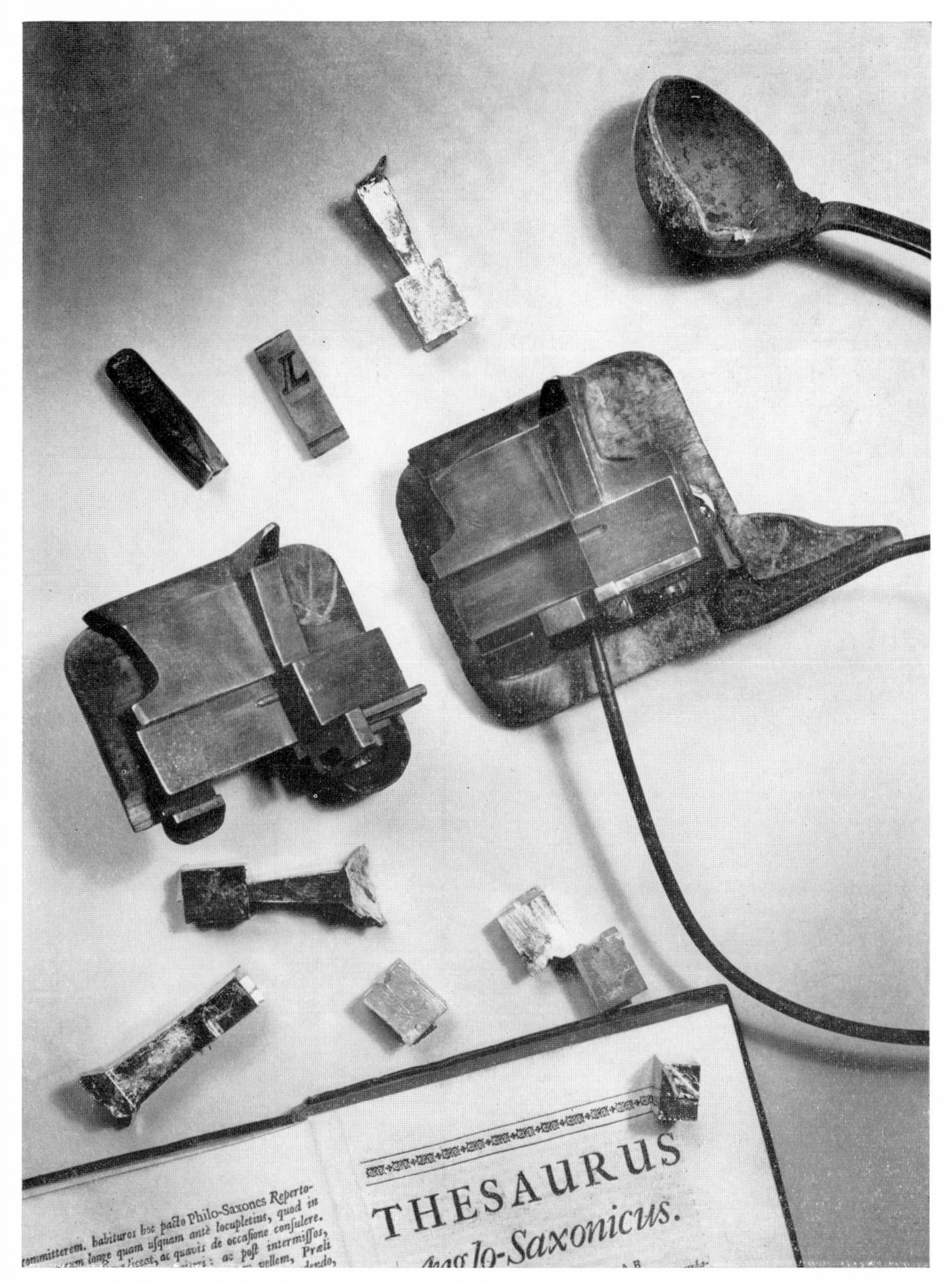

No. 64. The halves of a hand mould (of Canon body) with type cast in it and the punch and matrix for one of the letters

No. 6. Models for Hebrew letters cut in wood by Guillaume Le Bé, typefounder of Paris, in 1573, of which a photograph is shown in the exhibition

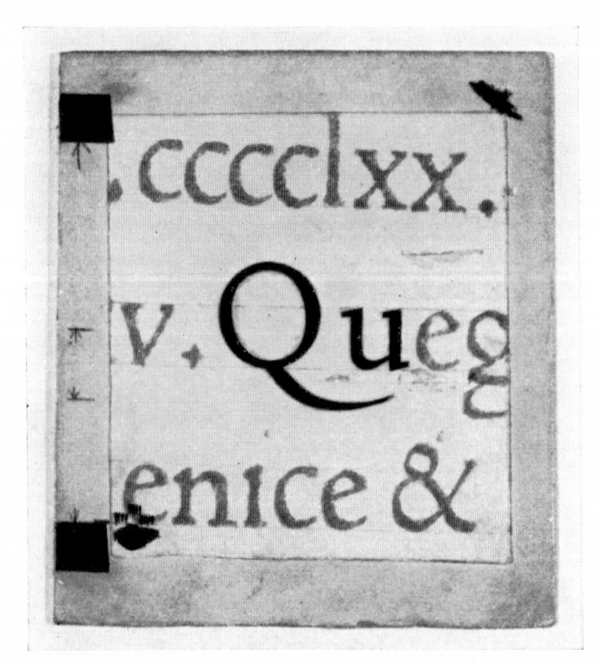

No. 8. A drawing for the type of the Doves Press made in Sir Emery Walker's studio in 1899–1900 on an enlarged photograph of the type of Nicolas Jenson

No. 11. Part of a letter from Eric Gill asking for changes to be made in the cutting of Perpetua roman

Nos. 12, 18. A punchcutter's workbench and tools

No. 27. Punches for Baskerville's Canon roman cut by John Handy about 1754

PLATE 4

No. 34. A press for striking punches in copper to make matrices

No. 45. Matrices for a type-face used in 1520

No. 63. A caster at the furnace using a hand mould

No. 252. A printing press of the design attributed to W. J. Blaeu (d. 1638) with modifications made at a later date

Nos. 103 ff. Printer's equipment of the early nineteenth century: a ball, galley and slice, candlestick, and sundries

No. 106. Frames for compositor's work made in 1668

Jacobs Op-tocht GENESIS, Cap. xlvij. *in Egypten.*

8 [e] Ende [13] dit zijn de Namen [14] der Sonen Israëls / die in Egypten quamen / Jacob / ende sijne Sonen: De eerst-geboren Jacobs / Ruben.

9 Ende Rubens Sonen; [15] Hanoch / ende Pallu / ende Hezron / ende Carmi.

10 [f] Ende Simeons Sonen; [16] Jemuël / ende Jamin / ende [17] Ohad / ende [18] Jachin / ende [19] Zohar: ende Saul de Sone eener [20] Canaanitischer Vrouwe.

11 [g] Ende de Sonen van Levi; Gerson / Kehath / ende Merari.

12 Ende [h] de Sonen van Juda; Er / ende Onan / ende Sela / ende Perez / ende Zerah: doch Er / ende Onan [21] waren gestorven in 't Lant Canaan: [i] ende Perez Sonen waren Hezron ende Hamul.

13 Ende Issaschars Sonen; Tola / ende Pua / ende [22] Job / ende Simron.

14 Ende Zebulons Sonen; Sered / ende Elon / ende Jahleël.

15 Dit zijn Leas Sonen / die sy Jacob gebaert heeft in [23] Paddan-Aram / met Dina sijne Dochter: alle [24] de Zielen sijner Sonen / ende sijner Dochteren waren [25] drie en dertig.

16 [k] Ende Gads Sonen; [26] Ziphion / ende Chaggi / Schuni / ende Ezbon / Eri / ende [27] Arodi / ende Areli.

17 [l] Ende Asers Sonen; Jimna / ende Jischva / ende Jischvi / ende Beria / ende Sera haer-lieder Suster: ende de Sonen Beria; Heber / ende Malchiël.

18 Dit zijn Zilpas Sonen / [m] die Laban sijne Dochter Lea [28] gegeven hadde: ende sy baerde Jacob dese [29] sestien Zielen.

moete na Gosen: ende [40] als hy sich aen hem vertoonde / [41] soo viel hy hem aen sijnen Hals / ende weende [42] lange aen sijnen Hals.

30 Ende Israël seyde tot Joseph: Dat ick [43] nu sterve / na dat ick u Aengesichte gesien hebbe / [44] dat gy noch leeft.

31 Daer na seyde Joseph tot sijne Broederen / ende tot sijnes Vaders Huys: Ick sal op-trecken ende Pharao boodschappen / ende tot hem seggen: Mijne Broeders / ende mijnes Vaders Huys / die in 't Lant Canaan waren / zijn tot my gekomen:

32 Eñ die Mannen zijn Schaep-herders / want 't zijn [45] Mannen die met Vee om-gaen / ende sy hebben hare Schapen / ende hare Runderen / ende al wat sy hebben / mede gebracht.

33 Wanneer het nu geschieden sal / dat Pharao u-lieden sal roepen / ende seggen: Wat is uwe Hanteeringe?

34 Soo sult gy seggen: Uwe Knechten zijn Mannen / die van onser Jeugt op tot nu toe met Vee om-gegaen hebben; soo wy / als onse Vaders: op dat gy in 't Lant Gosen moget wonen; [r] want alle Schaep-herder is den Egyptenaren [46] een Grouwel.

Dat sy daer in by een waren / ende t'samen in Vrede mochten wonen. ... Afgodische Egyptenaren afgesondert zijnde / den reynen Godts-dienst ... oeffenen.

Het xlvij. Capittel.

Joseph dient Pharao sijns Vaders Komste aen / ende brengt vijf sijner Broederen voor hem / vs 1 / &c. diese onder-vraegt / ende het Lant Gosen ingeeft / 3. Joseph brengt oock sijnen Vader voor Pharao / die hem vraegt na sijnen Ouderdom / ende wort van Jacob gezegent / 7. Joseph onderhoudt sijnen Vader met het gantsche Huys in Gosen / 11. De Egyptenaers / hebbende al haer Gelt voor Koorn uyt-gegeven / verkoopen door Hongers-noot het Vee / ende daer na Lyf ende Lant / aen Pharao / voor Koorn / 13. (uyt-genomen de Priesters 22 / 26.) 't Lant wort hen gelaten

No. 310. A stereotype plate believed to have been made by the process invented by Johann Müller and the corresponding page of a Dutch Bible printed at Leiden in 1718, represented in the exhibition by photographs

PLATE 9

No. 319. A 'mangle' press for moulding flong on formes to make stereotype matrices patented in 1861 by J. Dellagana

No. 319a. Stereotyping at Poppins Court, London, *c.* 1890

No. 396. A wooden rolling press for printing copper plates of the eighteenth or early nineteenth century

No. 397. A hand press for printing lithographs of a design introduced *c.* 1875

PLATE 11

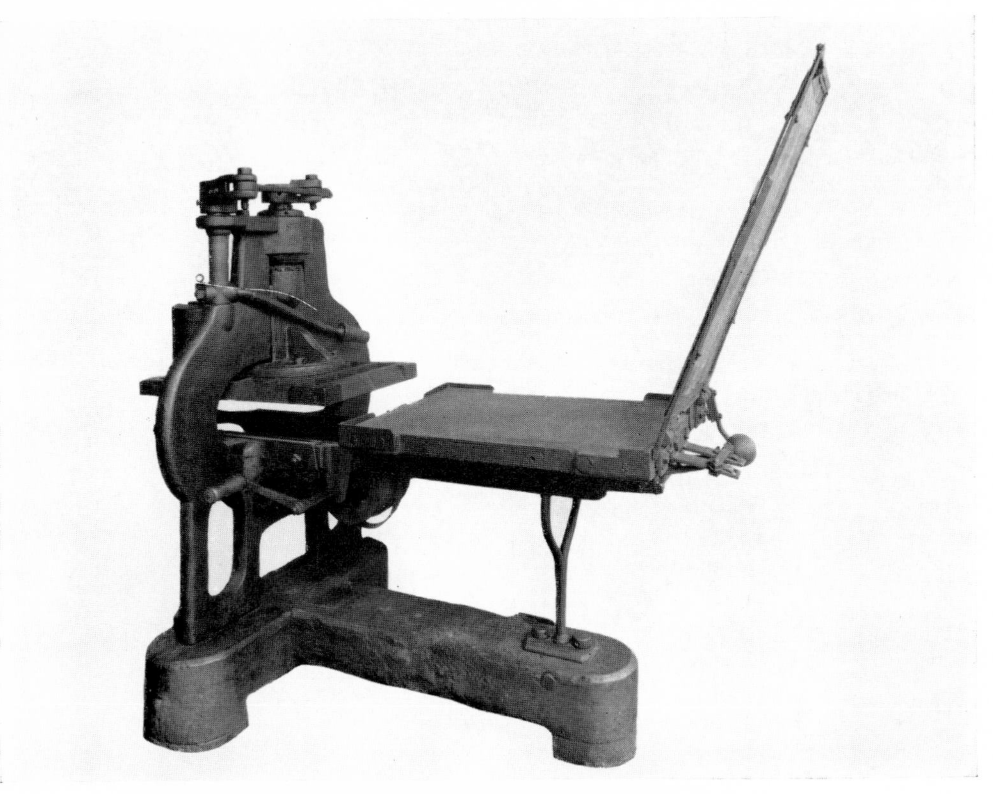

No. 398. An iron printing press of Earl Stanhope's earlier design (about 1800)

No. 399. A Ruthven printing press of the design patented in 1813

No. 407. A model of the printing machine made for *The Times* by Koenig and Bauer, completed in 1814

No. 421. Thomas Nelson's rotary printing machine, 1851

No. 423. The Ingle stop-cylinder printing machine, 1858

No. 422. David Payne's Wharfedale printing machine, 1858, of which this photograph is shown in the exhibition

PLATE 14

No. 460. The Brandt pivotal type-casting machine, invented in 1838

No. 461. A Wicks rotary type-casting machine made about 1881

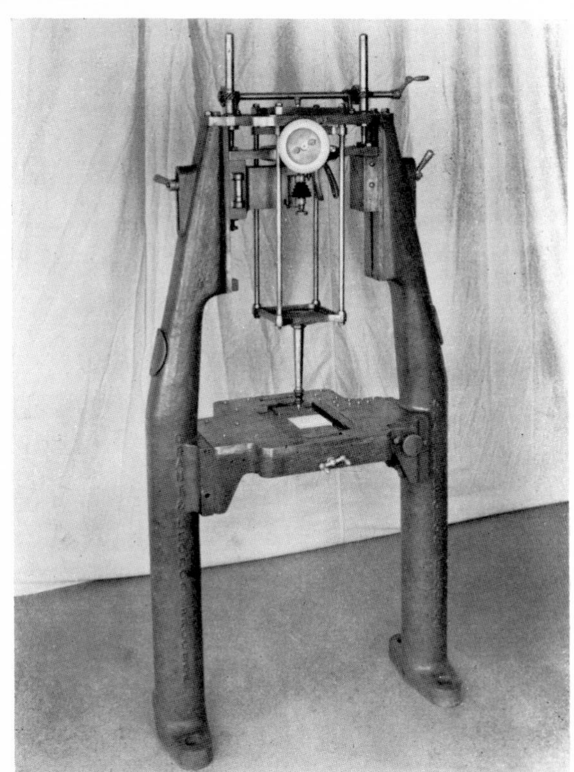

No. 475. A Grant-Legros punchcutting machine of the design patented in 1910

No. 473. A Pulsometer type-composing machine of the design patented in 1902; and (*below*),
No. 474, two views of the Pulsometer type-distributor patented in 1904

No. 469. The 'square-base' Linotype machine: a design introduced in 1890

No. 471. A Monotype weight-operated keyboard of 1897

No. 472. A Monotype caster of 1897, known as the 'limited-fount' caster

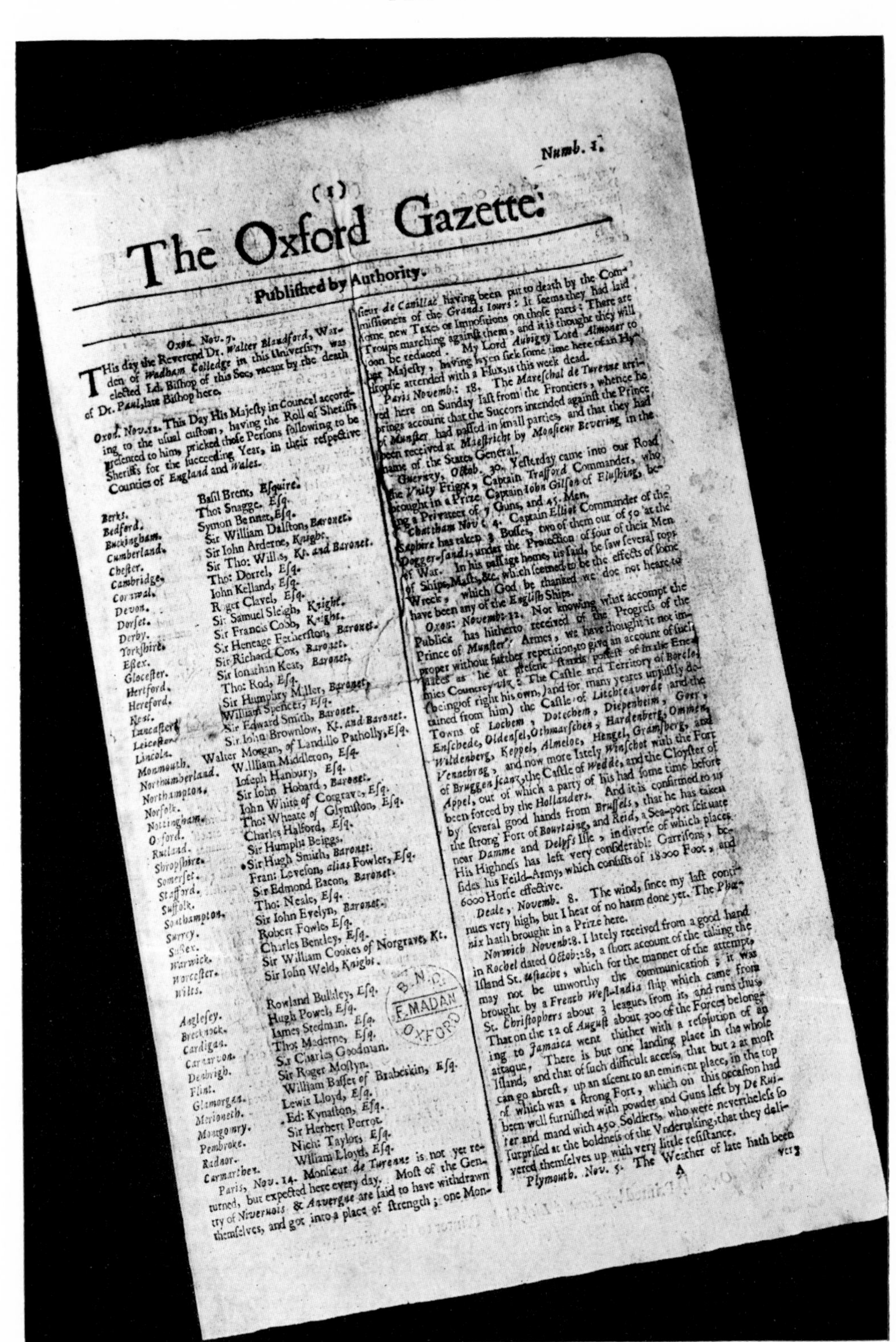

Numb. 1.

(1)

The Oxford Gazette.

Published by Authority.

Oxon. Nov. 7.

THis day the Reverend Dr. *Walter Blandford*, Warden of *Wadham Colledge* in this University, was elected Ld. Bishop of this Sec, vacant by the death of Dr. *Paul*, late Bishop here.

Oxon. Nov. 12. This Day His Majesty in Councel according to the usual custom, having the Roll of Sheriffs presented to him, pricked those Persons following to be Sheriffs for the succeeding Year, in their respective Counties of *England* and *Wales*.

Berks.	Basil Brent, Esquire.
Bedford.	Thos Snagge. Esq.
Buckingham.	Symon Bennet, Esq.
Cumberland.	Sir William Dalston, Baronet.
Chester.	Sir Iohn Arderne, Knight.
Cambridge.	Sir Tho: Willis, Kt. and Baronet.
Cornwal.	Tho: Dorrel, Esq.
Devon.	Iohn Kelland, Esq.
Dorset.	Roger Clavel, Esq.
Derby.	Sir Samuel Sleigh, Knight.
Yorkshire.	Sir Francis Cobb, Knight.
Essex.	Sir Heneage Fetherston, Baronet.
Glocester.	Sir Richard Cox, Baronet.
Hertford.	Sir Ionathan Keat, Baronet.
Hereford.	Thos Rod, Esq.
Kent.	Sir Humphry Miller, Baronet.
Lancaster.	William Spencer, Esq.
Leicester.	Sir Edward Smith, Baronet.
Lincoln.	Sir Iohn Brownlow, Kt. and Baronet.
Monmouth.	Walter Morgan, of Landillo Patholly, Esq.
Northumberland.	William Middleton, Esq.
Northampton.	Ioseph Hanbury, Esq.
Norfolk.	Sir Iohn Hobard, Baronet.
Nottingham.	Iohn White of Cotgrave, Esq.
Oxford.	Tho: Wheate of Glymston, Esq.
Rutland.	Charles Halford, Esq.
Shropshire.	Sir Humph: Briggs.
Somerset.	Sir Hugh Smith, Baronet.
Stafford.	Fran: Leveson, *alias* Fowler, Esq.
Suffolk.	Sir Edmond Bacon, Baronet.
Southampton.	Tho: Neale, Esq.
Surrey.	Sir Iohn Evelyn, Baronet.
Sussex.	Robert Fowle, Esq.
Warwick.	Charles Bentley, Esq.
Worcester.	Sir William Cookes of Norgrave, Kt.
Wilts.	Sir Iohn Weld, Knight.

Anglesey.	Rowland Bulkley, Esq.
Brecknock.	Hugh Powel, Esq.
Cardigan.	Iames Stedman. Esq.
Carnarvon.	Thos Madryne, Esq.
Denbigh.	Sir Charles Goodman.
Flint.	Sir Roger Mostyn.
Glamorgan.	William Basset of Brabeskin, Esq.
Merioneth.	Lewis Lloyd, Esq.
Montgomery.	Ed: Kynaston, Esq.
Pembroke.	Sir Herbert Perrot.
Radnor.	Nich: Taylors, Esq.
Carmarthen.	William Lloyd, Esq.

Paris, Nov. 14. Monsieur *de Turenne* is not yet returned, but expected here every day. Most of the Gentry of *Nivernois* & *Auvergne* are said to have withdrawn themselves, and got into a place of strength; one Monsieur *de Canillac* having been put to death by the Commissioners of the *Grands Iours*: It seems they had laid some new Taxes or Impositions on those parts: There are Troups marching against them, and it is thought they will soon be reduced. My Lord *Aubigny* Lord *Almoner* to her Majesty, having lyen sick some time here of an Hydropsic attended with a Flux, is this week dead.

Paris Novemb. 18. The *Mareschal de Turenne* arrived here on Sunday last from the Frontiers, whence he brings account that the Succors intended against the Prince of *Munster* had passed in small parties, and that they had been received at *Maestricht* by *Monsieur Bevering* in the name of the States General.

Guernsey, Octob. 30. Yesterday came into our Road the *Unity* Frigot, Captain *Trafford* Commander, who brought in a Prize, Captain *Iohn Gilson* of *Flushing*, being a Privateer of 7 Guns, and 45. Men.

Chattham Nov. 4. Captain *Elliot* Commander of the *Saphire* has taken 3 Busses, two of them out of 50 at the *Dogger-sands*, under the Protection of four of their Men of War. In his passage home, tis said, he saw several tops of Ships, Masts, &c. which seemed to be the effects of some Wreck, which God be thanked we doe not heare to have been any of the *English* Ships.

Oxon: Novemb: 12. Not knowing what accompt the Publick has hitherto received of the Progress of the Prince of *Munster's* Armes, we have thought it not improper without further repetition, to give an account of such places as he at present stands posseft of in the Enemies Countrey, viz: The Castle and Territory of *Borcelo*, (being of right his own,) and for many yeares unjustly detained from him) the Castle of *Litchtenvorde* and the Towns of *Lochem*, *Dotechem*, *Diepenheim*, *Goer*, *Enschede*, *Oldensel*, *Othmarschen*, *Hardenberg*, *Ommen*, and *Wildenberg*, *Keppel*, *Almeloe*, *Hengel*, *Gramsberg*, and *Vennebrug*, and now more lately *Winschot* with the Fort of *Bruggen Scanz*, the Castle of *Wedde*, and the Cloyster of *Appel*, out of which a party of his had some time before been forced by the *Hollanders*. And it is confirmed to us by several good hands from *Brussels*, that he has taken the strong Fort of *Bourtaing*, and *Reid*, a Sea-port scituate near *Damme* and *Delpfs Ille*, in diverse of which places His Highness has left very considerable Garrisons, besides his Feild-Army, which consists of 18000 Foot, and 6000 Horse effective.

Deale, Novemb. 8. The wind, since my last continues very high, but I hear of no harm done yet. The *Phœnix* hath brought in a Prize here.

Norwich Novemb: 8. I lately received from a good hand in *Rochel* dated *Octob:* 28, a short account of the taking the Island St. *Eustache*, which for the manner of the attempt, may not be unworthy the communication; it was brought by a *French West-India* ship which came from St. *Christophers* about 3 leagues from it, and runs thus. That on the 12 of *August* about 300 of the Forces belonging to *Jamaica* went thither with a resolution of an attaque. There is but one landing place in the whole Island, and that of such difficult access, that but 2 at most can go abrest, up an ascent to an eminent place, in the top of which was a strong Fort, which on this occasion had been well furnished with powder and Guns left by *De Ruiter* and mand with 450 Soldiers, who were neverthelesse so surprised at the boldness of the Undertaking, that they delivered themselves up with very little resistance.

Plymouth. Nov. 5. The Weather of late hath been very

A

No. 643. The *Oxford Gazette*, No. 1, 15 November 1665

[SATURDAY, JULY 25, 1778.] THE [No. 190.]

ROYAL  GAZETTE.

NEW-YORK: Published by JAMES RIVINGTON, Printer to the King's Most Excellent Majesty.

ASSIZE of BREAD. Flour at 35s. per Cent. Published February 2, 1778.

A WHITE Loaf of the finest FLOUR, to weigh 1 lb. 6 oz. for 14 Coppers, and in the same Proportion for Loaves of a lesser Weight.
JAMES ROBERTSON, M. G.

PRICE CURRENT, in NEW-YORK.

Wheat per Bushel,	22s.	od.	Muscovado Sugar,	5l.	10s.	Fine Salt,	4s.	od.
Flour,	35s.	od.	Single refin'd ditto,	25.	od.	Coarse Salt,	3s.	od.
Brown Bread,	45s.	od.	Molasses,	3s.	6d.	Indian Corn per Bushel,	7s.	od.
West-India Rum,	6s.	6d.	Beef per Barrel,	90s.	od.	Coffee,	1s.	6d.
New-England do.	5s.	od.	Pork,	5l. 10s.	od.	Chocolate,	26s. per dozen.	

HIGH WATER at NEW-YORK, this WEEK,

SAT. 45 m. after 10	Wed. 43 m. after 2
Sun. 29 m. after 11	Thu. 27 m. after 2
Monday 13 m. after 12	Friday 8 m. after 3
Tuesday 59 m. after 12	

TO BE SOLD,
AN ELEGANT LIGHT CHARIOT, In good Preservation, and Harness for two Horses. Inquire of the Printer, or of Mr. Hallet, Coach-maker, in the Broadway.

GENTLEMEN VOLUNTEERS,
THE best Encouragement will be given by Capt. HUCK, at No. 216, the corner of Queen-Street, and Maiden-Lane, near the upper end of the Fly-Market, to those Gentlemen Volunteers who enrole to serve his Majesty for two Years, or during the present Rebellion, in the Corps consisting of
CHASSEURS
AND
DRAGOONS,
Commanded by
Lieut. Col. EMMERICH,
A Compliment of One Guinea will be made to any person who shall bring to Capt. HUCK, an able bodied Recruit.

To be sold on the most reasonable Terms, for ready Cash, on board the ship Patuxent, lying at Pecks-Slip Wharf,
BOTTLED Porter of the best quality, in casks of eleven dozen. Do. Beer, in casks of eleven dozen. Portwine, do. in casks of six dozen. Sherry Wine, do. in casks of six dozen. Single refined and Lump Sugar in casks of about 3 cwt.

JOHN CAMPBELL,
Has just opened in the store formerly occupied by James Arten, at the East corner of Water and Wall-streets, adjoining the Coffee-House Bridge, an assortment of the following goods, which will be sold wholesale, on the most reasonable terms, for cash or ... short credit; to those purchasing any

A FEW hogsheads of loaf Sugar, and a few Chests of Bohea, Hyson, Singlo, and Congo Teas; also some Cheshire Cheese to be sold reasonable. Enquire of the printer.

To be Sold on very reasonable Terms,
A FEW Casks of the best Bristol Beer, Taunton Ale, and new Herefordshire Cyder, containing about 10 dozen each, and a few hampers of fine old Madeira, red and white Port and Lisbon Wine; Also, split Pease and Grots in jars. Enquire at FREDERICK WILLIAM GEYER's, Hanover-Square.

B. WADDINGTON,
Has just imported from LONDON, in the Alfred, Capt. Bolton, the undermentioned articles, which he will sell by WHOLESALE, on exceedingly low terms, for CASH, at his STORE, (late Mr. Desbrosses) No. 1, in QUEEN-STREET, opposite King-street.

A LARGE assortment of printed muslins, callicoes and cottons, the newest and most elegant patterns.
Yard wide Irish linens in boxes
Hempen and flaxen Russia towelling
3-4 wide brown raven ducks for trowsers, &c.
Russia sail cloth
Half bleached 7-8 dowlas
Ell-wide white hessens
Printed handkerchiefs
A variety of muslins
White and buff corded dimmities
Black Barcelona handkerchiefs, all prices
An assortment of fashionable gauzes
Gauze aprons, handkerchiefs, &c.
Black lining, modes and sattins
Coloured Persians
New figured and black ribbons
9-8 and ell-wide striped cotton Hollands
Womens cotton and worsted hose
3-4 wide striped and ...

JOHN CUNNINGHAM & Co.
Have just opened the Store formerly occupied by Messrs. Cameron and Blaikie, No. 192, in Queen-street, where they have the following Assortment of GOODS to dispose by Wholesale and Retail.

SCARLET, blue, white, buff, green, and fashionable coloured superfine Broad Cloths
Scarlet, blue, and green serjeants Cloth
Scarlet, blue, buff, and white Cassemirs
Superfine fashionable striped, figured, and spotted Orleans
Uniform white Shalloons and other trimmings
Fashionable enamel'd Buttons
Ochterlony and Warrington Sail Cloth, from No. 1 to 8, of an exceeding good quality
Sail and whipping Twine and Needles
Oznaburgs
Brown and white Irish Sheeting
3-4, 7-8, and 4-4 Irish Linens
3-4 and 7-8 Manchester cotton Check
3-4 and 7-8 striped Bed Tick
Ravens Duck, Russia Drab
Pomerania
Gulix Holland
A great variety of Callicoes and Chintzes
Cambricks, and Muslins
Humhums
Persians
Mens fine and coarse Shirts, ruffled and plain
Black Princes Stuff
Black silk Sattenets
Black silk Cravats and Barcelona Handkerchiefs
Dark Fustians
Drab Corduroy
Denims, rib'd, and Dutch Cords
Mens fashionable Hats from Oliphant
Coarse bound ditto
Mens strong and dress Didsbury's Shoes
Ladies best callimanco Shoes and Pumps
Writing Paper
Nuns and stitching thead
Gold and silver regimental Lace
Buttons for the 27th, 42d and 63d Regiments
A variety of navy and other fashionable Buttons
An assortment of Cutlery and tin ware
Nails from 3d to 20d
Sheathing do.
Crown Glass, 8 by 10 & 10 by 12
Green and Hyson Tea
Loaf Sugar---Nutmegs
Fig blue
Cheese
Draught and bottled Porter
Mustard---Corks---Pepper and Brimstone

JUST imported in the last Fleet from Corke, and to be sold by Jeremiah M'Carthy, at Mr. Fogarty's cellar, No. 13, lower end of the Fly Market, the following articles, viz. The best Irish Mess Pork, and New Rose Butter, and a quantity of the best Irish made shoes, together with some other commodities, which he means to sell on the most reasonable terms, for ready money only.

ALL persons willing to serve his Majesty King George the Third for two years, or during the present rebellion, in the regiment attached to the Royal Regiment of Artillery, commanded by Lieut. Colonel JOHN MORRIS, shall receive THREE POUNDS over and above the King's Bounty, a new suit of cloaths, and every other necessary fit to compleat a soldier; besides which, every man shall receive FIFTY ACRES OF GOOD LAND in the Province of New-York, over and above the King's Allowance, for which he shall receive a deed free from every expence.

Any serjeant or Soldier in his Majesty's service bringing an able bodied good RECRUIT, shall be handsomely rewarded.

An officer is ready to receive them at Kingsbridge, Fort Knyphausen, Cole's Ferry on Staten-Island, Powles Hook, Brooklyn ferry on Long-Island, at Col. Morris's, near the main-guard, Broad-street, and at the post-office in New-York.

TO BE SOLD,
By TERRILL and KEARNY,
In GREAT DOCK-STREET, No. 867.

MADEIRA, Port, Sherry, and Teneriffe } Wines
Loaf Sugar
Muscovado ditto
Chocolate
Florence oil
Hyson, Green, Shoushong and Bohea } Teas
Mustard
Pepper
Spices of all sorts, &c. &c. &c.

No. 645. The *Royal Gazette*, No. 190, New York, 25 July 1778

Nos. 96a, b. Typefounders' specimen books of the early nineteenth century

No. 611. Engraved boxwood blocks for initial letters used in 1673

No. 133. A page of Clarendon's *History of the Rebellion*, 1702–4, with the copper plates for the ornaments and the artist's design for one of them

Printers' keepsakes

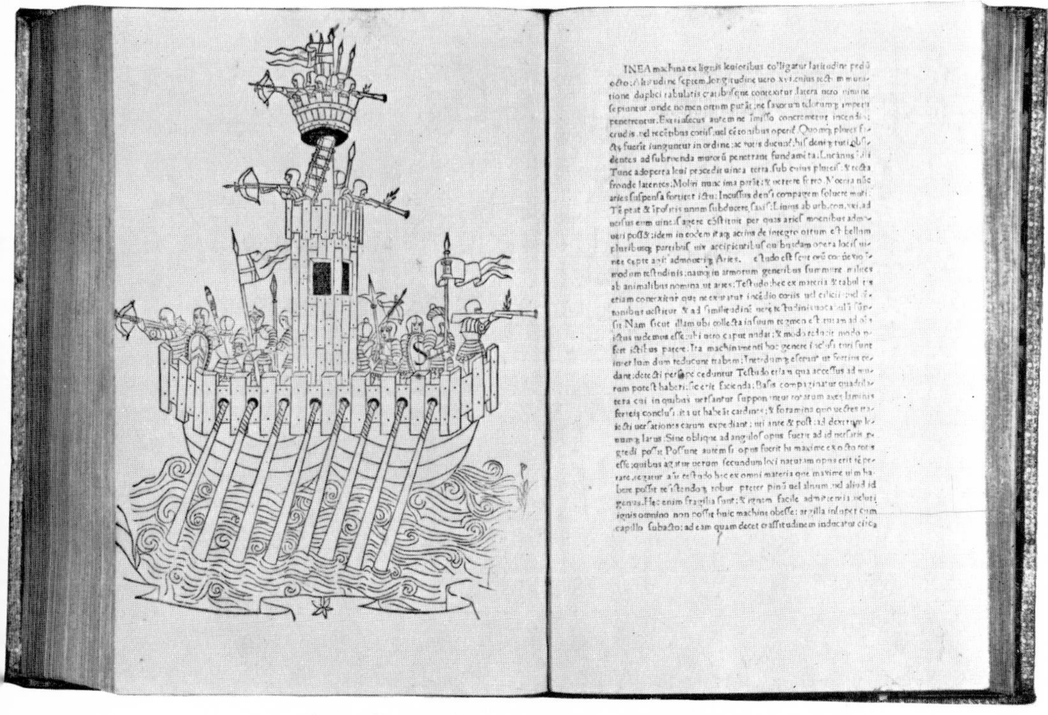

No. 142. The Earliest Technical Illustrations (*De re militari*, 1472)

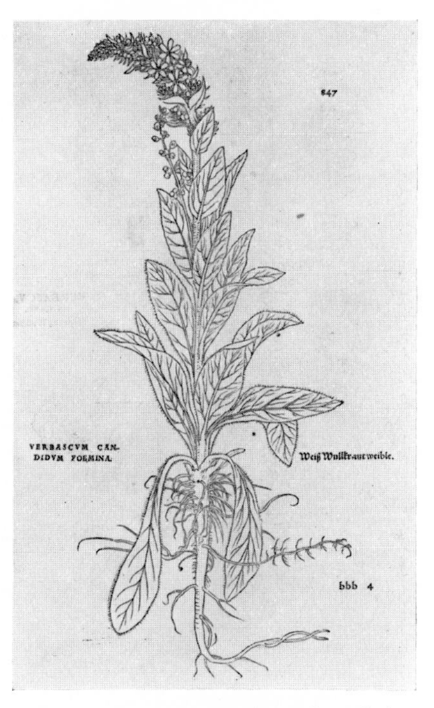

No. 200. A Famous Classical Herbal
(L. Fuchs, 1542)

No. 180. The Survival of Classical Architecture (Vitruvius, 1521)

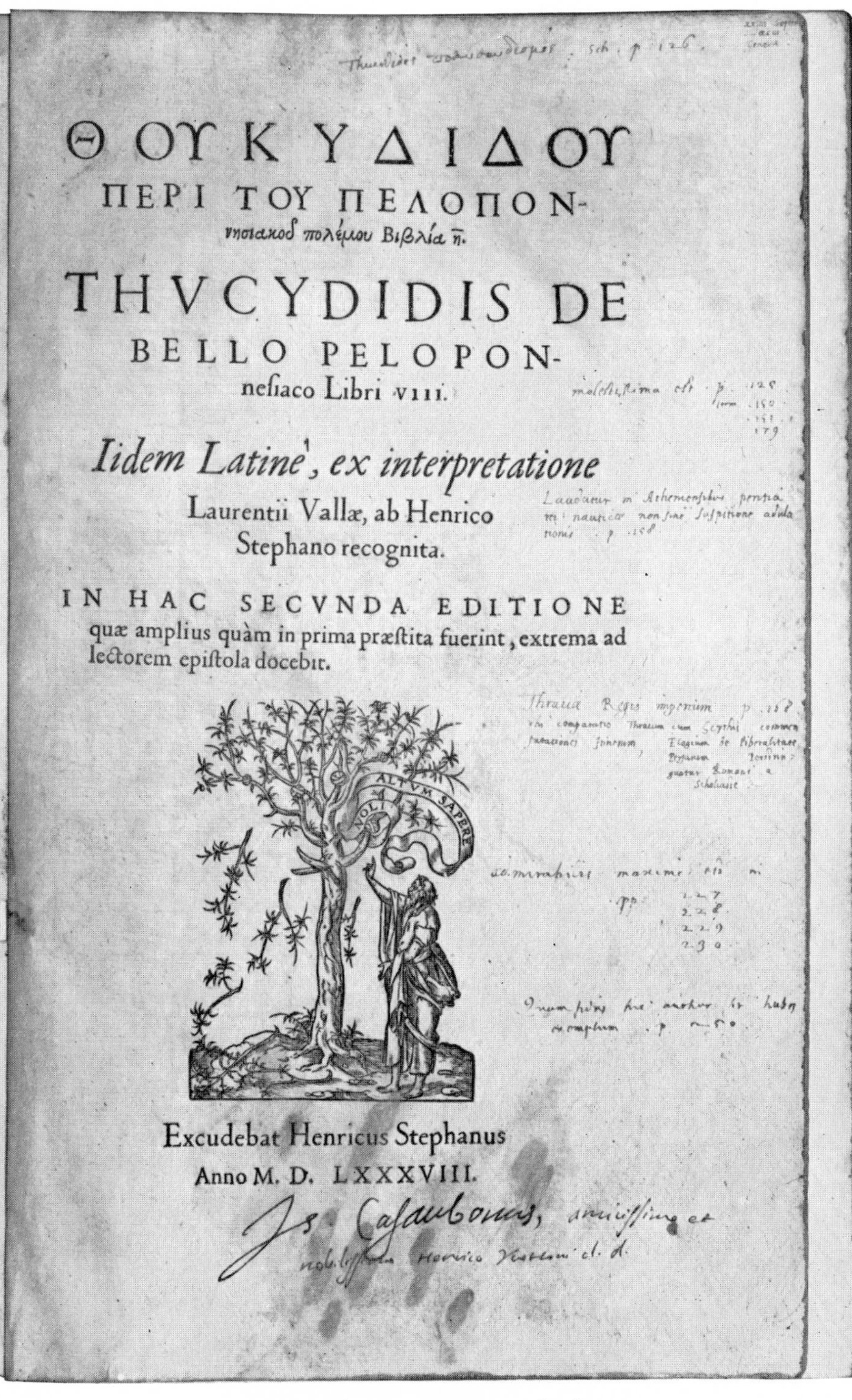

ΘΟΥΚΥΔΙΔΟΥ
ΠΕΡΙ ΤΟΥ ΠΕΛΟΠΟΝ-
νησιακοῦ πολέμου Βιβλία η̄.

THVCYDIDIS DE
BELLO PELOPON-
nesiaco Libri VIII.

Iidem Latinè, ex interpretatione
Laurentii Vallæ, ab Henrico
Stephano recognita.

IN HAC SECVNDA EDITIONE
quæ amplius quàm in prima præstita fuerint, extrema ad
lectorem epistola docebit.

NOLI ALTVM SAPERE

Excudebat Henricus Stephanus
Anno M. D. LXXXVIII.

No. 219. The Great Historian of Athens
(Thucydides annotated by Isaac Casaubon, 1588)

No. 366. Prison Reform (J. Howard 1777, binding by Edwards of Halifax, showing a fine painting of Howard beneath the vellum)

No. 369. The First Aerial Voyage (The Ascent of Montgolfier's balloon, 1783)

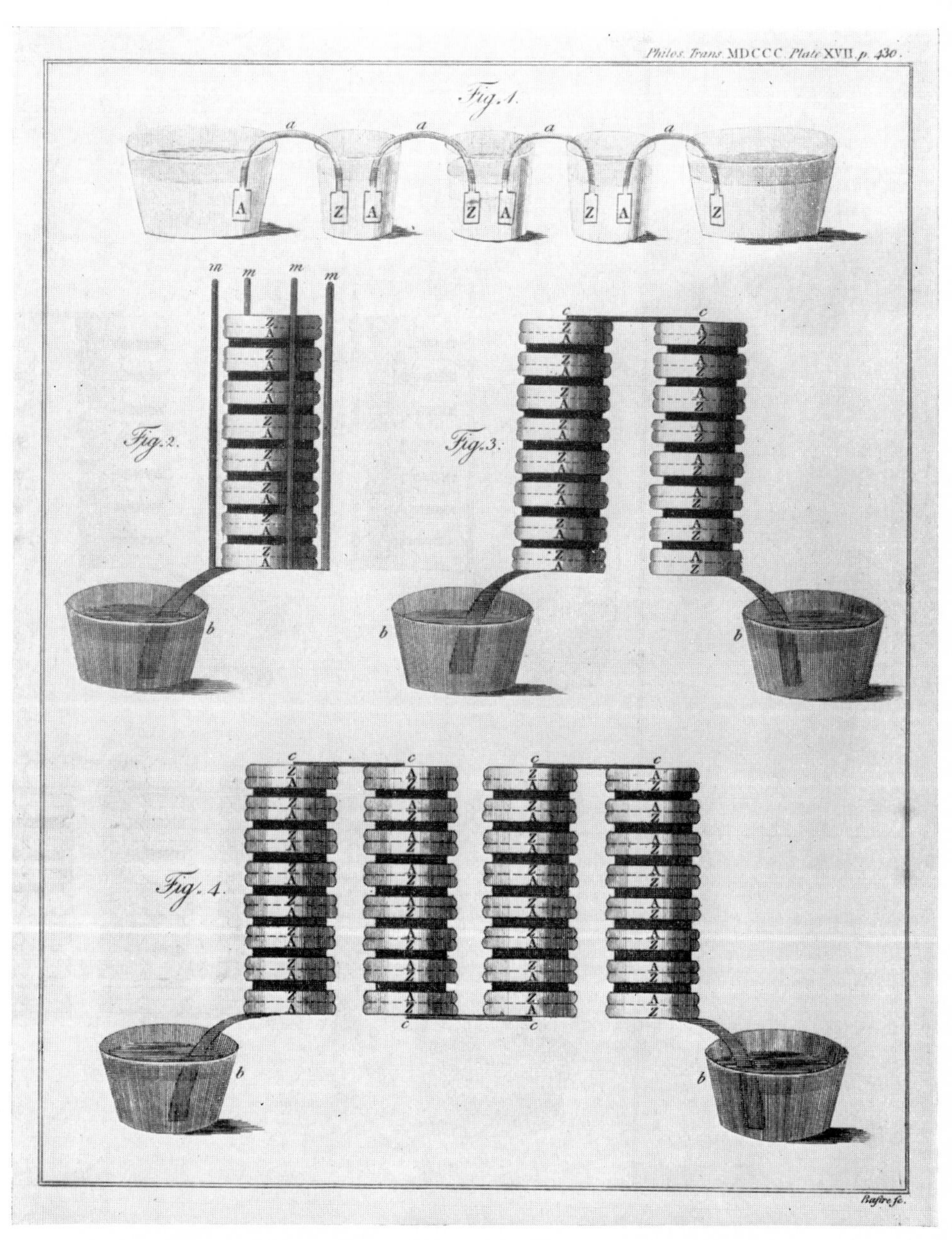

No. 432. The Invention of the Electric Battery (A. Volta, 1800)

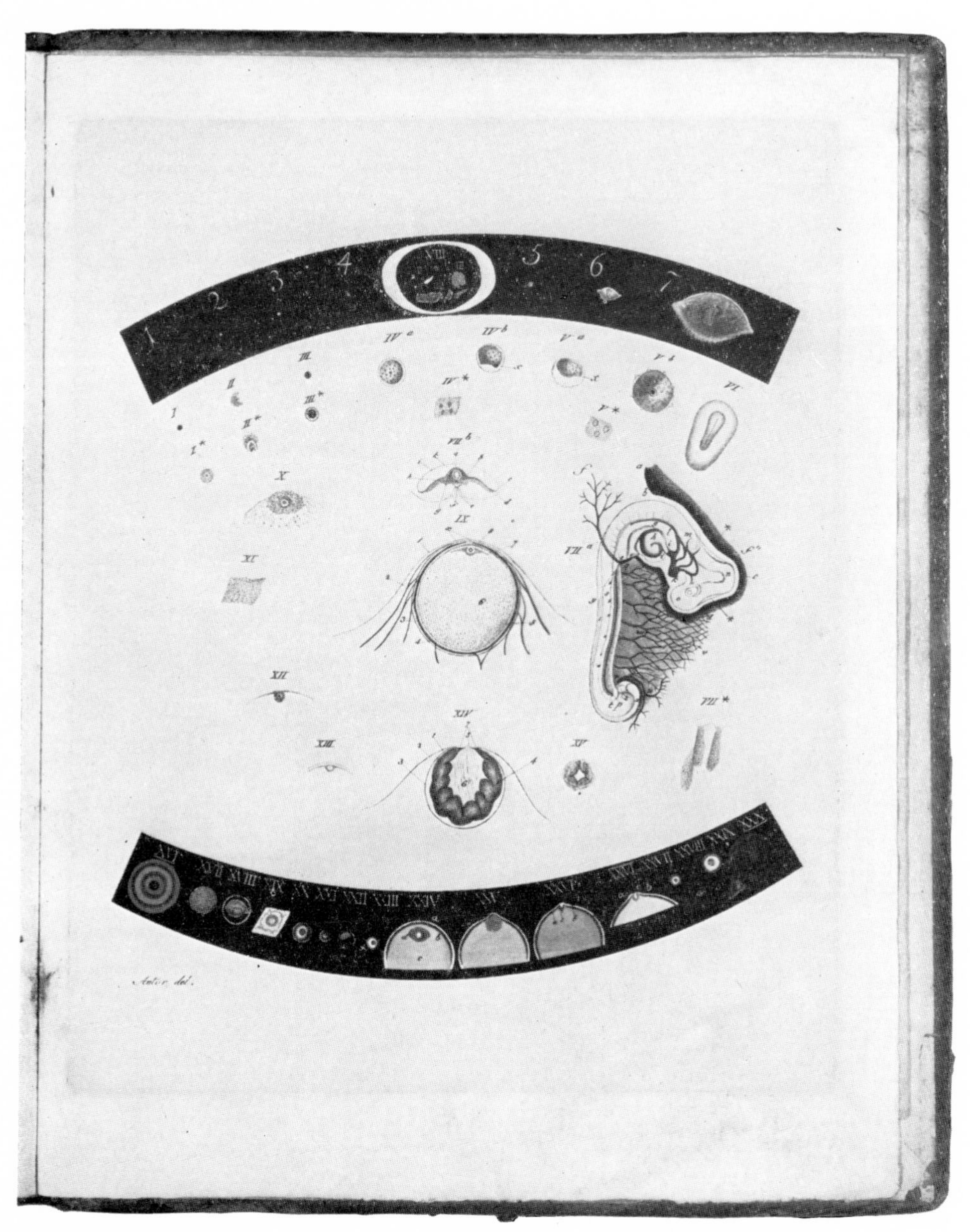

No. 479. The Discovery of the Mammalian Ovum (K. E. von Baer, 1827)

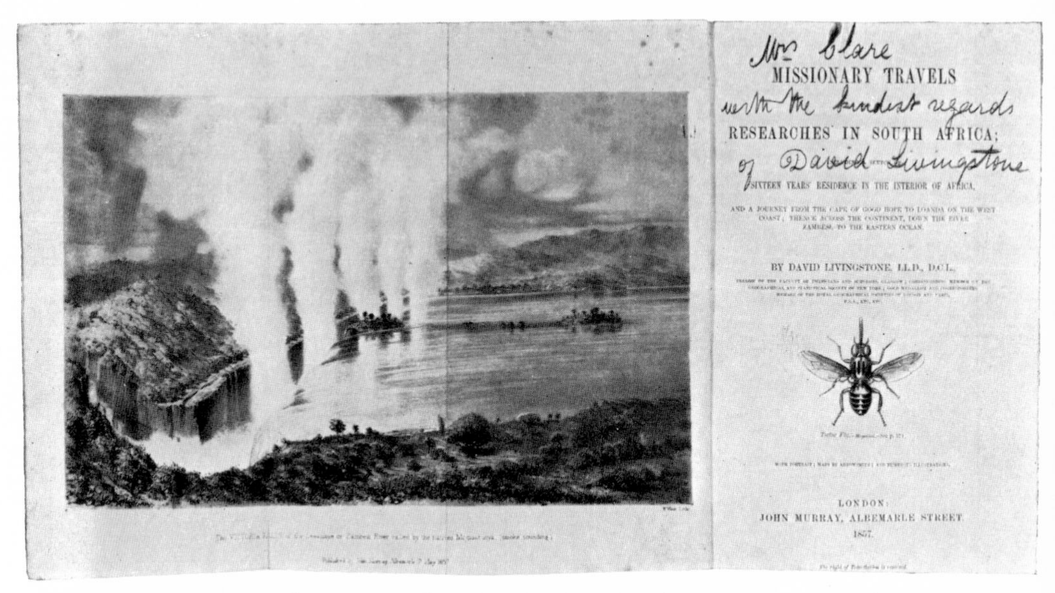

Mrs Clare
with the kindest regards
of David Livingstone

MISSIONARY TRAVELS

RESEARCHES IN SOUTH AFRICA;

SIXTEEN YEARS' RESIDENCE IN THE INTERIOR OF AFRICA,

AND A JOURNEY FROM THE CAPE OF GOOD HOPE TO LOANDA ON THE WEST COAST; THENCE ACROSS THE CONTINENT, DOWN THE RIVER ZAMBESI, TO THE EASTERN OCEAN.

BY DAVID LIVINGSTONE, LL.D., D.C.L.,

LONDON:
JOHN MURRAY, ALBEMARLE STREET.
1857.

No. 526. Christianity and Exploration in Africa (D. Livingstone, 1857)

No. 571. The First Practical Cinematograph
(A. & L. Lumière, 1897)

No. 587. The Boy Scout Movement
(R. Baden-Powell, 1908)

PRINTING AND THE MIND OF MAN

CATALOGUE OF
AN EXHIBITION OF FINE PRINTING
IN THE BRITISH MUSEUM

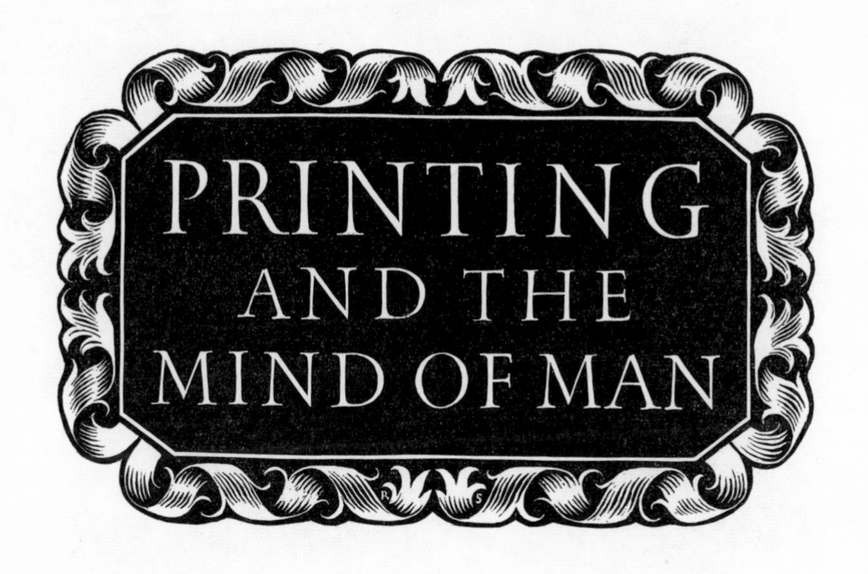

AN EXHIBITION OF

FINE PRINTING

IN THE KING'S LIBRARY OF

THE BRITISH MUSEUM

July–September
1963

PUBLISHED BY
THE TRUSTEES OF THE BRITISH MUSEUM

PRINTED IN GREAT BRITAIN

PREFACE

PRINTING AND THE MIND OF MAN is a special feature of the Eleventh International Printing Machinery and Allied Trades Exhibition (IPEX) held at Olympia and Earls Court from 16 to 27 July 1963 under the aegis of F. W. Bridges & Sons Ltd. and the Association of British Manufacturers of Printers' Machinery. It has three separate but complementary components.

Two of these—the historical evolution of printing techniques and the impact of printing upon Western civilization—will be shown in Earls Court for the duration of IPEX.

The third component, described here, is concerned solely with the physical appearance of the book. This display of fine printing will be on view in the King's Library of the British Museum during IPEX and for about six weeks thereafter.

Except for three books from the Department of Prints and Drawings (42, 149, 185) and no. 167, kindly lent by Mr. Herbert Spencer, the books exhibited all form part of the collections of the Department of Printed Books. Some of the finest (marked in the catalogue*) have been grouped in four upright cases in the centre of the room; the remainder have been arranged chronologically so as to illustrate the development of the art of printing. They have been chosen to represent the best typography of their day and should not be regarded as key books in the development of printing styles.

The selection has been made by a committee of members of the Department under the chairmanship of the Director of the Museum with the invaluable assistance of Mr. John Dreyfus. Acknowledgement must also be made of the help given to the committee in selecting the books and producing the following catalogue by members of the other committees concerned with PRINTING AND THE MIND OF MAN and, in particular, by Mr. Nicolas Barker, Mr. John Carter, and Mr. Percy Muir.

R. A. WILSON
Principal Keeper
Department of Printed Books

BRITISH MUSEUM
LONDON

CONTENTS

LIST OF ILLUSTRATIONS

THE ADVENT OF PRINTING

(c. 1455–1500)

THE invention of printing in the Western world was rendered necessary by the growth of the reading public at the close of the Middle Ages, and the inability of the manuscript trade to meet this expanding market. The basic problems were solved by Johann Gutenberg at Strassburg in *c.* 1436–9, and the technique perfected at Mainz in *c.* 1450–5, when the great Bible which commonly bears his name was produced. The essential and unique features of his invention were an adjustable hand mould, with punch-stamped matrices,for precision casting of type-sorts in large quantities; a type-metal alloy (probably lead with tin and antimony) with low melting-point and quick, undistorted solidification; a press adapted from those used by, among others, paper-makers and bookbinders; and an oil-based printing-ink. During the next decade this revolutionary invention spread to Bamberg, Strassburg, and Cologne, and was carried by German craftsmen to Italy in 1465, to Switzerland *c.* 1468, to France in 1470, and to Spain in 1472–3. From early in the 1470's presses were also active in the Netherlands, and it was from Bruges that William Caxton returned in 1476 to establish himself at Westminster as the first printer in his native England.

Printing was originally conceived as a process for the mechanical reproduction of manuscript. Type-design, layout, and decoration tended from the first to evolve autonomously, but were constantly stimulated and newly inspired by manuscript models. By the end of the century the printing houses of Europe had produced nearly 40,000 editions, the best of which remain unsurpassed in the beauty and variety of their craftsmanship.

*The 42-line Bible, c. 1455

1 Bible, in Latin. *[Johann Gutenberg, Johann Fust, and Peter Schoeffer, Mainz, c. 1455]*

The Gutenberg or 42-line Bible was, as far as is known, the first substantial book ever printed from movable type, and remains one of the finest. The copy in the Bibliothèque Nationale, Paris, contains a manuscript note by its rubricator and binder, Heinrich Cremer, Vicar of St. Stephen's at Mainz, stating that he finished his task on 24 August 1456. The printing of so large a work must have taken more than a year and therefore have commenced at least several months before the lawsuit decided on 6 November 1455 by which the partnership between Gutenberg and Fust, his financial backer, was dissolved. Forty-eight copies of this Bible are known, of which thirty-six are printed on paper and twelve on vellum, and twenty-one in all are perfect. The British Museum possesses one of each, both perfect.

The type is an ingenious and beautiful transposition into printed form of the manuscript book-hand customarily used for high-quality bibles and missals at this period in west Germany. The style is known as Textura, or 'weaving', as the equidistance of spacing between adjacent letters and the uprights of individual letters produces an interwoven effect, with an even balance of black and white throughout the page. The same type was used for headings and incipits in the 30-line *Indulgence* of 1454, and later in a *Donatus* of *c.* 1470 signed by Schoeffer. *Plate 1*

*The 36-line Bible, c. 1458–9

2 Bible, in Latin. *[Anonymous printer, Bamberg, c. 1458–9]*

The 36-line Bible is a later rival to the 42-line Bible of Gutenberg, Fust, and Schoeffer, from the text of which it was printed in a larger and coarser type of cognate design, and with a similar layout.

* Books so marked will be found in one of the four upright cases in the centre of the King's Library.

The type first appears in the 31-line *Indulgence* of 1454, and then with successive modifications in a series of small grammars and calendars (including the so-called *Astronomical Calendar* of 1448, which must now be dated *c.* 1457), next in the Bible itself, *c.* 1458–9, and lastly at Bamberg from 1460 onwards at the press of Albrecht Pfister, a much less-accomplished printer. On the evidence of paper and the discovery in that city of various press-waste fragments, the Bible was probably printed at Bamberg, perhaps under the patronage of the cathedral chapter. In presswork and type-design the 36-line Bible is inferior to the 42-line Bible, but remains sumptuous in intention and effect. It may well represent the capabilities of Gutenberg himself when deprived of the technical and aesthetic assistance of Schoeffer.

*Fust and Schoeffer, 1459

3 Psalter in Latin. *Johann Fust and Peter Schoeffer, Mainz, 29 August 1459*

The first edition of the Mainz *Psalter*, 14 August 1457, (of which the copy belonging to Her Majesty the Queen is shown in the Earls Court section of this exhibition) was intended for use in churches. In this second edition the contents are rearranged for monastic services according to the newly established Bursfeld Observance of the Benedictine Order, which had won wide acceptance in Western Germany. The colophon states that the edition was completed 'in honour of St. James', which suggests that it was authorized or commissioned by or otherwise associated with the Benedictine monastery of St. James at Mainz. The types and the elaborate two-colour printed capitals are the same as those used in the 1457 edition; and in both editions the whole of each page, including both the black text and the colour-printing, was printed at one pull of the press. All the thirteen known copies are on vellum; the British Museum possesses two, George III's here shown, and the Holkham copy.

The Mainz Catholicon, 1460

4 JOHANNES BALBUS, Catholicon. *[Possibly printed by Johann Gutenberg], Mainz 1460*

The *Catholicon*, a vast encyclopedic dictionary, together with two *Indulgences* of 1461 and 1462, and two theological tracts in the same type, may well have been the work of Gutenberg. The proud statement in the colophon, that it was printed 'without help of reed, stilus or pen, but by the marvellous concord, proportion and harmony of punches and types', and 'by the aid of the All-highest, who often reveals to the humble what he hides from the wise', suggests the voice of the inventor himself, while the type has many similarities to the smaller type of the 30-line *Indulgence* of 1454, which may well have been produced in the Gutenberg–Fust–Schoeffer office. The copy shown is one of eight known on vellum.

Fust and Schoeffer, 1462

5 Bible in Latin. *Johann Fust and Peter Schoeffer, Mainz, 14 August 1462*

The type of the 1462 or 48-line Bible is a medium gothic of humanistic design which departs entirely from the medieval severity of the 42-line Bible and Psalter types. It was no doubt cut specially for this work, in which it first appears. Many copies, including the one shown, were printed on vellum. A press correction in Matthew xxii found only in vellum copies suggests that these went through the press after the paper copies.

Fust and Schoeffer, 1465

6 CICERO, De officiis, and Paradoxa. *Johann Fust and Peter Schoeffer, Mainz 1465*

The Mainz *Cicero* is the first dated edition of any classical author, though the undated Cicero, *De oratore*, printed at Subiaco by Sweynheym and Pannartz, one copy of which was annotated by an early owner at some time before 30 September 1465, may possibly have preceded it by a few months. The type, which was first used in the *Durandus* of 6 October 1459, is the first small text-type, not counting the two small types used only in the 1454 *Indulgences*. It is here improved by thin leading between the lines, and in the *Paradoxa* is economically used as part of an incomplete Greek fount for the brief Greek quotations called for by the text. The headings are red-printed, and in this vellum copy rubrication strokes and initials, somewhat in the style of the printed capitals of the 1457 Psalter, are added by hand.

Sweynheym and Pannartz, 1465

7 LACTANTIUS, Opera. *[Conradus Sweynheym and Arnoldus Pannartz], Subiaco, 29 October 1465*

Sweynheym and Pannartz founded the first press in Italy in the Benedictine abbey at Subiaco near Rome towards the end of 1464. Sweynheym was a native of Mainz, and it is possible that he received his training there from Gutenberg or Schoeffer and became a refugee after the sack of Mainz in 1462. After printing four books at Subiaco, of which an entirely lost Donatus, *Latin Grammar*, was the first, and this *Lactantius* the third, the partners moved to Rome. Their Subiaco type may be regarded as the first roman, though its narrow face and thickness of line give it an appearance of gothic severity. The first complete Greek alphabet also appears in the *Lactantius*, though this was probably preceded by the incomplete Greek fount used in Fust and Schoeffer's Cicero, *De officiis*, produced at Mainz in the same year. The Subiaco roman inspired one of the finest types used by St. John Hornby at his Ashendene Press (no. 165).

Johannes de Spira, 1469

8 CICERO, Epistolae ad familiares. *Johannes de Spira, Venice 1469*

This vellum copy of the first book printed in Venice is one of an edition of only 100 copies, of which the British Museum possesses four. Johannes de Spira had obtained a five-year monopoly for printing in Venice, which fortunately for his future competitors expired on his death early in 1470, when his brother Vindelinus succeeded to his press. Their roman type, although the indecisiveness of certain letters still shows traces of its manuscript models, marks a decisive step in the autonomy of type-design and in the quest for a perfect roman.

Sweynheym and Pannartz, 1469

9 LIVY, Historia Romana. *Conradus Sweynheym and Arnoldus Pannartz, Rome [1469]*

In the autumn of 1467 Sweynheym and Pannartz moved from Subiaco to Rome and began a long series of editions of the Latin classics in a new roman type. Although inferior to their Subiaco type in the untidiness, tilting, and monotonous thickness of many sorts, this may be claimed as the first true and typical roman used in Italy (for in Germany it was preceded a few months before at Strassburg by the roman of Adolf Rusch, the 'R-Printer'). Its defects in detail are largely redeemed by the splendour of design with which it is used on the printed page. Of this Livy, here shown in a vellum copy illuminated with the Borgia arms, 275 copies were printed.

Johann Mentelin, c. 1469

10 VIRGIL, Opera. *[Johann Mentelin, Strassburg, c. 1469]*

Mentelin, the first printer at Strassburg, is said by a contemporary chronicler to have printed at the rate of 300 sheets a day as early as 1458, though his first datable book is the Latin Bible of which vol. 1 was issued not later than 1460. He died on 12 December 1478. His undated edition of Virgil, printed in a state of the type distinguished by its roman *a*-form and first used in 1469, is a candidate for the proud position of *editio princeps*, though the edition of Sweynheym and Pannartz at Rome in that year has at least an equal claim. In its severe gothic type Mentelin's edition appeals, as its German public would expect, to medieval rather than Renaissance standards of beauty and dignity.

Friburger, Gering, and Crantz, 1470

11 GASPARINUS BARZIZIUS, Epistolae. *Michael Friburger, Ulrich Gering, and Martinus Crantz, Paris [1470]*

As the colophon states, this is the first book printed in France. The bold and rounded roman type is modelled on the second roman of Sweynheym and Pannartz and on others of the earliest Rome presses, including that of Georg Lauer. The Paris press was set up under the patronage of two ex-rectors of the Sorbonne, Fichet and Heynlin, in the library of the Sorbonne itself, and before Fichet's retirement in 1473 produced more than twenty well-printed, mostly classical, texts.

Christophorus Valdarfer, 1470

12 CICERO, De oratore. *Christophorus Valdarfer, Venice 1470*

Valdarfer, a German from Ratisbon, was the third printer at Venice, being preceded there only by the De Spira brothers and Jenson. He produced a dozen books, of which this *Cicero* is the first, in 1470–1, all in the same rounded and broad-faced roman, which is noteworthy for the famous and widely imitated 'Valdarfer *h*', with its curved bowl and horizontal serif to the right below. In 1474 Valdarfer reappeared with new types (none of which, curiously enough, has the 'Valdarfer *h*') at Milan, where he worked until 1488, with a brief interval at Basel in 1479.

Speculum Printer, c. 1470

13 Speculum humanae salvationis, in Dutch. *[Printer of the Text of the Speculum, Utrecht, c. 1470]*

The text of this *Mirror of Human Salvation* tells the story of the Fall and Redemption, illustrated on each opening by three scenes from the Old Testament and one from the New. The text was printed in the normal manner from movable type with printer's ink in a press, but the illustrations were added separately from blocks belonging to an otherwise lost blockbook, and were printed not in a press but by the blockbook process of laying the paper on the incized block, moistened with a brown, water-based ink, and rubbing the uppermost side. The *Speculum* and other books in related types were once attributed to the semi-mythical Laurens Coster at Haarlem about 1440, but are now assigned to an anonymous press at Utrecht, *c.* 1470. The type is remarkable for the decorative hair-lines on *t* and other letters, and was no doubt modelled on a book-hand. Four editions of the *Speculum* were produced, two in Dutch, of which this is the first, and two in Latin, the second of which contains 20 leaves with both text and illustrations block-printed.

*Johannes Nicolai Alvise, 1472

14 ROBERTUS VALTURIUS, De re militari. *Johannes Nicolai Alvise de Verona, Verona 1472*

The treatise of Valturius on the art of war is illustrated with cuts of ingenious and futuristic contraptions which (like the White Knight's) were his own invention, but (like the White Knight's pudding) were doubtless never actually made. The printer has boldly followed his manuscript model in utilizing the entire page as a frame for these designs, thus anticipating mid twentieth-century innovations in the integration of text and illustration. These cuts, because they were too large to be printed in the forme at the same time as the type-page, were stamped in later by hand, as is shown by their slightly varying position in relation to the printed text in different copies of the book. Except for a small tract of local interest produced early in the same year, the *Valturius* was the only product of this press, the first at Verona; but its master is probably the same Giovanni Alvise who, in partnership with his brother Alberto, operated the second Veronese press in 1478–9.

Botel and Partners, 1473

15 ARISTOTLE, Ethica Nicomachea, Oeconomica *and* Politica. *[Henricus Botel, Johannes Planck, and Georgius vom Holtz, Barcelona 1473]*

Recent investigations of documentary and typographical evidence have shown that this *Aristotle* may be (with the possible exception of a group of books from a press which may have worked at Segovia, *c.* 1472–3) the earliest production of the printing-press in Spain. It is apparently the only work of a partnership formed in Barcelona by a contract dated 5 January 1473 in which Botel undertook to teach vom Holtz and Planck the art of printing. The massive roman type of the *Aristotle*, which is closely related to types used in the same year at Rome and Naples, was not used again; but when Botel and Planck renewed their partnership at Saragossa in 1478, they used the small gothic type in which the register to the *Politica* is printed. The rubrication in alternate red and blue, the thick white paper, and wide margins give the present copy a magnificence which is equally Italian and Spanish.

Nicolaus Jenson, 1474

16 GRATIANUS, Decretum. *Nicolaus Jenson, Venice, 28 June 1474*

Jenson, a Frenchman who is said to have learned printing at Mainz in 1458 at the order of Charles VII, King of France, worked at Venice from 1470 to his death in 1480, first as his own master, and after the slump of 1473 as head of a syndicate. After the 1473 recession, due to over-production of fine editions of the classics, the Venetian printers explored other fields, including the civil and canon law texts with surrounding commentary in which they soon became pre-eminent. For these gothic type was deemed appropriate, and Jenson therefore designed the large text-type and smaller commentary-type first used in this book, which were widely admired and copied. In a prefatory letter Jenson's foreman Francesco Colucia states that he has taken particular care with 'spelling, headings, full-stops, commas, question marks, and all other punctuation'. This copy is on vellum and luxuriously illuminated.

*Nicolaus Jenson, 1475

17 CICERO, Epistolae ad familiares. *Nicolaus Jenson, [Venice] 1475*

Jenson's roman, first used in the Eusebius, *De evangelica praeparatione*, of 1470, is the first to be consciously designed according to typographical ideals, and in liberation from manuscript models. It has influenced many noble founts in modern times, notably William Morris's 'Golden' (1890), the Doves Press roman of Cobden-Sanderson (1891), and the Riverside Press 'Montaigne' of Bruce Rogers (1901). As the advertisement issued *c.* 1482 by Jenson's partners truly affirms, 'his books do not hinder one's eyes, but rather help them and do them good. Moreover, the characters are so intelligently and carefully elaborated that the letters are neither smaller, larger nor thicker than reason or pleasure demand.' In paper copies Jenson's inking and presswork are all too often perfunctory, but on vellum, as here, he took pride in perfect craftsmanship. *(Plate 2a)*

Heinrich Quentell, c. 1478

18 Bible, in the West Low German dialect. *[Heinrich Quentell, Cologne, c. 1478]*

The second Cologne Bible contains eight more woodcuts in the Book of Revelations than the first, a Low Saxon version printed by Quentell shortly before. These, as Hind remarks, are 'perhaps the most epoch-making of all contemporary Bibles for the influence the woodcuts had on Bible illustration in general for generations'. Quentell's first dated book appeared in 1479, and the two Cologne Bibles are probably his earliest, but certainly his most important productions. In his later career, which continued till 1501, he became the most prolific of the Cologne printers.

William Caxton, c. 1478

19 GEOFFREY CHAUCER, The Canterbury Tales. *[William Caxton, Westminster, c. 1478]*

After learning the art of printing at Cologne in 1471–2, and producing six books from his own press at Bruges in 1473–5, Caxton moved to England and set up the first English press in the precincts of Westminster Abbey in the autumn of 1476. He there printed a vellum indulgence (exhibited at Earls Court) in time for the only surviving copy to be sold on 13 December 1476, followed by an undated *History of Jason*, the *Dictes* of November 1477, a number of verse tracts by Chaucer and Lydgate, and this first edition of *Canterbury Tales*. All these are in his second type, a large *bâtarde* which he had already utilized in one book at Bruges. It is modelled on the book-hands used at Bruges in high-class vernacular manuscripts for the Burgundian court.

Giovanni Alvise, 1479

20 AESOP, Fables, in Latin and Italian. *Giovanni Alvise, Verona, 26 June 1479*

This first edition of the Italian *Aesop* contains sixty-six lively and charming woodcuts in a style which suggests the cutter (but not the artist) of the 1472 *Valturius*. The printer freely uses a varied and attractive set of 'flowers', an unusual feature in fifteenth-century printing, and ingeniously encloses these between rules to decorate the borders of the cuts. More than a dozen rival editions followed, all now exceedingly rare, before the end of the century.

Gerard Leeu, 1480

21 Dialogus Creaturarum. *Gerard Leeu, Gouda, 3 June 1480*

Gerard Leeu, one of the most prolific and enterprising of the early printers in the Low Countries, worked at Gouda from 1477 to 1484 and thereafter at Antwerp, where he died in 1493 in a quarrel with one of his workmen during the printing of a new edition of Caxton's *Chronicles of England*. He produced seven editions, in Latin, Dutch, and French, of the *Dialogus creaturarum*, of which the first is shown. Each has the same woodcuts, in a naïve and humorous style which suits the light-hearted animal fables of the text, and with an economy of outline which contrasts effectively with the blackness of the type-page.

*Jean Dupré, 1481

22 Missal, in the use of Verdun. *Jean Dupré, Paris, 28 November 1481*

Dupré's *Verdun Missal* was the second missal printed in France, preceded only by the same printer's first work, the *Paris Missal* of the previous 22 September. In illuminated copies on vellum, as became increasingly the practice in the fifteenth-century Paris book-trade, the woodcuts were used with more or less freedom as models by the illuminator. This is the Holkham Hall (Earl of Leicester) copy, the only other being that in the Bibliothèque Nationale, Paris. Dupré specialized in liturgical and decorative printing until the end of the century, and often supplied material to printers in other towns, as for the Abbeville *Augustine*, 1487, also shown. He should not be confused with his namesake Jean Dupré at Lyons, though there was evidently some connexion both in business and in family between the two printers.

Erhard Ratdolt, 1482

23 EUCLID, Elementa. *Erhard Ratdolt, Venice, 25 May 1482*

As he remarks in his dedication to Giovanni Mocenigo, Doge of Venice in 1478–85, Ratdolt here solves the technical problem of producing the essential marginal diagrams together with the text, which had hitherto prevented the printing of Euclid. This is the very copy which was presented to the doge, and is on vellum with the dedicatory letter printed in gold ink (made by substituting gold-dust for lampblack in the normal printer's ink formula) and with the doge's illuminated arms. Ratdolt, who worked at Venice in 1476–86, and thereafter at Augsburg until 1528, was one of the most original and accomplished of the early fine printers.

Lienhart Holle, 1482

24 PTOLEMY, Cosmographia. *Lienhart Holle, Ulm, 16 July 1482*

The type of the Ulm *Ptolemy* is a distinctive large roman with agreeable gothic features, modelled on the autograph manuscript of the editor, Nicolaus Germanus, which still survives, and accompanied by large *Maiblumen* (i.e. lily of the valley) initials. The volume is illustrated with thirty-two woodcut and gaily hand-coloured maps, each on a folding sheet tipped in. This copy is on vellum. The Ulm type was imitated by St. John Hornby at his Ashendene Press, notably in the *Don Quixote* of 1928.

Colard Mansion, 1484

25 OVID, Metamorphoses, an allegorized version in French prose. *Colard Mansion, Bruges, May 1484*

The text is a free paraphrase of Ovid's work in the manner of medieval romance, with ethical and theological moralizations of each episode. The cuts are closely related to the Flemish miniatures found in manuscripts of this work, but Mansion's illustrator has shown vigour and charm in translating his models into terms of block-cutting. Mansion's fine, bold text-type, still larger than the Caxton type 2 on which it is modelled, is a typographical version of the Bruges book-hand. Mansion worked as a calligrapher as early as 1450, probably became Caxton's pupil (but not, as was once thought, his master) in 1473–5, and produced at his own press in 1476–84 a score of notable books. He absconded from Bruges about June 1484, no doubt ruined by the expenses of this magnificent *Ovid*, resumed work as a calligrapher at Abbeville, and is heard of no more.

Gérard and Dupré, 1486

26 SAINT AUGUSTINE, De civitate Dei, in French. 2 volumes. *Pierre Gérard and Jean Dupré, Abbeville, 24 November 1486, 12 April 1486/7*

The Abbeville *Saint Augustine*, in A. W. Pollard's words, is 'the first really magnificent French illustrated book, in which paper and print and woodcuts of artistic value all harmonise'. The press material was supplied by Dupré, who later co-operated similarly in provincial presses at Rouen, Angoulême, Nantes, and Châlons-sur-Marne, but was apparently not present in person, as he continued to work in Paris throughout the activity of the Abbeville press. The woodcuts, which were later acquired by Vérard, are modelled on manuscript illuminations, for they closely resemble the illustrations in a British Museum manuscript of the same text (Royal 14. D. 1).

Bernardus Nerlius, 1489

27 HOMER, Works, in Greek. *Bernardus Nerlius, Florence, [after 13 January 1488/9]*

In order to ensure a contemporary appearance for their Greek types, fifteenth-century printers were in general committed to the adaptation of cursive manuscript forms, with their profuse and unpleasing contractions and complex accentuation, despite the enormous number of different sorts which these models necessitated. The type of this *editio princeps* of Homer is a recasting with many new sorts, making a total of more than 300, of that used in the 1476 *Lascaris* printed at Milan by Dionysius Paravisinus, which was the first book printed throughout (except for a preface and colophon in roman) in Greek. The accents are embodied in the vowel-sorts, not printed separately. Both states of the type were cut and the printing supervised by the Cretan Demetrius Damilas. Seen in its contemporary context the type is graceful and fluid, and the Florence *Homer*, with its careful presswork and fine paper, is the stateliest fifteenth-century edition of any major Greek classic.

William Caxton, c. 1489

28 BONAVENTURA, Speculum vitae Christi, in English. *William Caxton, Westminster, [c. 1489]*

This popular *Life of Christ* was translated into English *c.* 1410 by Nicholas Love, the Carthusian prior of Ingleby, Yorkshire; it remained a firm favourite for over a hundred years, and was recommended by Sir Thomas More in his *Apology*. This is Caxton's second edition, a close reprint in the same type (no. 5) of his first edition, *c.* 1487, of which only the Cambridge University Library copy is known.

The woodcuts are greatly superior to the coarse work produced by the two artists previously employed by Caxton. The copy shown is one of only three known copies of any Caxton edition (with the exception of indulgences and a Donatus fragment) printed on vellum.

Pierre Levet, 1489

29 FRANÇOIS VILLON, Œuvres. *Pierre Levet, Paris 1489*

Pierre Levet, active from 1485 to 1502, specialized in cheap quarto and octavo tracts of legal, theological, and classical texts for the use of Sorbonne students, but occasionally produced a more notable work. This first edition of Villon was no doubt meant for the same public, for Villon had taken his bachelor's degree in the University of Paris in 1449; and the crime for which the poet narrowly escaped hanging in 1463 (after which he disappeared), was the theft at Christmas, 1456, of 500 gold crowns from the College of Navarre by the gang of robber-students of which he was the leader. The woodcuts are from borrowed blocks first used in Guy Marchant's edition of the *Danse Macabre*, 1485. The figure of a man with a dagger is made to do duty, not inappropriately, for Villon himself, who had killed his man with this weapon in a brawl over a girl on 5 June 1455, but the cut of Villon's friends on the gallows is original, and is given startling force by its very crudity.

Giovanni Ragazzo, 1490

30 Bible, in Italian. *Giovanni Ragazzo, Venice, 15 October 1490*

The Malermi Bible, so called after its translator Niccolò Malermi, was first printed by De Spira at Venice, 1 August 1471, but is best known from the illustrated editions, of which this is the first, The 384 small woodcuts are among the most charming products of the Venetian popular style, and are the work of two designers, the better of whom was chiefly responsible for the Old Testament, while his colleague worked mainly on the New Testament. The initial *b* with which many of the cuts are signed is found equally on the work of either artist, and must therefore belong only to the block-cutter. The plan of this edition was no doubt inspired by Lucantonio Giunta, one of the most enterprising publishers in Venice between 1490 and 1510, who commissioned Ragazzo to print it.

Antonius Zarotus, 1490

31 JOHANNES SIMONETA, Commentarii rerum gestarum Francisci Sfortiae, in Italian. *Antonius Zarotus, Milan 1490*

This history of the life and reign of Francesco Sforza, Duke of Milan from 1450–1466, is here seen in the vellum presentation copy made for his son Ludovico il Moro, then regent of the duchy during the minority of his nephew Giangalezzo, whom Ludovico murdered and superseded in 1494.

The illuminations are by one of the masters who collaborated on the Bona Sforza Book of Hours (B.M. Add. MS. 34294), and include portraits of Francesco and Ludovico, a moor's head, and the Sforza arms. After acting as foreman to the prototypographer of Milan, Pamfilo Castaldi, in 1471, Zarotus opened his own office with at least seven presses in 1472, specialized in classical and Italian literature, and continued to work until 1507, though with diminished activity during his last decade.

Jacob Meydenbach, 1491

32 Hortus Sanitatis. *Jacob Meydenbach, Mainz, 23 June 1491*

As the title *Garden of Health* indicates, the many printed herbals of the fifteenth century were intended, in an age of mainly herbal medicines, as manuals for the physician and pharmacist rather than as textbooks of botany. They are now prized for the simple charm of their woodcut illustrations. This first edition of the Latin text contains cuts modelled, with much independence and equal merit, on those in the German version, the *Gart der Gesundheit*, printed by Peter Schoeffer in 1485, together with many new cuts attributable to the Master of the Ulm *Aesop*, making a total of 527.

Antoine Vérard, 1491

33 OROSIUS, Historiae. *Antoine Vérard, Paris, 21 August 1491*

Vérard was originally a calligrapher and illuminator for aristocratic patrons, and his successful aim as a printer was to produce equivalent books for a wider public by mechanical means. Although not the first of his volumes with woodcuts, which began in 1485, the *Orosius* marks the beginning of Vérard's steady output of finely printed and illustrated books of chivalry, in which he became preeminent. The small cuts of battle scenes were his own property, and often reappear in his later work, but the larger cuts and the great capitals, together with the types, derive from Pierre le Rouge, who had used them in his *Mer des Histoires*, 1488–9, and may well have printed the *Orosius* to Vérard's order. The repetition of the two powerful S-capitals on facing pages is daringly effective.

Nicolaus Spindeler, 1491

34 Tirant lo Blanc. *Nicolaus Spindeler, Valencia, 20 November 1491*

Despite the claim of the alleged translator, Johanot Martorell, to have rendered this romance into Catalan from a Portuguese version of an English original, it is very probable that *Tirant lo*

Blanc is in fact his own work. The text is unusually realistic and humorous; the hero, like Don Quixote, dies in bed and makes a will; and Cervantes was evidently influenced by the tale.

The border of this first edition, containing branch-work, hunting scenes, and a battle between a wild man and a centaur, together with a shield bearing the sacred monogram IHS and surrounded by the printer's name, is one of the most splendid to be found in early Spanish books. An original feature is the use of a sectional block, with a design of vine-branches and tendrils, to divide the columns of the text. The heading-type and text-type present large and small versions of the distinctive rounded gothic style which found such favour with Spanish printers and readers up to the mid sixteenth century, and seems to portray the severe magnificence of the Spanish national character.

Anton Koberger, 1493

35 HARTMANN SCHEDEL, Liber chronicarum. *Anton Koberger, Nuremberg, 12 July 1493*

The *Nuremberg Chronicle*, a history of the world from the creation to the year 1492, is the most lavishly illustrated book of the fifteenth century, containing 645 different cuts and 1,164 repeats, a total of 1,809. The illustrations include many authentic two-page views of the great cities ot Europe, though some of these are borrowed from Breydenbach, including the panorama of Venice. The artists are named in the colophon as Michael Wolgemut (the teacher of Dürer) and Wilhelm Pleydenwurff. Koberger, from 1473 to his death in 1513, was one of the most prolific of early German printers, and exported his output not only to the rest of Germany but throughout Europe.

Laurentius de Alopa, 1494

36 Anthologia Graeca. *Laurentius de Alopa, Florence, 11 August 1494*

The *Greek Anthology*, a collection of amatory, obituary, humorous, and occasional Greek verses both classical and late, was edited by the Byzantine monk Planudes in 1301 in the version here first printed.

The type was designed by Joannes Lascaris, the librarian of Lorenzo the Magnificent, who collected Greek manuscripts for his master and turned to printing after Lorenzo's death. Lascaris, deciding, as he remarks in his dedication to Piero de' Medici, that 'ordinary Greek types are difficult to cast and too complicated to fit together in composition', devised an entirely majuscule type without ligatures, an experiment first repeated by Bodoni some three centuries later. The accents and breathings are set on the line above as separate sorts. This press was the most prolific in fifteenth-century Greek printing next to Aldus's, and also produced first editions of Euripides, Apollonius Rhodius, and Callimachus. A vellum copy is shown.

*Wynkyn de Worde, c. 1495

37 BARTHOLOMAEUS ANGLICUS, De proprietatibus rerum, in English. *Wynkyn de Worde, Westminster, c. 1495*

Caxton's foreman, Wynkyn de Worde, inherited his deceased master's press in 1491, and continued, until he moved to Fleet Street in 1500, to print in his tradition and often with his types. As the colophon remarks, Caxton was the 'first prynter of this boke, in Laten tonge at Coleyne'; and a Latin *Bartholomaeus* was in fact produced *c.* 1472 by the anonymous Cologne press at which Caxton learned to print. The colophon further reveals that the paper (water-marked with an eight-point star in a circle) was made by John Tate the Younger, 'whiche late hathe in Englond doo make this paper thynne': here, therefore, is the first book printed on English paper. The *Bartholomaeus* is typical of De Worde's best presswork, and is here seen in an exceptionally large and clean copy. Between 1500 and his death in 1535 De Worde increasingly preferred to attack a wider market with cheaper books in smaller format. *Plate 2b*

Fernandes and De Saxonia, 1495

38 LUDOLPHUS DE SAXONIA, Vita Christi, in Portuguese. *Valentin Fernandes de Moravia and Nicolaus de Saxonia, Lisbon, 14 May–20 November 1495*

The *Life of Christ*, the first printed work in the Portuguese language, and the first in Portugal to contain woodcuts, is the finest Portuguese book of the fifteenth century. It was printed at the command of King John II and his queen Leonora, whose woodcut arms appear on the title-pages of each of the four volumes. After completing the *Life of Christ* the two German partners severed company and set up presses of their own.

Aldus Manutius, 1496

39 CARDINAL PIETRO BEMBO, Aetna. *Aldus Manutius, Venice, February 1495/6*

Aldus's first productions, the Lascaris, *Erotemata*, of 28 February 1495, and other works of that year, including the first volume of his monumental *Aristotle*, were in Greek, and therefore required only small quantities of roman type, which he apparently procured from other printers. His first individual roman type has been called Bembo in modern times, from the author of this book in which it is first used. It is not generally realized that Aldus greatly improved his *Aetna* type, and discarded the original sorts (except for a few persistent but unintentional wrong-fount admixtures) as early as 1499, when he designed a modified version (found for example in no. 45) using the original lower case with a new, larger, and lighter upper case. Indeed, the original majuscules are perceptibly undersized and over-dark. This most modern in appearance of fifteenth-century romans exercised enormous influence on the subsequent development of type-design. *Plate 3a*

*Stephan Plannck, 1496

40 Missale Romanum. *Stephan Plannck, Rome, 31 October 1496*

Plannck is chiefly known for his vast output, in the years 1480–1500, of small tracts, especially of single sermons and other speeches made before the Papal court; but he also produced two *Missals* and two *Pontificals* which are masterpieces of liturgical and musical printing. A special copy of the 1496 *Missal* is shown, printed on vellum and illuminated for Petrus Arrivabene, Bishop of Urbino in 1491–1504.

Phillipe Pigouchet, 1498

41 Horae ad usum Romanum. *Philippe Pigouchet, Paris, 16 September 1498*

The first Paris-printed *Book of Hours* with woodcut decoration was produced by Vérard in 1486. Before the end of the century several hundred editions of this popular book of private devotion were printed in Paris, usually on vellum, with cuts and lively borders in imitation of manuscripts, for which metal soon became a more usual and satisfactory medium than wood. Pigouchet in particular, often, as here, working for the publisher Simon Vostre, printed half a dozen or more every year from 1491 onwards, with increasingly varied and elaborate decoration, and the British Museum alone possesses seventeen of his editions. The copy shown is unusual for the largeness of the vellum, and a normal-sized copy of the same edition, also in the Museum, has perceptibly narrower margins.

*Anton Koberger, 1498

42 Apocalypse, in German. *[Anton Koberger, Nüremberg], 1498*

Various woodcuts in incunabula, notably those in the Brant, *Narrenschiff*, printed by Johann Bergmann at Basel, 1494, have been attributed on stylistic grounds to Dürer's earliest period. The great full-page cuts to the *Apocalypse*, with their truly apocalyptic power and sublimity, are his first masterwork. The two tall columns of the text make an excellent balance to the cuts, being printed in each case on the verso of a cut, so that each opening shows text to the left and a cut to the right. Michael Wolgemut (1434–1519), to whom Dürer was apprenticed in 1486–9, worked for Koberger on the *Schatzbehalter*, 1491, and the *Nuremberg Chronicle*, 1493, and perhaps introduced his pupil to the printer. Koberger produced two editions of the *Apocalypse* in the same year, one with Latin and the other, here shown, with German text.

*Mathias Hus, 1499

43 Danse Macabre. *Lyons, Mathias Hus, 18 February 1499*

Various versions of a *Danse Macabre* or *Dance of Death* were printed in the fifteenth century in German, Latin, and French, each with verse dialogues between Death and persons in various stations of society, and forceful illustrations of Death dragging his victims away. Both the illustrations and the text of the French version were based on frescoes in the church of the Holy Innocents in Paris, which were destroyed in 1669. The woodcuts printed by Hus are for the most part based on those in the editions of Guy Marchant, Paris, 15 April–22 May 1492, or of Couteau and Ménard, Paris, 26 June 1492; but the cut of the printer's office here shown was apparently made specially for Hus's edition, presumably by his own engraver, and may well represent, with necessary simplification and plus the skeletons, the actual appearance of his own establishment. This is the earliest known illustration of a printing-press. The compositor, with his case of type, composing-stick, and the two-page forme on the bench beside him, is setting from copy propped up before him; the pressman, with his right hand on the invisible handle, is arrested on the point of pulling the press; his colleague is already inking the next forme with the ink-balls; and in the adjoining bookshop the shopman is halted in the act of reading a volume of his wares. The text is printed in a neat *bâtarde* type of the kind normally used in French vernacular texts at this period.

*Zacharias Callierges, 1499

44 Etymologicum magnum. *Zacharias Callierges, Venice, 8 July 1499*

Aldus had armed himself with a monopoly privilege for his Greek types in 1495 on the grounds of their 'two new features' (meaning apparently his modelling of the letters on the contemporary business-hands and the kerning of the accents into the vowels), and successfully eliminated his imitators Bissolus & Co. in 1498. Such was the originality of the type designed by Callierges, however, that his publisher Nicolaus Blastos was enabled in the September of the same year to obtain a privilege for his 'very fine Greek type, in one piece with its accents, a thing never yet so well or finely achieved'. The red-printed initials and head-pieces in Byzantine style, the latter embodying the name of the publisher (Nicolas the Greek), are of unexampled splendour, and show the continuing inspiration from manuscript models which is one of the ruling themes of the fifteenth-century book.

*Aldus Manutius, 1499

45 FRANCISCUS COLONNA, Hypnerotomachia. *Aldus Manutius, Venice, December 1499*

The *Hypnerotomachia Poliphili* (i.e. 'The Strife of Love in a Dream of the Lover of Polia') is a dream-allegory, written in a macaronic mixture of Italian, Latin, and Greek, in which the author, a Dominican friar, tells the story of his love for the beautiful Polia, who has been doubtfully identified as the niece of the Bishop of Treviso. Colonna reveals his name in an acrostic formed by the first letter in each chapter, which reads: *Poliam frater Franciscus Columna peramavit.* The illustrations, which form the masterpiece of the Venetian classical style, are the work of an unknown artist, and even the initial *b* with which several are signed may belong only to the block-cutter. The book is equally remarkable for these cuts, the unframed strapwork capitals, the type, which is the improved version of the *Aetna* type with larger and lighter upper-case, the presswork, and the harmony of the whole. *Plate 3b*

THE SIXTEENTH CENTURY

THE sixteenth century in its typography clearly reflects the spirit of the Renaissance, especially in Italy and France. In the former country, the great figure of Aldus Manutius at Venice opens the century with his stream of first editions of the Greek and Latin classics. His roman, greek, and newly introduced italic types—he never printed in black letter—were of pure Renaissance inspiration and design. The Aldine style was to dominate the typography of Europe for upwards of two centuries. But the publishing impetus of the pocket-size Aldine classics did not inhibit improvements on his italic type on the part of other Italian printers. The formal, less sloped, cursive hand practised in the Vatican Chancery (hence known as *Cancellaresca*) was translated, notably by Lodovico degli Arrighi, writing-master and printer, into a variety of elegant types which found great favour with the new school of printers in Paris: Henri Estienne, first of an illustrious family, Simon de Colines, and Geoffroy Tory, whose taste and enterprise, in tune with the italianate enthusiasms of King François I, made Paris the capital of fine book-making in the second quarter of the century. Paris Books of Hours printed between 1500 and 1550, of which there is an enormous number of editions, are one of the most beautiful class of books ever produced.

The Aldine roman type was refined and improved by a succession of brilliant punchcutters, Garamond and Granjon being the most celebrated names. In these Gallic versions the roman type invaded not only Lyons, where Jean de Tournes was the best printer, but also Rome, Florence, Venice, and the printing houses of the Low Countries, in particular that of Christopher Plantin at Antwerp. The gothic types of Germany and their derivatives meanwhile found most favour in England and Spain.

Nuremberg (unknown printer), 1501

46 ROSWITHA, Opera. [Edited by Conradus Celtes.] *Nuremberg 1501*

The first book printed by an unnamed printer (possibly Friedrich Peypus) for the Nuremberg group of humanists calling themselves the Sodalitas Celtica, whose leaders were Conradus Celtes and Ulrich Pinder. He printed ten or more books between 1501 and about 1512. The text type of the *Roswitha* is a roman of Italian style.

Roswitha was a Benedictine nun of Gandersheim in Lower Saxony, born at some time between A.D. 912 and 940. She wrote eight poems or metrical legends of the saints, six religious plays, and a long unfinished poem called *Panegyric of the Othos*. Her manuscript was discovered by Conradus Celtes in the library of the Benedictine monastery of St. Emmeran at Ratisbon at the end of the fifteenth century and was first printed in this edition of 1501. The woodcut frontispiece, which has been attributed to both Dürer and Cranach, represents the nun offering her works to the Emperor Otho II in the presence of her Abbess Gerberg.

Aldus Manutius, 1501

47 VIRGIL, Opera. *Aldus Manutius, Venice 1501*

The first book printed by Aldus Manutius in his newly invented italic type, designed largely for the printing of the classics in a smaller and handier form than was previously available. Several copies were printed on vellum, to be illuminated for particular patrons. Isabella d'Este, Marchioness of Mantua, received her vellum copy from Aldus in July 1501 and it is probably this very copy, annotated by her son Cardinal Ercole Gonzaga in 1529 and by Vincenzo Gonzaga,

4th Duke of Mantua, in 1594, which is here shown. *Plate 5b*

*Johann Grüninger, 1502

48 VIRGIL, Opera. *Johann Grüninger, Strassburg 1502*

Johann Reinhard (usually known as Grüninger from his birth-place Grüningen, or Markgröningen in Württemberg) printed his earliest dated book at Strassburg on 28 August 1483, his last known work being the German New Testament of 1532. He was throughout his career a printer on a large scale, employing an enormous number of different types and working for publishers as far afield as Basel, Speier, and Nuremberg. At Strassburg he was his own publisher and bookseller. He probably owes his principal fame to the fine edition of Virgil here shown, in which he uses five roman types in addition to a Greek and a Gothic. The edition was based on manuscripts of Virgil found in Germany, and was edited by Sebastian Brant (1457–1521), a prolific Strassburg writer best known for his *Narrenschiff*, or *The Ship of Fools*.

Grüninger's types had a wide influence in Germany, but it is as a printer of illustrated books that he is best appreciated. His first book containing woodcuts dates from 1491. The illustrations for this *Virgil* were executed by at least three different artists.

*Gershom Soncino, 1507

49 MARCUS VIGERIUS, Decachordum christianum. *Gershom Soncino, Fano 1507*

The Jewish printer Gershom Soncino was the son of the printer of the first Hebrew Bible, and spent a wandering life, during the course of which he set up presses in no fewer than nine Italian towns. Eventually his persistence in printing the many fine Hebrew books which bear his name forced him to leave Italy, first for Salonica and then for Constantinople where he died in 1534. At the beginning of his stay at Fano, in 1503, Soncino acquired an italic fount from Francesco Griffo, who cut Aldus's type for *Aetna*; he may also have produced the fine roman for the *Decachordum*.

This vellum copy was sent with a manuscript dedication by the author to Henry VII; a similar copy, with a dedication to Louis XII, is in the Bibliothèque Nationale. On both occasions Vigerius apologized for sending the book unbound, but he used quite different excuses to the two kings.

*Piero Pacini, 1508

50 BISHOP F. FREZZI, Quatriregio. *For Piero Pacini, Florence 1508*

Piero Pacini (active in Florence from 1495 to 1514) was once thought to be a printer but is now known to have been a publisher only. It is possible that the *Quatriregio* was printed by Gianstefano di Carlo da Pavia, although that printer's earliest dated work appears to be of 15 November 1511; and the *Quatriregio* shows a change-over of types half-way through the book. Its printing may therefore have been shared by two presses. The *Quatriregio* is an allegorical poem on the four kingdoms, temporal and mundane in this life, Inferno and Purgatory, and finally Paradise. Piero Pacini apparently took a special interest in book-illustration, for no book issued from his house without adornment of some sort. The *Quatriregio* woodcuts are probably by several artists.

Arnald Guillen De Brocar, 1514

51 Polyglot Bible. *Arnald Guillen de Brocar, Alcalá de Henares 1514–17*

The Complutensian Bible (so called because Complutum is the Roman name for Alcalá de Henares, the small town near Madrid where it was printed) is by far the most famous landmark in all Spanish printing. It is the first of the great polyglot Bibles, giving the text in Hebrew, Aramaic, Greek, and Latin. Work on the Bible is said to have begun in 1502, but the publication of the whole set of six volumes was not completed until 1522. The New Testament was printed first, its colophon bearing the date 10 January 1514; the Appendix (vol. 6) in 1515; and the Old Testament last, being completed on 10 July 1517.

This Bible does *not* contain (as has often been thought) the earliest Greek type ever used in Spain, for there is Greek in an edition of Perottus printed at Barcelona in 1475; but, in the words of Robert Proctor, the Greek type of the New Testament is 'undoubtedly the finest Greek fount ever cut'. The Greek of the Old and the New Testaments is not the same. That designed for the New Testament was evidently cut on the model of the writing in the archetype manuscript sent to Cardinal Ximenez at Alcalá by Pope Leo X from the Vatican Library. The Greek type of the Old Testament is a small and poor fount: the printer in his preface claims that the Greek of the Old Testament is only a translation, and therefore not worthy of his finest type.

About 600 copies of the edition were printed at Guillen de Brocar's press in the new university, which Cardinal Ximenez had founded in 1510.

*Johann Schönsperger the Elder, 1517

52 MELCHIOR PFINZING. Der Teuerdank. *Johann Schönsperger the Elder, Nuremberg 1517*

The *Teuerdank* was printed at Nuremberg in 1517 and at Augsburg in 1519. In its first edition, here shown, it is the only book recorded from the third press of Johann Schönsperger the Elder, whose chief activity was at Augsburg (1482–1520). An allegorical chivalrous romance, it was first circulated in manuscript about 1505 and was planned by the Emperor Maximilian I, who is represented by the hero himself. Pfinzing was the chief editor. The woodcuts are from designs by Hans Leonhard Schäuffelein (*c.* 1480–*c.* 1540), engraved by Jost von Negker (*c.* 1485–*c.* 1544) and others.

Between 1513 and 1524 eight varieties of Fraktur type were cut. (Fraktur, meaning 'broken', is the fourth of the *bastarda*, or vernacular, types used in Germany, the others being Schwabacher, Upper-Rhine and Wittenberg.) The Teuerdankschrift, one of the first Frakturs, was designed by Vincenz Rockner and cut by Hieronymus Andreae. *Plate 4*

*Richard Pynson, 1519

53 Missal, in the use of Sarum. *Richard Pynson, London 1519*

Pynson was a Norman by birth, and appears to have learnt to print at Rouen with Guillaume le Talleur. He arrived in London between 1486 and 1490. His address in the sixteenth century was within Temple Bar at the corner of Chancery Lane and Fleet Street next to St. Dunstan's Church. He became King's Printer in 1508, in which year he used the first roman type in England. Pynson died early in 1530, having printed over 370 books.

The Missal is printed on vellum, in red and black, with two sizes of gothic type. The date, 'nono kalendas Ianuarii, M.D.XX', shows that the book was actually completed on 24 December 1519.

Giacomo Mazzochi, 1521

54 Epigrammata antiquae urbis. *Giacomo Mazzochi, Rome 1521*

Giacomo Mazzochi, who in the colophon of this book describes himself as bookseller to the Roman Academy in April 1521, was a keen antiquary as well as a printer, and the book here shown is his own compilation of inscriptions of ancient Rome. The pages of well-spaced centred lines of roman catalogues show him capable of a dignified typographic style.

Mazzochi was a bookseller from 1505, and began to print in 1509. 165 books are known to have been printed or published by him between 1505 and 1524.

Hieronymus Andreae, 1525

55 ALBRECHT DÜRER, Underweyssung der messung. *Hieronymus Andreae, der Formschneider, Nuremberg 1525*

In 1522 at Nuremberg Andreae cut a series of Fraktur types, used in this book, which became the standard of that design. Dürer (1471–1528), who was born at Nuremberg, succeeded in finishing and publishing during his lifetime only two theoretical books, of which the first is that on geometry and perspective or measurements here shown: his book on fortification came out in 1527.

De Colines for Tory, 1525

56 Book of Hours. *Simon de Colines for Geoffroy Tory, Paris 1525*

During the life of Henri Estienne the Elder, Simon de Colines looked after his types and probably most of the technical side of his business, and on his death married his widow and carried on the firm. In 1526 he moved to new premises, where he continued business with great success until his death in 1546. The *Horae* of 1525 is one of the most famous Books of Hours, a class of printing in which Paris had a virtual monopoly, and a fine example of perfect harmony between type and decoration. The borders are said to have been designed by Geoffroy Tory, a native of Bourges, who was active as a bookseller and printer in Paris from 1525 to 1533. Tory had spent a considerable time in northern Italy and acted as a strong Italianizing influence in French book-production.

Lodovico degli Arrighi, 1527

57 MARCUS HIERONYMUS VIDA, De arte poetica. *Ludovicus Vicentinus, Rome 1527*

Between 1510 and 1527 Arrighi, a native of Vicenza, published at Rome about fifteen books, but he is only known as a printer between about 1522 and 1527; he probably perished in the Sack of Rome in the latter year. He was the author of one of the best-known and most authoritative writing-books, which did much to spread the calligraphic style—of which he was a master—practised in the Papal Chancery. His books are printed in two kinds of italic without any form of decoration. His first italic is 'a very exuberant fount with long ascenders and descenders and swash capitals, such as were used later by Marcolini at Venice. His second italic [here shown] is larger, more severe, and perhaps better adapted for general purposes' (A. F. Johnson). This second type had considerable influence on the design of italic types in the sixteenth century.

Geoffroy Tory, 1529

58 GEOFFROY TORY, Champfleury. *Geoffroy Tory and Gilles de Gourmont, Paris 1529*

Geoffroy Tory (*c.* 1480–1533) was equally active as illustrator, publisher, and printer. He tells us himself that he drew the illustrations for *Champfleury* while the borders may also be presumed to be his own work. The book was probably printed for him by Gilles de Gourmont: the type is closely similar to a type of Gourmont's. The book contains 'the art and science of due and true proportion of attic letters, also called antique letters, and commonly Roman letters proportioned according to the human body and countenance'.

Tolomeo Janicolo, 1529

59 G. G. TRISSINO, Dialωgω del Trissinω intitulatω Castellanω. *Tolomeo Janicolo, [Vicenza 1529]*

Giangiorgio Trissino was a spelling reformer among his other activities. His works were printed by Arrighi at Rome in 1524, using a few Greek letters in addition to the roman alphabet. After Arrighi's death, Trissino transferred his patronage to Janicolo at Vicenza, who had acquired Arrighi's type and has consequently enjoyed most of the credit for this beautiful italic. Janicolo's activity at Vicenza seems to be restricted to the year 1529, but he also printed at Venice in 1547 and 1548: what he did between those dates remains a mystery.

Francesco Marcolini, 1537

60 SEBASTIANO SERLIO, Regole generali di architetura. *Francesco Marcolini da Forlì, Venice 1537*

Marcolini printed about a hundred books in Venice between 1535 and 1559. He became a member of the circle of Pietro Aretino and printed many of his books. It was doubtless his interest in architecture which led him to print the works of Serlio. He also printed Alessandro Vellutello's famous illustrated edition of Dante, using two sizes of italic type, of which he made conspicuously good use. In the latter part of his career Marcolini came under the influence of Giolito, and he seems to have copied or borrowed the latter's initials.

Denis Janot, [1539]

61 GUILLAUME DE LA PERRIÈRE, Le Théâtre des bons engins. *Denis Janot, Paris [1539]*

Denis Janot was active as a printer in Paris from 1529 until his death in 1545. Guillaume de la Perrière (1499–*c.* 1565) was a native of Toulouse.

The first true emblem book was the *Emblematum libellus* of Andrea Alciati, first printed at Augsburg in 1531 and then at Paris in 1534; this is the first by a Frenchman. An unillustrated edition of De la Perrière's book came out in 1536, and in 1539 followed two editions, one printed in roman type and the other in a formal italic, with 101 woodcuts and engraved borders. The vellum copy of the edition in roman type here shown is said to be unique. Janot's device of a vase of thistles, accompanied by the mottoes 'Patere et abstine' and 'Nul ne s'y frotte', appears in this book without his initials on the vase. Thistles occur also in a number of the frames surrounding the text and illustrations. Three sizes of Garamond roman type are used in this book, and a notable feature is the characteristic swash *e* with which many words end. *Plate 5a*

Giovanni Antonio da Castiglione, 1541

62 BONAVENTURA CASTIGLIONE, Gallorum Insubrum Antiquae Sedes. *Giovanni Antonio da Castiglione, Milan 1541*

Although the vast majority of italic types are sloping, and sloping capitals were later cut to accompany them, yet it is possible to have upright italic. The first printer to employ these types was Alessandro dei Paganini at Toscolano and Venice in the 1520's. A fine example is to be found in books printed at Milan by Castiglione (active mainly between 1535 and 1550) and the example here shown is perhaps his best.

[Richard Grafton? or Edward Whitchurch? for] William Bonham, 1542

63 The Workes of Geffray Chaucer. *'Printed by' Wyllyam Bonham, London 1542*

William Bonham (active from before 1535 to 1557) was one of those stationers whose names are found in colophons stating that they have 'imprinted' the books in question, but who were publishers only and not printers. This fine edition of Chaucer may have been printed by Edward

Whitchurch or Richard Grafton, two of the leading London printers of the day, whose types—at any rate about this time—are so nearly the same that it is virtually impossible to distinguish one printer's work from the other.

Étienne Roffet, 1545

64 GIOVANNI BOCCACCIO, Le Decameron, translated into French by Antoine Le Maçon. *For Étienne Roffet, Paris 1545*

Francis I, King of France (1494–1547), in his privilege dated from St. Germain en Laye on 2 November 1544, explains that this translation of the *Decameron* into French by Antoine Le Maçon, 'nostre amé & feal cõseiller receueur general de noz finances en Bourgoigne, tresorier de lextraordinaire de noz guerres', was undertaken at the request of the king's sister, Marguerite d'Angoulême (1492–1549), Queen of Navarre, and that the translator has given it to the printer Étienne Roffet to print. Both the imprint and the colophon, however, state that the book was printed for, not by, Roffet, who is described as a bookseller dwelling 'on the Pont Saint Michel at the Sign of the White Rose'. He also held the office of Royal Binder, 1533–48, and it is almost certain that he was not in fact a printer. He was one of four brothers who followed the same profession as their father, Pierre Roffet. But whether Étienne was the printer or simply the bookseller of this edition, it is a beautiful piece of printing in both roman and italic types, with woodcuts and initials of masterly craftsmanship, and it is one of the best examples of the influence of the Italian Renaissance on French book-production.

It is interesting to remember that Queen Marguerite, who commissioned this translation, was herself the author of the *Heptameron*, which is modelled on Boccaccio's *Decameron*, and the book here exhibited also includes an Italian dedicatory address to the queen by Emilio Ferretti, written at Lyons on 1 May 1545.

Louis Cyaneus, 1546

65 FRANCESCO COLONNA, Hypnerotomachie, ou Discours du songe de Poliphile. *Louis Cyaneus for Jacques Kerver, Paris 1546*

The printer Louis Cyaneus (Blaublom or Blaamobloen) came from Ghent, and was a printer-bookseller in Paris from 1528 to 1546. Jacques Kerver was a university bookseller of Paris, active from 1535 until his death in 1583. The book here shown is particularly distinguished not only for its clear roman and italic types, but also for its splendid initials and above all its typical sixteenth-century woodcuts, which compare well with those in the 1499 edition printed by Aldus at Venice (no. 45).

Jean Martin in his dedicatory letter to Count Henry de Lenoncourt explains that this is an anonymous translation into French of the original Italian written in 1467 (the author, Francesco Colonna, is not named), which he himself has freely adapted. The *Hypnerotomachie* became very popular in France, where other editions followed in 1554, 1561, and 1600.

Paris (printer unknown), 1547

66 VITRUVIUS, Architecture. Translated into French by Jean Martin. *Chez Iacques Gazeau, Paris 1547*

The imprint on the title-page shows that the book was sold by Jacques Gazeau, who was a bookseller active from 1542 to 1549, in the rue Saint Jacques at the Sign of the Shield of Cologne. The colophon, on the other hand, states that it was printed for the widow and heirs of Jean Barbé, who had the same address as Gazeau and may have been his brother-in-law. Barbé, whose activity is only documented from 1545 to 1547, must have died in the latter year, and the Vitruvius was evidently issued as a memorial to him, for it bears a woodcut portrait of him both on its title-page and at the end. The woodcuts are by Jean Goujon (*c.* 1515–*c.* 1570), the famous French sculptor, who writes at the end of the book a series of notes to the reader explaining his methods in illustrating and interpreting Vitruvius. Goujon had travelled in Italy and acknowledges his debt to various Italian master-artists. The printer of the *Vitruvius* remains unknown, but the book is characterized by several clear roman and italic founts of type and at least three sets of decorative initials.

*Jacques Roffet, 1549

67 C'est l'ordre qui a este tenu a la nouuelle et ioyeuse entrée, que . . . Prince, le Roy . . . Henry deuzieme . . . à faicte en sa bonne ville & cité de Paris . . . le sezieme iour de Iuin M.D.XLIX. *Chez Iacques Roffet, Paris 1549*

This book is especially distinguished by its woodcuts and initials. The illustration here shown depicts the king riding into his capital. The printer is not named: but on the other hand, Roffet himself is described as 'imprimeur iuré de nostre bõne ville & cité de Paris' in the King's Privilege. Jacques Roffet, son of Pierre and brother of Étienne, was active 1548–51.

Robert Estienne, 1549

68 PAOLO GIOVIO, Vitae duodecim Vicecomitum Mediolani Principum. Ex Bibliotheca Regia. *Robert Estienne, Paris 1549*

Robert Estienne I, born in 1503 at Paris, became King's Printer for Hebrew and Latin in 1539, and for Greek in 1540. It was his custom to add the words 'ex Bibliotheca Regia' to the title-pages of books which he printed from manuscripts, or possibly in some cases from earlier printed editions, in the Royal Library in Paris. In 1541 King Francis I entrusted him with the task of obtaining from Claude Garamond, the engraver and typefounder, three sets of Greek type for the royal press, the 'Grecs du Roi' which became the most prized possession of his family. Robert Estienne maintained the high reputation of his family for scholarly and fine printing, and even in mid sixteenth-century Paris his books were outstanding.

Robert Estienne, 1550

69 *Της Καινης Διαθηκης Άπαντα* . . . Nouum Iesu Christi D.N. Testamentum. Ex Bibliotheca Regia. *Robert Estienne, 'Regiis typis', Paris 1550*

The third and largest size of Garamond's 'Grecs du Roi' appeared first in the New Testament of 1550; it is one of the most famous editions of the Greek text, for in it, for the first time, the text was divided up into numbered verses. Robert Estienne takes care to add to the imprint of this book the fact that he is printing it 'with royal types', or 'Grecs du Roi'. In 1551, shortly after the publication of this New Testament, Estienne fell into dispute with the faculty of theology, and he was forced to move from Paris to Geneva, where he died on 7 September 1559. Garamond died in 1561.

Steven Mierdman, 1551

70 WILLIAM TURNER, The New Herball. *Steven Mierdman, London 1551*

Steven Mierdman, born about 1510 at Hooge Mierde, a little village in Holland near the Belgian frontier, became a freeman of the city of Antwerp on 16 November 1543, the year in which he printed his first book there. He came to England as a refugee and had settled here by 1549. He printed in London from 1550 to 1553, and fled to the Continent on the accession of Queen Mary, settling at Emden. The *New Herball* is printed in two sizes of black letter, with the captions to the woodcut illustrations in an italic type which stems from Arrighi and had been introduced to England some twenty years earlier. The largest size of woodcut initials are a notable feature; they are based on extravagant German calligraphic originals. The book was sold in London by John Gybken, another foreigner, and completed in a second part which was printed in 1562 at Cologne by Arnold Birckman.

Gabriel Giolito, 1553

71 OVID, Le Transformationi (Metamorphoses), translated into Italian by Lodovico Dolce. *Gabriel Giolito, Venice 1553*

This copy on vellum is one of the most handsome books printed by Gabriel Giolito de' Ferrari and Brothers, the most prolific publishing house in Italy in the sixteenth century. Nearly a thousand books are recorded from this press between 1540 and 1592. The year 1555 may be remarked as that in which 'a typefoundry, independent of any particular printer or group of printers, was opened as a commercial speculation in Venice . . . Gabriele had been at work about thirteen years with characters of his own, displaying his conception of a good type, before his press was invaded by the undistinguished and undistinguishable flood of mediocre characters produced wholesale by speculating type-founders' (Horatio F. Brown). The Ovid of 1553 therefore comes shortly before this innovation. *Plate 6*

Étienne Groleau, 1555

72 L'Histoire Palladienne (The Romance of Paladin, Prince of England). *Étienne Groleau for Jean Dallier, Paris 1555*

This edition exists in three issues: one with Jean Dallier's name in the imprint and Étienne Groleau's in the colophon; a second with Groleau on the title-page and a different device, and a third 'Pour Ian Longis Libraire'. The copy here exhibited is the Dallier-Groleau issue. The privilege for the book was granted to Vincent Sertenas, bookseller, on 10 November 1553. The printing was completed on 20 September 1555. Jean Dallier worked from 1545 to 1574, and Étienne Groleau (Groulleau) from 1543 to 1563, specializing in vernacular texts, among them the famous *Amadis de Gaule* (1548) and a translation of Josephus (1557) with decorations attributed to Tory. The book is a good example of a close collaboration between several (in this case five) printers and booksellers in the production of one book.

Michel Vascosan, 1556

73 ORONTIUS FINAEUS, De rebus mathematicis. *Michel Vascosan, Paris 1556*

The mathematician Oronce Fine (1494–1555) was also an artist, and designed some of the borders and initials appearing in his books, which bear the initials O. F. All his books, printed first by Henri Estienne, then Simon de Colines, and finally by Vascosan, reveal their author's passion for fine printing. Vascosan, a native of Amiens, was a son-in-law of Badius Ascensius, the humanist and printer. He became King's Printer, and was active from 1530 to 1577. His work as a printer is characterized by its simplicity, and he used no device. 'The book is a masterpiece of restrained style, through the beauty of its types and the elegance of their arrangement' (Updike).

Robert Granjon, 1558

74 PHILIPPUS GUALTERUS, Alexandreidos libri decem. *Robert Granjon, Lyons 1558*

Robert Granjon, the famous type-designer and the printer of this book, is first heard of in 1545. He worked as a printer and typefounder both on his own account and in the employ of others, residing in Paris, Lyons (1557–62), Antwerp, and Rome, where, in 1588, all trace of him is lost. The type in which this book is printed is now known as *civilité*, from the fact that it was early used for a book written by Erasmus to teach the young good manners, *La Civilité puerile*, whose popularity caused the type to be used for many such books right up to the nineteenth century. It was cut by Granjon in imitation of the French handwriting of the day, and was meant to be the French counterpart of the Italian italic and the German Fraktur. The privilege which Granjon obtained from Henri II reserving to himself the use of what he called his *lettre françoyse d'art de main* clearly indicates the hopes its designer entertained for it; it is printed on the leaf following the title-page of this book.

*John Day, 1559

75 WILLIAM CUNINGHAM, The Cosmographical Glasse. *John Day, London 1559*

William Cuningham, M.D., was born in 1531, probably in Norfolk, and was educated at Cambridge and Heidelberg. Between 1556 and 1559 he lived at Norwich, of which city he gives a very curious map in the book here exhibited. He was a physician, astrologer, and engraver. Several of the woodcuts in the *Cosmographical Glasse* are his own work.

The book is printed in an italic type, and may be one of the earliest books printed on Day's presses—he owned four at the time of his death in 1584. The fine series of pictorial initials were evidently designed especially for this book.

Jean le Royer, 1560

76 JEAN COUSIN, Livre de perspective. *Jean le Royer, Paris 1560*

Cousin was a painter, sculptor, and author of two books on design. Jean le Royer, born in 1528, was originally an engraver, but was appointed by Henry II as *imprimeur du Roy ès mathématiques* and worked from 1560 to 1581, and probably later. His address to the reader shows that this book was his first effort. The decorations and initials are by Cousin, and the diagrams of perspective are chiefly engraved by Le Royer.

It is one of the most magnificent of all sixteenth-century French books, baroque decoration, perspective diagrams, a noble roman, and a lively italic blending in a *coup de maître* of simplicity and elegance.

*Jean de Tournes I, 1561

77 JEAN DUVET, L'Apocalypse, figurée par Maistre Iehan Duuet. *Jean de Tournes, Lyons 1561*

Jean Duvet, whose real name may have been Drouot, was born *c.* 1485 and died about 1562. He is here described as former goldsmith to the kings. His set of engravings for the *Apocalypse* is his masterpiece, executed, it is believed, before 1555, and published in 1561 at Lyons by Jean de Tournes, although the printer's name is not given in the book. Duvet is the first identifiable French engraver on metal. The twenty-two copper-plate engravings of this book show Duvet to have been an artist of exceptional individuality, who did not conform with the typical Renaissance style, but was nevertheless influenced to some extent by Raphael. His figures are far more frenzied and tormented than those of Dürer's *Apocalypse*, which seem by comparison almost peaceful.

Jean de Tournes the Elder began printing at Lyons in 1542 and died in 1564. His career was distinguished by his patronage of artists, among them the famous wood-engraver Bernard Salomon, and he did much to popularize the use of typographic ornaments, especially the arabesques which had originated earlier in the century at Venice.

Christopher Plantin, 1565

78 HADRIANUS JUNIUS, Emblemata. *Christopher Plantin, Antwerp 1565*

Plantin, by birth a Frenchman, began to print in 1555. He published many illustrated books, including a series of emblem books of which this is the most beautiful. It contains fifty-eight wood-engravings by Arnold Nicolai and Gerard Jansen van Kempen. It is said that Junius intended the book as a new year gift to his friends, and this may account for the great typographical skill expended on it. It is a particularly charming example of the work of one of the greatest of all the sixteenth-century printers.

*Christopher Plantin, 1571

79 Biblia sacra, Hebraice, Chaldaice, Graece, & Latine. *Christopher Plantin, Antwerp 1569–73*

The second of the great polyglot Bibles, and the book on which the reputation of Plantin as a printer and publisher mainly rests. This polyglot was begun in 1568 and finished in 1573, the languages included being Hebrew, Aramaic, Greek, Latin, and Syriac. About 1,200 copies were printed, thirteen of them on vellum, of which this is one. The work was begun under the patronage of Philip II of Spain, but Plantin was almost ruined by the king's failure to supply any of the promised funds, although he was later compensated by a monopoly for printing service books. Plantin died in 1589.

Mateusz Wierzbięta, [1578]

80 ALEXANDER GUAGNINUS, Sarmatiae europeae descriptio. *Mateusz Wierzbięta, [Cracow 1578]*

Alessandro Guagnini of Verona, 'a Golden Knight and prefect of infantry', wrote the preface to this book at Cracow on 20 June 1578 and dedicated it to Stephen, King of Poland. The printer, Mateusz Wierzbięta or Wirzbięta, began work at Cracow in 1554, but his first dated book appeared only in 1557. He was a Calvinist and printed many works by non-Catholics, until in 1603 his books were placed on the *Index*. He died in 1605, aged 82.

Augsburg, 'Ad insigne pinus', 1595

81 HORAPOLLO, Hieroglyphica, a Davide Hoeschelio fide codicis Augustani ms. correcta, suppleta, illustrata. *Ad insigne pinus, Augsburg 1595*

The press which bore the address 'At the sign of the pine-tree' in Augsburg was active from 1594 to 1619. It was run by a group of local humanists, chief among them being David Höschel, librarian and *Rektor* of the St.-Anna Gymnasium. They specialized in the production of Greek and Latin texts, and wherever possible they first consulted available manuscripts. It is clear from the title of the book here shown that David Höschel had access to a codex of Horapollo in Augsburg before he printed it, and did not rely on previously printed texts. The beautiful Greek type used by the press has been identified with that of Robert Granjon.

Horapollo (more properly called simply Horus) was a fifth-century A.D. Egyptian scribe who attempted to collect and perpetuate the hieroglyphics of his country; but a Greek translation of his work, made by a certain Philip who lived apparently a century or two later than Horapollo, is all that has come down to us.

THE SEVENTEENTH CENTURY

ALL over Europe this century was marked by a disastrous lowering of standards in everyday printing, the reasons for which were partly political and partly economic. Typographic design was almost at a standstill, presswork was slovenly, and paper of poor quality. The types in use were generally obtained from Holland, but Dutch types and matrices were often derived from sixteenth-century French punches in the possession of a German foundry, that of the Luthers at Frankfurt. Proper consideration was only given to appearance when a special *de luxe* edition—a Bible, an emblem book, or an account of some royal occasion—was put in hand, and even then the presswork was likely to be very indifferent. Yet the printer did sometimes rise to the occasion, and some of the illustrated books of this century are fully up to the level of their more publicized successors of the eighteenth century.

As early as 1640 steps were taken in Paris which were to lead to a revival in printing standards by Richelieu's establishment of the Imprimerie Royale, whose leisurely procession of well-made books culminated in Louis XIV's commission, in 1692, for the design of a wholly new, regal, proprietary type. This, after prolonged and scientific gestation, was brought to birth by Philippe Grandjean; and the 'Romain du Roi' made its first public appearance, to dazzle printers and *cognoscenti* by its brilliance and accuracy of cutting, in a magnificent folio (no. 101) ten years later.

G. E. von Löhneyss, 1609

82 GEORG ENGELHARD VON LÖHNEYSS, Della Caualleria. 2 volumes. *[At the author's private press], Remlingen 1609–10*

Von Löhneyss (or Loehneissen), who died in 1625, entered the service of the Hereditary Princes of Braunschweig-Wolfenbüttel in 1583 and held the positions of Master of the Horse and Superintendent of Mining. He established his own press at Remlingen in Bavaria and printed his own books there. The initials, printer's ornaments, woodcuts and copper plates used in these books are all said to have been based on his designs. The books are somewhat old-fashioned in style, but are notable for their spacious layout and careful presswork.

Robert Barker, 1611

83 The Holy Bible. Newly translated out of the originall tongue. *Robert Barker, London 1611*

The first edition of the so-called 'Authorized' or King James Version of the Bible in English was printed by Robert Barker (1570–1645), who held a partnership in the Royal Printing House from 1589 until 1599 and then succeeded his father, Christopher Barker I, as Royal Printer. The layout of the page differed little from that of the last folio edition of the Bishop's Bible, which Robert Barker had printed in 1602, but the adoption of a larger black-letter type-face gave it a more dignified and spacious appearance. The presswork is very much better than that found in most books of the period.

Pauwels van Ravesteyn, 1619

84 THEODORE RODENBURGH, Eglentiers Poëtens Borst-weringh. *Pauwels van Ravesteyn, Amsterdam 1619*

Dutch printers of the early seventeenth century seem to have been typographically more adventurous than those of the rest of Europe, and in this book van Ravesteyn sometimes mixes roman, italic, *textura*, and *civilité* types on the same page. The *civilité* type shown differs considerably from the smaller size of this type familiar in French books of the sixteenth century. It was, however, also the work of Granjon; before 1575 he cut punches for it, which are still preserved in the Plantin-Moretus Museum in Antwerp. Pauwels Aertzen van Ravesteyn came of a well-known Amsterdam family of printers. He is first heard of as a compositor in 1608. When he died in 1655 he owned four presses.

Paris (unknown printer), 1624

85 THOMAS BILLON, Sibylla Gallica. *Paris 1624*

The printer of this book has not been identified. Its most notable features are the attractive layout permitted by a text which consists largely of anagrams and snatches of verse, and the fine engravings. The allegorical portraits of Louis XIII and his consort are the work of Crispin de Passe the Younger (*c.* 1597–1670), a Flemish artist who was working in Paris between 1617 and 1630.

Balthasar Moretus I, 1634

86 SILVESTRA PIETRASANTA, De symbolis heroicis. *Ex officina Plantiniana Balthasaris Moreti, Antwerp 1634*

Balthasar Moretus I (d. 1641) was the grandson of Christopher Plantin and worthily carried on the printing traditions of the great Antwerp firm after the death of his father, Jan Moretus, in 1610. This well-printed emblem-book dates from the period when both Catholics and Protestants had realized that this type of book, formerly produced for the frivolous pleasure of courtiers, was equally suitable for the allegorical interpretation of spiritual truths. The frontispiece, as in many books printed by Moretus, is engraved by Cornelis Galle the Elder after a design by Rubens, but the Plantin–Moretus archives reveal that the emblems which are exhibited were evidently originally engraved on copper by artists in the employ of the Jesuit fathers and then re-worked for Moretus between December 1633 and June 1634 by the skilled hand of André Pauwels. The book would appear to have been a commercial failure, for the edition published in 1682 at Amsterdam with the imprint 'apud Janssonio–Waesbergios & Henr. Wetstenium' is a re-issue of unsold sheets of this 1634 Moretus edition.

*John Raworth, 1639

87 JEAN PUGET DE LA SERRE, Histoire de l'entrée de la Reyne Mère du Roy très-chrestien dans la Grande-Bretaigne. *Jean Raworth, for George Thomason and Octavian Pulleyn, London 1639*

This book and its companion on the entry of Queen Marie de Medici into the Low Countries which is usually found bound with it, are the only folios which John Raworth printed in his short career which lasted from 1638 to 1645. It is interesting that at this unpromising date an English printer, whose bread-and-butter work was quarto plays, news-books, and theological controversy of the usual dreary sort, could produce such a handsome-looking and relatively well-printed volume. The frontispiece and portraits were probably etched by Wenzel Hollar, but the interesting topographical plates appear to be the work of a less-skilled hand. This is one of the large paper copies.

Imprimerie Royale, 1642

88 Biblia Sacra. 8 volumes. *E Typographia Regia, Paris 1642*

The Imprimerie Royale was founded by Louis XIII in 1640 on the advice of Cardinal Richelieu in a deliberate endeavour to raise the standards of printing in France. The cardinal fully appreciated the power of the printing-press as an aid to government and as a means of religious propaganda, and the aims of the new national printing office included 'The multiplication of the principal monuments of religion and letters'. Advice was sought from a number of technical experts, and although the first director was Sublet de Noyers, the King's Superintendent of Buildings and Manufactures, the printing was from the first under the control of Richelieu's personal bookseller, Sébastien Cramoisy (1585–1669). The French ambassador in Holland was instructed to try and discover the Dutch secret for producing a deep black printing-ink and to recruit four pressmen and four compositors from that country. The best paper and types were obtained and, finally seven presses were set up in the Louvre. Within the first two years of its operation the Imprimerie Royale produced over seventy folios including this handsome and typical Bible in 8 volumes. The head-pieces and initials were probably engraved by Claude Mellan, who was also responsible for engraving a number of frontispieces for the Press including three designed by Poussin. The 36-point roman type used closely resembles, but is not identical with, Jean Jannon's *gros canon*, of which the Imprimerie Nationale owns the original punches, and from which the Garamond of today is derived. *Plate 7*

Vitale Mascardi, 1642

89 COUNT GIROLAMO TETI, Aedes Barberinae ad Quirinalem. *Mascardus, Rome 1642*

Vitale Mascardi succeeded Giacomo Mascardi in the 1630's as head of one of the most important printing offices in Rome. Little seems to be known of the author of this splendid description of the Palazzo Barberini in Rome, but by the time that a second edition was published in 1647 he appears to have been dead. The majority of the engravings illustrating the wall-paintings and ceilings painted by Pietro da Cortona are signed by Cornelis Bloemaert. Others, however, are the work of Camillo Cungi, Johann Friedrich Grenter, and Michel Natalis, and it is not clear who was responsible for the admirable initials, head-pieces, and tail-pieces which harmonize so happily with the well-spaced type.

Pierre Moreau, 1644

90 JEAN BAUDOIN, Les Saintes metamorphoses. *P. Moreau, Paris 1644*

Pierre Moreau, a professional calligrapher in Paris, issued engraved writing manuals in 1626 and 1633 and a book of devotions, *Les Saintes prières de l'âme chrétienne*, which he designed, engraved throughout, and continued to print from 1631 to 1644. In 1643 he was appointed one of the printers in ordinary to Louis XIII with permission to produce and sell both engraved books and those printed in types of his own invention, which last he mentions in his imprint 'En l'Imprimerie des nouveaux Caractheres de P. Moreau'. These were a script type, three sizes of *bâtarde italienne* and one based on the hand known as *ronde*. At least eleven books were issued in these types between 1643 and 1648. Virgil's *Aeneid* in French is the most celebrated of these, but the type shows to better advantage in the *Baudoin* exhibited. *Plate 8b*

*Thomas Roycroft, 1653–7

91 Biblia Sacra Polyglotta. Edited by Brian Walton. 6 volumes. *Thomas Roycroft, London 1657*

The printing of Walton's polyglot Bible, considered the most accurate of the four great polyglots of the sixteenth and seventeenth centuries, was completed in the short space of four years. It was published by subscription and, after the prospectus printed by James Flesher in 1652 had earned unfavourable comment, the work was entrusted to Thomas Roycroft (active 1651–77). The exotic founts of type appear to have been supplied by English typefounders (limited to four by the Star Chamber decree of 1637) and the arrangement of the different languages on the page showed a considerable improvement on that found in the earlier polyglots. The volume exhibited shows the text of Ezekiel in Hebrew, Latin, Greek, Aramaic, Syriac, and Arabic.

Elzevier, 1655

92 Le Pastissier françois. *Louys et Daniel Elzevier, Amsterdam 1655*

The taste of the early nineteenth-century collectors for a 'tall Elzevir' has left this Dutch family with an exaggerated reputation for excellent printing. The founder of the firm, Louis I, began as a binder in 1580, opened a bookseller's shop in Leiden in 1587 and issued his first book in 1593. By the time of his death in 1617 two of his sons were established in The Hague and Utrecht, but the main branch of the business was carried on in Leyden and Amsterdam, and these were the only two cities in which the firm printed. Its fortunes declined towards the end of the seventeenth century and the last branch closed in Leyden in 1712. Like other printers of the day they obtained most of their type from the Egenolff-Berner foundry at Frankfurt. 'The Elzevier editions are distinguished for their high ideals, their unimpeachable correctness and perfect impression, but they are not valued as models of the typographic art, except in so far as they show what can be achieved with a comparatively modest stock.'

*Augustin Courbé, 1658

93 JEAN DESMARETS DE SAINT SORLIN, Les Délices de l'esprit. *Florentin Lambert, Paris 1661*

This book is a re-issue by Florentin Lambert in 1661 of the sheets of the edition of 1658 with the imprint of Augustin Courbé, Henri le Gras, and Jacques Roger, who had published in 1657 the same author's *Clovis* in quarto, with similar illustrations and decorations. As Courbé in 1637 was styled 'Imprimeur et Libraire de Monseigneur le Duc d'Orléans' he may have been the printer. The elaborate intaglio ornamentation on the title-page and above and below the illustrations is matched by similar woodcut head-pieces and initials at the beginning of each chapter. Both are believed to have been designed by the illustrator, François Chauveau, and this gives the book its outstanding unity of style. This copy, prepared for presentation to Louis XIV's consort, Queen Marie Thérèse, is in a magnificent contemporary Parisian inlaid binding. *Plate 9*

Balthasar Moretus II, 1663

94 Missale Romanum. *Balthasar Moretus, Antwerp 1663*

Balthasar Moretus II (1615–74) succeeded his uncle, Balthasar I, in 1641, and it was not until after his death that the press founded by

Christopher Plantin began to lose its pre-eminence. During the seventeenth century liturgical printing maintained a reasonably high standard and, although this book contains handsome copper-plate engravings by Cornelis Galle, an unillustrated opening is exhibited to show the dignified, but not ponderous, layout and the good two-colour presswork.

Imprimerie Royale, 1676

95 OVID, Metamorphoses, translated into French verse by Isaac de Benserade. *Imprimerie Royale, Paris 1676*

Sébastien Cramoisy died in 1669 and was succeeded as director of the Imprimerie Royale by his grandson, Sébastien Mabre-Cramoisy (1642–87). Under him the Press devoted much of its time to the production of the *Cabinet du Roi*, a series intended to leave no doubts in the mind of posterity of the greatness of Louis XIV. These volumes were, however, collections of plates, rather than books, and the best examples of typography of this period are to be found among the smaller illustrated works. Benserade's *Ovid* with its charming vignettes (some by Sebastien Le Clerc, but the majority by François Chauveau), clearly foreshadows the French illustrated book of the eighteenth century.

Imprimerie Royale, 1677

96 [CHARLES PERRAULT], Labyrinte de Versailles. *Imprimerie Royale, Paris 1677*

This attractive octavo shows a happy balance between the layout of the text and the facing illustrations. These depict the various fountains at Versailles illustrating *Aesop's Fables*, and were engraved by Sébastien Le Clerc, who for once was not hampered by having to engrave the work of others, and was able to show his true qualities as a book-illustrator. Unlike many of the Imprimerie Royale books this one seems to have sold well and was reprinted in 1679. *Plate 8a*

Johann Baptista Mayr, 1682

97 JOHANN WEIKHARD FREIHERR VON VALVASOR, Theatrum mortis humanae. *Johann Baptista Mayr, Laibach 1682*

Valvasor (1641–93) was the historian and topographer of Carniola—the province of the Austrian Empire in which Laibach (the modern Ljubljana) was situated. He established his own copper-plate printing-press in his castle at Wagensberg and had the letterpress of this book printed in Laibach at a press established in 1678 under the management of J. B. Mayr, a Salzburg printer and bookseller. The text, with Latin in roman type and German in Fraktur, is more attractively laid out than in most German printing of the seventeenth century. The engravings are by Andreas Trost, who was apparently working at Wagensberg at this time, from designs by Johann Koch.

Louis Senault, c. 1685

98 Heures nouvelles tirées de la Sainte Ecriture. Written and engraved by the author. *L. Senault, Paris [c. 1685]*

Louis Senault, another professional calligrapher, followed Pierre Moreau in producing two writing books (one dated 1668) and then concentrating on successive editions of a devotional work printed from the same plates. But while Moreau finished by producing printed books with some of the characteristics of handwriting, Senault endeavoured to preserve in his engraved books the full flavour of a contemporary manuscript. After his death his daughter, Elisabeth Senault, produced some equally attractive smaller engraved *Heures nouvelles* dedicated to the Grand Dauphin.

Henry Hills, Junior, 1687

99 Aesop's Fables, with his life: in English, French, and Latin. Illustrated with sculptures by Francis Barlow. *H. Hills, Jun., for Francis Barlow, London 1687*

This book owes its inclusion to the charming etchings of Francis Barlow, for which the printer did no more than provide an adequate setting. Hills, who succeeded to his father's share in the King's Printing House in 1689, subsequently earned considerable notoriety as a pirate of other printers' copyrights. The French text is printed in roman type, the Latin is in italic, and the English verses which 'the Ingenious Mrs. A. Behn' had been 'so obliging as to perform' are etched beneath the illustrations. This is the dedication copy presented by Barlow to William, Earl of Devonshire.

Robert Everingham, 1697

100 VIRGIL, The Works. Translated by John Dryden. *[Robert Everingham] for Jacob Tonson, London 1697*

Jacob Tonson the Elder does not seem to have started to print before the end of the seventeenth century, and it can be inferred from a remark in one of Dryden's letters to Tonson that the 1698 edition of the Virgil (and hence this of 1697 which is clearly from the same press) was printed by Robert Everingham. The plates, etched by Pierre Lombart and Wenzel Hollar after designs by Francis Clein, had already appeared in John Ogilby's translation of Virgil, printed by Thomas Warren in 1654. But although Warren's edition had some attractive initials and head-pieces, its layout compares very unfavourably with Everingham's.

THE EIGHTEENTH CENTURY

THE 'Romain du Roi' of 1702, with its short, flat serifs and a sharper contrast between thick and thin strokes than the prevailing types (all variations on the form of letter first evolved by Garamond, which later printers called 'old face') foreshadowed a new fashion in type-design. Yet much that appears as the new fashion has little to do with type, but results from a return to the virtues of black and white from the inexpensive greys of routine printing. More white space in and around the type, more generous margins, fresh white paper set against letters more intensely black and more crisply printed can entirely change the effect of a type-face, as eighteenth-century anecdote reveals.

Typography was often the neglected partner of the engraved illustration and ornament of the early examples of those *éditions de luxe* which have ever since commanded the enthusiasm of French connoisseurship. Fournier's elegance at mid-century and F. A. Didot's glacial perfection in its latter decades raised Paris standards, as Ibarra and de Sancha raised them to a level never before achieved in Madrid; yet it was the productions of an amateur, John Baskerville of Birmingham, with their wide-spread, rather pallid typography and their smooth 'hot-pressed' paper, which 'went forth to astonish the librarians of Europe'. And not librarians only: for it was Baskerville's books which encouraged Bodoni of Parma to shed his French manner and to develop types with an absolute and geometric contrast between thick and thin strokes which, combined with an austere nobility of layout, made him the idol of European taste, the model for later members of the Didot family, and a powerful influence on Baskerville's English successors, Bell, Bulmer, and Bensley. Thus he became spiritual father of—what he would doubtless have disowned—the 'modern face' types of the next century.

***Imprimerie Royale, 1702**

101 Médailles sur les principaux événements du règne de Louis le Grand. *Imprimerie Royale, Paris 1702*

The French Académie des Sciences in the seventeenth century set about compiling a *Description et perfection des arts et métiers*, of which printing as the art which preserves all others was the first to be studied. In 1693 a committee headed by Jacques Jaugeon started work, and after studying many models, both printed and manuscript, presented a series of suggested letter-forms which were engraved by Louis Simonneau.

Basing himself on these theoretical studies, Philippe Grandjean (1666–1714) cut the first series of the types known as the 'Romains du Roi', first used in book form in the present volume. They have a fresh clean look; their chief peculiarity is that the fine unbracketed serifs extend on both sides of the upright stroke of letters with ascenders. The more pronounced distinction of thick and thin strokes is another characteristic which foreshadows the coming of 'modern face'.

The medals which provide the excuse for this celebratory volume were mainly designed by A. Coypel and the decorations including the engraved borders for each page were by Jean Berain. The team of engravers was led by Louis Simonneau.

Oxford Press, 1703

102 EDWARD HYDE, EARL OF CLARENDON, The History of the Rebellion and Civil Wars in England. 3 volumes. *Oxford, Printed at the theater, 1702–4*

The name of the University of Oxford appeared on the title pages of several earlier printers, but it was not until Dr. John Fell's (1625–86) reforms that the foundations of the present University

Press were laid. This was in fact done by Fell and three others forming a private company which leased the privilege of printing from the University. Fell seems to have looked after the typographical side of the business; much material was imported from Holland, and in 1676 Peter Walpergen, a Dutchman, was engaged as type-founder. It was he who cut the types shown here, which are certainly the most distinguished produced in England in the seventeenth century. The engraved decoration is by Michael Burghers (d. 1727) another Dutchman who worked for the Press in Oxford from *c.* 1673 to 1727. The copy shown is one of those printed on fine paper.

Plate 10

John Watts, 1718

103 MATTHEW PRIOR, Poems on several occasions. *[John Watts] for Jacob Tonson and John Barber, London 1718*

John Watts (d. 1763) was probably the most important English printer of the first half of the century; his output was enormous and extremely varied, and he was as successful with a handsome folio like the present as with Maittaire's duodecimo classics. He lent William Caslon, the type-founder, £100 to start in business; and the ornamentation of his books, whether engraved or woodcut, is notable for its high standards. In this volume the engraved decorations are by L. Cheron; the copy shown is a large paper subscription copy.

Johann Valentin Lüders, 1727

104 FRANÇOIS DE SALIGNAC DE LA MOTHE FÉNELON, Télémaque. Translated into German by Benjamin Neukirch. 3 volumes. *Johann Valentin Lüders, Ansbach 1727–39*

Germany produced very little in the first half of the eighteenth century that in any way compares with the luxury books produced elsewhere. This translation of Fénelon's ever-popular continuation of the *Odyssey* is a surprising exception, produced at the expense of the Margrave of Brandenburg. The type is well spaced and well inked, the paper is of good quality, and the illustrations dignified if not inspired. The first volume is shown open at a plate designed by Johann Christian Sperling (1690–1746) and engraved by Winter.

John Pine, 1733

105 HORACE, Opera. 2 volumes. *Aeneis tabulis incidit Iohannes Pine, London* 1733–7

John Pine (1690–1756) may well have been the pupil of Bernard Picart, the great French engraver at Amsterdam: he was the best English engraver in the first half of the century. His edition of Horace is engraved throughout, text as well as ornament, though it is said that the text was first set in type and an impression transferred to the plate before it was engraved.

The results are a unity between decoration and text which at times suggests Didot's *Horace* of 1799; a contrast between thick and thin strokes in the letters which naturally follows from the engraving process but which foreshadows the type design of Baskerville, Bodoni, and Didot; and the wide 'leading' between the lines of text which did so much to give their pages a brilliant effect.

*Pierre Prault, 1734

106 J. B. POQUELIN DE MOLIÈRE, Œuvres. 6 volumes. *[Pierre Prault], Paris 1734*

François Boucher (1703–70) in his early years lodged with the father of Laurent Cars, the engraver; when he produced the thirty-three designs for this edition of Molière, Cars engraved them with a great feeling for Boucher's style. The decorative engravings were designed by Boucher, Blondel, and Oppenord, engraved by Cars and Joullain. The volume was printed by Pierre Prault, member of a famous Paris printing family, in a well-leaded old-style type.

Benjamin Franklin, 1744

107 CICERO's Cato major, or his discourse of old-age. *B. Franklin, Philadelphia 1744*

Benjamin Franklin (1706–90) started printing as the younger brother and apprentice of James Franklin in Boston; after a quarrel with his brother he left for Philadelphia and in 1724 came to England. In his nineteen months in England he worked for Samuel Palmer and for John Watts, and his experience in England was as valuable to him as a printer as it was subsequently to prove to him as a statesman. In 1728 he joined with Hugh Meredith in starting a new printing office in Philadelphia, ordering the press and types from London. He rapidly became successful in his printing and in public life; he purchased and reconstructed the *Pennsylvania Gazette* in 1729, became public printer for Pennsylvania in 1730, founded the first circulating library in 1731. His business rapidly increased and by 1748, when he went into partnership with David Hall, the profits amounted to about £1,000 per year.

Franklin regarded the *Cato major* as his finest piece of printing and it is a very workmanlike job, printed no doubt with freshly arrived Caslon types from England, for there were no type-foundries in America. The translation is by James Logan, President of the Council and Chief Justice of Pennsylvania; Franklin in his preface claims that it is the 'First Translation of a *Classic* in this *Western World*'.

*Charles-Antoine Jombert, 1755

108 JEAN DE LA FONTAINE, Fables choisies, mises en vers. 4 volumes. *Charles-Antoine Jombert, Paris 1755–9*

Jean Baptiste Oudry (1686–1765), the famous animal-painter, had drawn most of the designs for the *Fables* as far back as 1729–34; it was M. de Montenault who eventually persuaded a group of rich bankers to finance their publication as illustrations for this edition. The pen-and-wash drawings had not been designed for engraving, and Charles Nicolas Cochin (1715–90) had to redraw them completely for the engravers. J. J. Bachelier, the flower-painter, designed floral tail-pieces which were cut in wood by J. B. Papillon and Nicolas le Sueur. The text is set in a dignified old-style fount and the whole work perfectly represents the taste of the first half of the century.

The first volume is shown of a large paper copy open at a plate engraved by P. E. Moitte.

*John Baskerville, 1757

109 VIRGIL, Bucolica, Georgica, et Aeneis. *John Baskerville, Birmingham 1757*

John Baskerville (1706–75) seems to have started life in Birmingham as a writing master, made a fortune by the manufacture of japanned goods, and turned to printing as a rich man's hobby, but with a passion which belied the 'amateur' status for which the jealous London trade mocked him. His aim was to perfect the 'finish' of a book by improving not only type-design but ink, paper, and printing techniques; in this he was most influential.

His types were cut for him by John Handy; they are more delicate and lighter than the standard Caslon letter. In book design, Baskerville relied almost entirely on typographic effect. He made his own deep black ink and was the first to use wove paper, specially manufactured for him by James Whatman, in order to have a smoother printing surface. This was further improved by 'hot-pressing' the printed sheets between hot copper plates when they came from the press. The *Virgil* was his first book and shows all the characteristics of his technique.

Robert Foulis, 1758

110 VIRGIL, Bucolica, Georgica, et Aeneis. *Robert and Andrew Foulis, Glasgow 1758*

Robert Foulis (1707–76) learnt his trade as a barber but he had some education at Glasgow University before he became (1741) bookseller and later (1743) printer to the University. His brother Andrew (1712–75) was closely associated with all his projects, though it was not until about 1748 that he became Robert's official partner. Their types were produced by Alexander Wilson (1714–84), the Glasgow founder, who subsequently became Professor of Astronomy; an interesting point is that they never leaded their type, but achieved the same spacious effect by having it cast on a larger body. The quality of their books depends on good paper, inking, and presswork; and the result is a workmanlike simplicity. This edition was printed in both octavo and quarto format; the copy shown is an octavo.

Joseph Gérard Barbou, 1762

111 JEAN DE LA FONTAINE, Contes et nouvelles en vers. 2 volumes. *[J. G. Barbou], 'Amsterdam' [Paris] 1762*

This edition is known by the name of the *fermiers-généraux* after the financiers who promoted it and put up the capital for the production of the plates. It is the most famous monument of the trend towards a small luxurious book; the plates after Charles Eisen are etched and engraved to a jewel-like perfection, while Pierre Philippe Choffard was responsible for the fresh and delicate vignettes. It is probable that the printing was done by Barbou, who certainly acted as publisher.

The copy shown from the Grenville library contains many proof states and rejected plates, and also an original design by Choffard. The first volume is shown open at 'Les deux amis'; the plate is engraved by J. Aliamet. *Plate 12b*

Pierre Simon Fournier, 1764

112 PIERRE SIMON FOURNIER, Manuel typographique, utile aux gens de lettres, & à ceux qui exercent les différentes parties de l'art de l'imprimerie. 2 volumes. *'Imprimé par l'auteur . . . & se vend chez Barbou', Paris 1764–6*

P. S. Fournier (1712–68) came of a type-founders' family; his father and elder brother successively managed the Le Bé foundry. He took up type-cutting and typefounding about 1737, and issued his first specimen book at the age of 30. He seems to have sought consciously to integrate all the best features of early types with the modern spirit of the 'Romain du Roi'; and his types dominated European printing for fifty years, just as his introduction of new ornamental rules and decorative units set a new fashion in the ornamentation of books.

In spite of his distinguished career, Fournier's attempts to obtain permission from the Chamber of Syndics to print his *Manuel typographique* himself seem to have failed, and despite the imprint the book is said to have been printed by Barbou. The first volume, which describes the technical details of printing, is set in a thin condensed letter known as 'poétique' because it was designed to enable the long lines of French Alexandrines to be printed without overrunning.

Joseph Gérard Barbou, 1767

113 VIRGIL, Opera. 2 volumes. *Barbou, Paris 1767*

Joseph Gérard Barbou (1723–*c.* 1790) was perhaps the most famous of a family of printers and booksellers who had been active in Lyons and Limoges since the sixteenth century. He was the fifth son of Jean Barbou of Limoges (1688–1736) who ran an increasingly large business, the printing side largely devoted to liturgical and theological works: he was also very active in the paper trade.

Antoine Coustelier had in the 1740's started a series of classics to take the place of the Elzevier texts; they were illustrated with plates after Cochin, Eisen, and others. In 1753 Barbou took over the series, reprinting and extending it; and adding the typographical elegance created by a skilful use of Fournier's types.

The *Virgil* shown here has a frontispiece and seventeen plates by Cochin, engraved for the Coustelier edition of 1745 by Duflos. The wood-engraved tail-pieces are by J. B. M. Papillon; one of the engraved head-pieces is signed by Delafosse.

Johann Thomas Trattner, 1767

114 MICHAEL DENIS, Ode auf die Genesung Marien Theresiens. *Joh. Thomas Edler von Trattner, Vienna 1767*

Johann Thomas Trattner (1717–98), unlike most distinguished printers of the period, was not born into a printing family but was the son of a peasant, and his rise to prominence was the result of his energy and business sense. In 1759 he built what was popularly known as the 'typographischer Pallast', containing printing works, bindery, foundry, warehouses, and retail departments; by 1788 he had eight retail shops and many outlets in other cities; he also ran a finance house.

As a typefounder he seems to have collected founts from any source he could; the most distinctive feature of his work was his wide range of type ornaments, largely based on Fournier's work. This poem by the distinguished Austrian bibliographer Denis shows the kind of use he made of them.

Imprimerie Royale, 1768

115 TACITUS, Tibère, ou les six premiers livres des Annales de Tacite. Translated by the Abbé de la Bléterie. *Imprimerie Royale, Paris 1768*

In the eighteenth century the Imprimerie Royale printed few editions of the classics; this elegant translation in 3 volumes is an exception. Like other publishers, it employed the fashionable illustrators; the plates and head-pieces in this volume are designed by Hubert Gravelot (1699–1773). The text is set in various sizes of the 'Romain du Roi' which gives the page an open look. The first volume is shown open at a plate engraved by J. Aliamet.

Orell, Gessner, Füssli & Co., 1770

116 SALOMON GESSNER, Schriften. 5 volumes. *Orell, Gessner, Füssli u. Comp., Zürich 1770–2*

Salomon Gessner (1730–88) was the son of a printer and was apprenticed to a printer in Berlin; but he soon turned to literature and art. He wrote his most famous books in his twenties and then in 1761 he helped to found the firm of Orell, Gessner & Co.; it became Orell, Gessner, Füssli & Co. in 1770 and by the end of the eighteenth-century was the best-known Swiss publishing house.

The firm published a steady series of editions of Gessner's works, and for each he etched new sets of plates. The second volume of this edition is shown open at a head-piece by Gessner.

Imprimerie Royale, 1771

117 GEORGES LOUIS LECLERC, COMTE DE BUFFON, Histoire naturelle des oiseaux. 10 volumes. *Imprimerie Royale, Paris 1771–86*

The family of Anisson, which directed the Imprimerie Royale from 1691 until 1794 when E. A. J. Anisson-Dupéron was guillotined, printed a number of scientific works of which this is the most important. The 'Romain du Roi' looks very modern inside the neo-classic border which was added to the large paper copies; the presswork varies in quality, but at its best gives a brilliant effect. The first volume is shown; the large paper copies of this volume are dated 1771, whereas the ordinary paper copies are dated 1770.

* Joaquín Ibarra, 1772

118 Sallust, La Conjuración de Catilina y la Guerra de Jugurta. *Joaquín Ibarra, Madrid 1772*

Joaquín Ibarra (1725–85) was Spanish Court printer and stood in relation to this branch of the Bourbon family as Bodoni did to the Parma Court. The two knew and influenced each other's work; Bodoni writes of this book as 'the stupendous Sallust . . . printed with so much *finitezza* at Madrid'.

The types used were cut by Antonio Espinosa; the setting of the various parts of the book is beautifully related. Ibarra made his own brilliant black ink and hot-pressed his paper. Most of the plates and ornaments were designed by M. S. Maella, but the engraved title-page was designed and cut by E. Monfort.

The translation is by the Infante Don Gabriel Antonio de Borbon, second son of Carlos III. The present copy is one of 120 large-paper presentation copies. It contains a note by Thomas Grenville, 'Mr. Waddelove, chaplain to the English Ambassador Lord Grantham, procured the types from the Baskerville Font'—this is probably only a legend. *Plate 11*

Noël le Mire, 1772

119 Charles Louis de Secondat, Baron de Montesquieu, Le Temple de Gnide. *'Chez le Mire, graveur', Paris 1772*

Charles Eisen (1721–78) after some early paintings devoted his life to producing designs for book-illustration; he was particularly gifted in portraying *galant* scenes. The Goncourts wrote: 'Inspiré de Boucher, sorti de son style, il s'en dégage par l'affinement, la délicatesse de sa manière.' His designs are here engraved by Noël le Mire (1724–1801), one of the foremost French engravers who also published the volume. The text is engraved by Droüet. Many of the books Eisen illustrated are not well printed (or, indeed, well written), and the delicacy of his style contrasts oddly with bad presswork. Here the engraved text admirably matches the delicacy of the plates.

Antonio Zatta, 1772

120 Ariosto, Orlando Furioso. 4 volumes. *Antonio Zatta, Venice 1772–3*

Venetian printers in the eighteenth century, particularly G. B. Albrizzi and Antonio Zatta, produced many books with pleasant engraved designs and later in the century made use of Fournier-style types; the finished books, however, often lack a feeling for overall design and are usually marred by a lack of finish in the engraving and in the presswork. One common practice of Venetian printers was to use engraved rococo borders entirely surrounding the type-page; they are most frequently found in congratulatory poems on weddings and official inaugurations, but they were also added to large-paper copies of this edition of the *Orlando Furioso*. Most of the decorations and the plates were designed by Pier Antonio Novelli (1729–1804) and engraved by Giuliano Zuliani (1730–1814) and others. The first volume of a copy on vellum is shown.

*John Baskerville, 1773

121 Ariosto, Orlando Furioso. 4 volumes. *Baskerville, Birmingham, for P. and G. Molini, 1773*

This edition is an exception to the general rule that Baskerville's books relied on their typographical design alone; it contains forty-six plates by Moreau le jeune, Eisen, Cochin, and Cipriani. It was commissioned by the brothers Molini who were established in London, Paris, and Florence and was an attempt to introduce new standards of printing into the market for luxury books.

The book was printed in both quarto and octavo. The present copy is a quarto; the second volume is shown open at a plate by J. M. Moreau le jeune, engraved by N. de Launay.

Antonio de Sancha, 1773

122 Parnaso Español. 9 volumes. *Antonio de Sancha, Madrid 1768–78*

Antonio de Sancha (1720–90) started life as a bookseller and publisher; volumes 1–5 of the *Parnaso Español*, 'an anthology of the most famous Castilian poets', were printed for him by Ibarra, but volume 6 onwards were printed by himself. It is said that he went to Paris to study printing, and sent his sons there too; this volume is a good example of a fusion of French grace (the types are by Fournier) and Spanish control. The seventh volume (1773) is shown.

Joaquín Ibarra, 1780

123 Cervantes, Don Quixote. 4 volumes. *Joaquín Ibarra, Madrid 1780*

This edition was planned by the Spanish Academy from the first as a piece of fine printing as well as a correct text; the minutes of the Academy in 1773 contain details of the type-sizes to be used. Type was newly cast from matrices prepared for the Biblioteca Real by Geronimo Gil. The paper was specially made at the mills of Joseph Florens in Catalonia. 1600 copies were printed.

The plates and ornaments were designed by A. Carnicero, J. del Castillo, J. Brunete, B. Barranco, P. Arnal, G. Gil, and G. Ferro.

The first volume is shown open at a plate designed by Joseph del Castillo and engraved by Fernando Selma.

*Benito Monfort, 1781

124 FRANCISCO PEREZ BAYER, De numis hebraeo-samaritanis. *Monfort, Valencia 1781*

Benito Monfort (1716–85) learnt his trade under Antonio Bordazar in Valencia and became the outstanding printer there. Bordazar had published in 1732 proposals for printing liturgical books in Spain, *Plantificación de la Imprenta de el Rezo Sagrado*, which show the type used here. According to Bordazar, Charles II of Spain had brought the matrices from the Netherlands and they were then in the possession of Juan Gomez Morales, a typefounder in Madrid.

This is therefore an example of how modern a book can look through a severe but elegant handling of an old type face; and of how much improved a seventeenth-century type is by leading, good ink, good paper, and good presswork.

Jacques Gabriel Clousier, 1783

125 J. C. RICHARD DE SAINT-NON, Voyage pittoresque, ou description des royaumes de Naples et de Sicile. 4 volumes. *J. G. Clousier, Paris 1781–6*

This enormous work, directed by Saint-Non (1727–91) and illustrated by Choffard, Cochin Fragonard and others, was influential in the vogue for classical motifs in decoration. The printing by Clousier, *imprimeur au roi*, is in old-style types; there are many plates by a variety of artists throughout the work. The third volume is shown open at a headpiece designed by Fragonard, etched by Augustin St. Aubin and finished with the burin by B. A. Nicollet; the woodcut tail-piece opposite is signed by Jean Beugnet.

*François Ambroise Didot, 1783

126 JEAN RACINE, Œuvres. 3 volumes. *Didot l'aîné, Paris 1783*

François Ambroise Didot (1730–1804) was one of the most important members of the Didot family, for several generations the most prominent in French printing. In this series of French and Latin classics commissioned by the king for the education of the dauphin, the royal authorization specifically refers to Didot's perfection of type and paper, in which he seems to have been following the example of Baskerville. The first *papier vélin* is said to have been made for him in 1780 by the Johannot mills at Annonay; it produces a splendid surface for the delicate strokes of the newly cut transitional type. These types may have been cut by Pierre Louis Vaflard or by Didot's younger son Firmin Didot, later famous as a typefounder.

John Bell, 1791

127 MARY ROBINSON, Poems. *J. Bell, British Library, London 1791*

John Bell (1745–1831) was a man of many interests. Throughout his life he was an active newspaper publisher. In 1774, after Alexander Donaldson had been upheld by the House of Lords in his right to reprint books when the statutory copyright term had expired (the London booksellers opposed to this a common law perpetual copyright), Bell published a *Shakespeare* (1774), a *British Theatre* (1776–8), and *The Poets of Great Britain* (1777–82). These were printed at York and Edinburgh beyond the reach of the irate London trade, who commissioned Dr. Johnson to write his *Lives of the Poets* for their rival edition. The series that Bell published were notable for the elegance he brought to what were essentially cheap editions.

Bell's interest in design is shown by the fact that he started his own letter-foundry in 1788 with Richard Austin as punchcutter, but in the following year he went into partnership with Simon Stephenson who subsequently took over the business. It was Bell who in 1785 first abandoned the use of the long ſ in favour of the round one, largely for the reason that it gave a page a more open effect. During the long period he ran his own press he was punctilious in the quality of his paper, ink, and presswork.

The book shown is set in a long primer type of Edmund Fry & Co, cast on a small pica body.

Giovanni Battista Bodoni, 1791

128 ANACREON, *Μελη. [G. B. Bodoni], 'in aedibus palatinis', Parma 1791*

Giovanni Battista Bodoni (1740–1813) was the son of a Piedmontese printer. He served his apprenticeship in Rome and there he first cut types. On his way to England to seek his fortune in 1768 he was asked to take charge of the Stamperia Reale in Parma: and there he spent the rest of his life, designing more and more new types and perfecting the production of luxurious books in a variety of styles.

The *Anacreon* shown here combines an inscriptional quality with the graceful charm of his earlier style. It was published both in octavo and 16mo; this is one of three copies on vellum.

*Giovanni Battista Bodoni, 1793

129 VIRGIL, Opera. 2 volumes. *G. B. Bodoni, Parma 1793*

In 1791 Bodoni was permitted to set up his private press in addition to the royal printing office which he directed; the products of this press were aimed at the international market of book-collectors. This edition of *Virgil*, printed in his most severe 'modern face' types, was one of the most admired products; it was, however, severely criticized by the Didots, now commercial rivals, for its inaccuracies; a number of cancel leaves were subsequently printed. Twenty-five copies were printed on superfine paper, twenty-five on Annonay laid paper, and three on vellum; the copy shown is on Annonay.

*William Bulmer, 1795

130 OLIVER GOLDSMITH and THOMAS PARNELL, Poems. *W. Bulmer & Co., Shakespeare Printing Office, London 1795*

William Bulmer (1757–1830) was born in Newcastle where he was a friend of Thomas Bewick; he later worked for John Bell in London. About 1787 George Nicol was looking for a printer who could print a text for the 'Boydell Shakespeare' fine enough to match the magnificent engraved plates, and he put Bulmer in charge of the Shakespeare Press. Nicol had engaged William Martin of Birmingham to cut type specially for him; he was the brother of Robert Martin, Baskerville's foreman, and his handsome modern design shows Baskerville's influence. Bulmer was helped in his search for a rich black ink by Robert Martin; and he relied on Whatman for his paper.

The advertisement to this volume says: 'Much pains have been bestowed on the present publication, to render it a complete specimen of the arts of type and block-printing.' The wood-engravings by Thomas Bewick (1753–1828) and John Bewick (1760–95) are technically brilliant and much better printed than in any of their other books; but they lack some of the spontaneity of their usual work.

*Pierre Didot, 1795

131 JEAN DE LA FONTAINE, Contes et nouvelles en vers. 2 volumes. *P. Didot l'aîné, Paris 1795*

Jean Honoré Fragonard (1734–1806) first sketched some designs for La Fontaine in 1773 with no thought of publication; and he produced two subsequent suites of more finished illustrations, the last in 1790. The publication was never completed, for the French Revolution had destroyed the market and the taste for this type of book; only the first two volumes appeared, and only the first was illustrated with sixteen engravings after Fragonard. The plate shown is engraved by Jean Baptiste Patas. *Plate 12a*

Thomas Bensley, 1797

132 JAMES THOMSON, The Seasons. Illustrated with engravings by F. Bartolozzi, R.A., and P. W. Tomkins . . . from original pictures painted for the work by W. Hamilton, R.A. '*The letter-press by T. Bensley. The types by V. Figgins*', *London 1797*

Thomas Bensley (d. 1835) was the son of a London printer and started business as a not very distinguished printer himself. In the 1790's, however, he began to produce a number of *de luxe* editions whose quality is comparable with those of Bulmer. His types were the first designed by Vincent Figgins, a more delicate and, in the event, more influential face than the Martin type used by Bulmer.

Bensley's brilliance is perhaps best seen in the layout of his title-pages; that shown here is one of the most sensational. The frontispiece is a stipple engraving by P. W. Tomkins after a drawing by William Hamilton.

Pierre Didot, 1797

133 PIERRE JOSEPH BERNARD, Œuvres, ornées de gravures d'après les desseins de Prud'hon. *P. Didot l'aîné, Paris 1797*

Pierre Prud'hon (1758–1823) produced little book-illustration. His work is interesting because it combines a neo-classicism very suitable to the modern-face types of Didot with a sentimental voluptuousness. He produced four plates for this edition; that shown was engraved by Jacques Louis Copia. This copy is one of 150 on *papier vélin*.

R. Noble, 1797

134 EDWARD YOUNG, The Complaint, and the Consolation; or, Night Thoughts. *R. Noble for R. Edwards, London 1797*

In 1795 William Blake (1757–1827) had illustrated a number of his own books with no commercial success; he had done little original work for other authors, but a good deal of professional engraving of other men's work. It is not known whether the idea of illustrating the *Night Thoughts* came from Blake or from Richard Edwards, youngest son of the famous Halifax bookbinding family. Edwards provided Blake with the text of the poem inlaid in blank sheets of drawing paper, and Blake drew 537 illustrative borders from which to select 150 subjects that he would engrave. There can have been little public demand, for only the first of four parts was ever issued, containing 43 designs. Edwards claimed in his prospectus: 'These engravings are in a perfectly new style of decoration, surrounding the text which they are designed to illustrate.'

Gabriel de Sancha, 1797

135 CERVANTES, Don Quixote. 5 volumes. *D. Gabriel de Sancha, Madrid 1797–8*

Antonio de Sancha died in 1790, and this edition he had planned was produced by his eldest son; it is notable among their works for its restrained style. The plates were designed by R. Ximeno, A. Navarro, Monnet, Camarón, and Paret.

Two hundred and fifty copies were printed on large paper, and six on vellum; this is one of the vellum copies. The second volume is shown, open at a plate designed by Navarro and engraved by Moreno Texada.

Pierre Didot, 1798

136 VIRGIL, Bucolica, Georgica, et Aeneis. *P. Didot l'aîné, Paris 'anno reip. VI', [1798]*

Firmin Didot (1764–1836) was the younger son of F. A. Didot and took over his typefoundry in 1789 at the same time as his elder brother Pierre took over the printing side of the business. Firmin subsequently became a printer and paper-maker in his own right.

In 1795 he started experiments with a stereotyping process, and by 1798 he had developed a method invented by Gatteaux which he applied to standard authors, producing an elegant series of cheap editions in 18mo of which this was the first. It was available as cheaply as 75 centimes, though copies were also available on three better grades of paper.

The brilliant small types may be the work of Henri Didot (1765–1852). This copy is one of the few printed off before stereotypes were made.

*Pierre Didot, 1799

137 HORACE, Opera. *P. Didot l'aîné, 'in aedibus palatinis', Paris 1799*

In 1798, Pierre and Firmin Didot working together as printer and type designer produced a folio *Virgil* followed by the *Horace* shown here. These were the first 'éditions du Louvre', so called because when the Imprimerie Nationale moved from the Louvre in 1795 the government allowed Didot to occupy their premises. He was thus able to follow Bodoni in using the imprint 'in aedibus palatinis'. There is no doubt that these editions were produced in direct rivalry with Bodoni; in 1797 the Institut National set up a committee to consider advance sheets of the *Virgil*, and their report is largely devoted to pointing out how in most respects the type is preferable to Bodoni's. The paper came from Essonne and the ink is the deep black dear to the period. The edition was limited to 250 copies.

The engraved headpieces were designed by Charles Percier (1764–1838), the architect who was one of the chief exponents of the Empire style; they were engraved by Girardet. They are modelled on Roman bas-reliefs and have a frigid formal quality which perfectly matches the typography.

THE NINETEENTH CENTURY

THE nineteenth century has been regarded as the Cinderella of printing—dull, inartistic, and no match for its predecessors. The first twenty years saw few innovations. Men already in the field, Bulmer, Bensley, and Charles Whittingham the Elder, continued to produce sound, well-printed books in the 'classical' tradition. The appearance of the steam-press, however, and the growth of an industrialized society, clamouring for educative material, was to revolutionize the conception of printing and depress taste. There was an inevitable falling-off in standards all round, although the work of individual printers shows that machine methods were not necessarily a bar to good printing. In England, William Pickering, a publisher of scholarly and antiquarian taste, with a feeling for the fine typography of the old books he reprinted, obtained a consistently high standard both in *pastiches* and in his original works from the printers he used. Notable among these was Charles Whittingham the Younger, whose printing of Lady Willoughby's *Diary* in 1844, set in Caslon's 'old face' types, was an innovation which had an immediate impact, since for several decades only the 'modern face' types made popular by the example of Bodoni had been used. The revolution, though slow in action, had far-reaching results and similar 'revivals' took place in Paris, Lyons, and Basle.

Throughout the century illustration played a dominant role, particularly in France. Restraint was thrown to the winds, and decoration in the form of lithography and wood-engraving, admirable in itself, led to a serious debasement in the design of type. There was a lack of balance between text and design. The illustration was no longer an attractive adjunct, but became the *raison d'être* of the book itself. Instances of this are seen in Delacroix's dramatic lithographs for *Faust* (1828), and Manet's striking illustrations for Poe's *The Raven* (1875). Superb as is Curmer's *Paul et Virginie* (1838), the abundance of woodcuts almost overwhelms the type.

There was a serious need for discipline and a leavening of standards of typography. William Morris came to the fore in the last decade of the century, and sought with Messianic zeal to redeem printing from the slough into which it had sunk. But in his anxiety to avoid the defects of his time, the cramped thin-faced types, poor paper, and slovenly presswork, he went too far in the opposite direction. In praising the standards and techniques of the fifteenth-century printers he accpeted their faults as well; and in damning the deterioration that had taken place since, he ignored the value of the real improvements which had accompanied them. But if his views on typography now seem misguided—and much of the blame attached to Morris belongs to his more erratic imitators—his insistence on a proper attention to all the components of the manufacture of books is the fundamental cause of the higher standards which prevail today.

*William Bulmer, 1802

138 The Arabian Nights, translated by the Reverend Edward Foster. With engravings from pictures by Robert Smirke, R.A. *W. Bulmer & Co., London 1802*

William Bulmer was one of three outstanding master-printers in England at the beginning of the nineteenth century; he continued the tradition of printing in a 'classical' as opposed to a 'romantic' style. Despite the technical advances of growing industrialization, he still paid great attention to paper, presswork, and inks. *The Arabian Nights* is one of his finest productions. It is set in Martin's type, of which Bulmer had a monopoly for his earlier works, but, whereas his Goldsmith and Parnell *Poems* of 1795 looks back to the eighteenth century, *The Arabian Nights* belongs to the new century.

*Bodoni, 1818

139 G. B. Bodoni, Manuale tipografico. 2 volumes. *'Presso la Vedova', Parma 1818*

Giovanni Battista Bodoni died on 30 November 1813. The *Manuale*, which had been partly assembled by Bodoni himself before his death, was first issued in March 1818, as a memorial to him, by his widow, Paola Margherita (1758–1841). It was produced in a limited edition of about 150 copies under the direction of Luigi Orsi, who had worked as foreman under Bodoni. It contained hundreds of examples of modern-face types —roman, italic, Greek, and exotic, many of which had been selected and arranged after critical examination by Bodoni. Several editorial and literary changes were probably carried out in the *Manuale*, and some of the material rearranged after Bodoni's death. The *Manuale* very likely contains types used, but not designed, cut, or cast, by Bodoni. It did not include all available Bodoni alphabets, but 285 of the 667 existing founts were used. It was printed on a special size of wove paper, manufactured by Pasquale Bozzani.

Plate 13a

Grass, Barth & Co., 1818

140 Johann August Barth, Pacis annis MDCCCXIV et MDCCCXV Foederatis Armis Restitutae Monumentum. *Ex officina Grassii Barthii et Societatis, Bratislava [1818]*

This work was designed as a memorial volume to celebrate the Peace of 1815. It consists of texts in a variety of languages, compiled by German and other scholars. The first edition, 1816, contained only forty-three languages; the second edition, 1818, contained over one hundred. The 1818 edition, shown here, is distinguished by the lithographed borders and ornaments surrounding the text, which are the first examples of printing in several colours entirely from stone, without any subsequent retouching by hand. The printing business which later became Grass, Barth & Co. was first established in 1504, and set up a type-foundry under Georg Baumann the Elder around 1600. It ceased operating about 1729. Johann August Barth revived the foundry about 1800.

William Savage, 1822

141 William Savage, Practical Hints on Decorative Printing. *[William Savage], London 1822–[1823]*

William Savage (1770–1843) came to London from Yorkshire in 1797, and about two years later was appointed printer to the Royal Institution. He started printing on his own account about 1803. Savage was particularly interested in coloured inks, and, contrary to the practice of George Baxter (1804–67) a quarter of a century later, experimented with a view to producing an ink which would have no oil in its constituents. By using balsam capivi and dried turpentine soap instead, he produced an ink suitable for making colour prints. He then set about publishing a book which should demonstrate the application of his new coloured inks to letterpress work of a pictorial and decorative nature. His *Practical Hints on Decorative Printing* was announced in 1815, but was not completed until 1823. Savage decided to print nearly all the colour work himself. Savage's work had little immediate influence, but the process later patented by Baxter (which had considerable success), differed only in the addition of a metal key plate and the use of colours with an oil-vehicle. Savage later wrote what was for long the standard work on printing-inks (1832), and an invaluable *Dictionary of Printing* (1841).

The ornamental title-page, shown here, was drawn by T. Willement and engraved by Branston. It was produced with eight blocks and with the addition of the title of the book printed in gold by William Blanchard.

John Johnson, 1828

142 James Northcote, One Hundred Fables, embellished with two hundred engravings on wood. *J. Johnson, London 1828*

Northcote's *Fables* illustrates a practice which became common in the nineteenth century of introducing an interpreter between the designer and the engraver. The designs are generally by

Northcote, but William Harvey prepared them for reproduction by various engravers. Harvey was a pupil of Bewick. The engravings are finely executed and give the impression of being made on copper rather than on wood. The ornamental letter at the beginning of each Fable and the vignette at the end were designed entirely by Harvey, and herald the beginnings of Victorian baroque. The printer, John Johnson (1777–1848) worked for a time with Thomas Bensley. From 1813 to 1817 he, as compositor, with a pressman, John Warwick, operated a private press at Lee Priory in Kent for Sir Egerton Brydges. Later Johnson removed to Holborn, setting up a printing business on his own. Here he printed *Typographia*, one of the most popular early manuals of printing (1824), and other elaborately illustrated books such as Northcote's *Fables*.

Charles Motte, 1828

143 JOHANN WOLFGANG VON GOETHE, Faust. *Charles Motte, Paris [1828]*

Lithography was first introduced into France by Frédéric André, who established a workshop in Paris in 1800. From 1815 onward *lithos* were produced in abundance. Eugène Delacroix (1799–1863), who designed and drew on stone these dramatic lithographs for *Faust*, was an interesting early example of the painter-illustrator, who sought to interpret the spirit of the text without any regard for the typography. The lithographs were printed separately, and earned for Delacroix a reputation as the leader of the 'École du Laid'. This divorce of illustration from type, seen here, foreshadows the development of the modern French illustrated book.

Firmin Didot Frères, 1835

144 J. TAYLOR, C. NODIER, and A. DE CAILLEUX, Voyages pittoresques et romantiques dans l'ancienne France. (Picardie: vol. 1) *Firmin Didot Frères, Paris 1835*

This extensive and ambitious work, conceived by Baron Taylor and backed by financial support from the State, was published in parts under the various imprints of the Didot family, from 1820 to 1878. It was intended to be not only an album of views of historic monuments throughout France, but a treasure-house of *chef-d'œuvres* of lithography executed by famous French and English artists. The 3 volumes comprising Picardy alone, published between 1835 and 1845, contained more than 1,100 drawings, lithographs, and engravings. The flamboyant decoration displayed in the first volume of the part dealing with Picardy, shown here, derived its inspiration from an excessive zeal for reproducing the art of the Middle Ages, characteristic of this period. The borders are executed by Célestin Nanteuil (1813–73) who allowed his designs to run riot with arches, traceries, and carvings. The introduction of photolithography in 1863 was a serious blow to the *Voyages*, already becoming too expensive to complete.

Léon Curmer, 1838

145 J. H. BERNARDIN DE SAINT-PIERRE, Paul et Virginie. *L. Curmer, Paris 1838*

Wood-engraving made a triumphant re-entry into France in the 1830's. There was a reaction against line-engraving, the impetus coming from England. Léon Curmer (1801–70) founded his publishing firm in 1834, and was an enthusiastic participator in the artistic expression of his time. His *Paul et Virginie* is a superb example of book-making in the romantic manner. A multitude of different designers and engravers shared in its production. Many of the engravers were English. As a piece of printing the presswork is excellent, but it is broken up too much by the engravings. The blocks occupy so much more space than the text that they overwhelm it through their sheer abundance. The elaborate picture initials are an interesting but hardly conscious imitation of the illuminated initials of the Middle Ages. The designs shown here are by Jean Meissonnier, Louis Steinheil, Tony Johannot, and Paul Huet.

F. A. Brockhaus, 1840

146 FRANZ KUGLER, Geschichte Friedrichs des Grossen. Illustrated by Adolph Menzel. *F. A. Brockhaus for J. J. Weber, Leipzig 1840 [1840–2]*

The appearance of Kugler's *Geschichte Friedrichs des Grossen*, published in parts between 1840 and 1842, with its fascinating wood-engravings after Adolph Menzel (1815–1905), was a turning-point in the history of German book-illustration. Menzel scoured the royal art collections, the Zeughaus, and museums in Berlin and Potsdam for material on which to model his drawings and thus recreate the atmosphere of Frederick's court. He took infinite pains over his designs, and was, therefore, justifiably annoyed over the treatment they received at the hands of the craftsmen of Andrew Best and Leloir, who were first engaged by Weber to make the engravings. No single engraver was responsible for any one drawing, the original designs being bandied about from one man to another, according to his skill as a figure, architectural, or landscape engraver. This inevitably led to deviations from Menzel's original intentions, and made him determined to train a group of German engravers who would be able to execute his ideas with precision and understanding. Menzel was afterwards commissioned by Frederick William the Fourth to illustrate a *de luxe* edition of the Works of Frederick the Great (1843–9), issued in a limited number of copies for presentation only.

H. Fournier et Cie, 1844

147 [TAXILE DELORD], Un autre monde. Illustrated by J. J. Grandville. *H. Fournier, Paris 1844*

Un autre monde is an interesting example of wood-engraving in the service of caricature. J. J. Grandville, or to give him his real name, Jean Ignace Isidore Gérard (1803–47), achieved fame in 1829 by the publication of his masterpiece *Les Métamorphoses du Jour*. He belonged to a group of politically minded artists, who expressed their hatred of the current régime in two journals, *La Caricature* and *La Caricature provisoire*. Grandville was singularly adept at pinpointing the weaknesses of his fellow men. He combined this gift with a strange element of fantasy, bordering on surrealism, and a sympathetic understanding of animals, all of which helped to differentiate his work from that of his contemporaries.

The Chiswick Press, 1844

148 [HANNAH MARY RATHBONE], So much of the Diary of Lady Willoughby as relates to her Domestic History. *The Chiswick Press, London 1844*

The Diary of Lady Willoughby marks an important point in the revival of 'old face' types. It was the first book to be wholly printed in Caslon's type, although Charles Whittingham the Younger (1795–1876) had been experimenting with this type for several years previously. From 1840 he had been using Caslon capitals on title-pages printed for William Pickering, and had several books in hand for that same publisher to be set in Caslon. The *Diary* was an artistic and commercial success, and led to the gradual reintroduction of old faces into English typography. By 1860 Caslon had become a favourite type for devotional books. The Chiswick Press was founded by Charles Whittingham the Elder, uncle of the printer of the *Diary*. The name of the Press was first used in imprints of 1811, and persisted for a century and a half, with an especially distinguished period at the end of the nineteenth century under C. T. Jacobi. From its earliest days, the Press was highly esteemed for the excellence of its wood-engravings and use of ornament, and, after its amalgamation in 1919 with William Griggs, for its work in collotype.

J. G. Cotta, 1846

149 JOHANN WOLFGANG VON GOETHE, Reineke Fuchs, illustrated by Wilhelm von Kaulbach. *J. G. Cotta'scher Verlag, Stuttgart and Tübingen 1846*

Reineke Fuchs is an excellent example of Cotta's presswork in the first half of the nineteenth century. The illustrations by Wilhelm von Kaulbach (1805–74), already well known as an artist, established his reputation as a book-illustrator. His first important work, 'Apollo among the Muses', had been painted in the Odeon in 1826. He subsequently executed several wall-paintings in the palace of Duke Maximilian, consisting of scenes from the works of Wieland, Klopstock, Hermann, and Goethe. He also illustrated editions of Shakespeare, Schiller, and Goethe. His designs for *Reineke Fuchs*, several of which are of a decidedly sensual nature, were engraved on steel by Rudolph Rahn and Adrian Schleich.

The printing and publishing firm of Cotta, founded in the eighteenth century, was in 1846 at the height of its reputation. A pioneer in installing König and Bauer's steam-presses, Cotta became one of the most prolific and successful firms in Germany.

*The Chiswick Press, 1847

150 OLIVER BYRNE, The First Six Books of the Elements of Euclid, *The Chiswick Press for William Pickering, London 1847*

This gay and amusing experiment in printing, 'in which coloured diagrams and symbols are used instead of letters for the greater ease of learners', was produced by William Pickering during his association with Charles Whittingham the Younger. It is a curious work in which Caslon's pica old face is combined with Chiswick Press initials and ornaments, and supplemented by diagrams and symbols printed in brilliant colours. The author, Oliver Byrne, was Surveyor of H.M. Settlements in the Falkland Islands.

Bradbury and Evans, 1857

151 ALFRED TENNYSON, Poems. *Edward Moxon, London 1857*

Moxon's edition of Tennyson's *Poems* was illustrated by almost all the distinguished artists of the period. Two very dissimilar groups of artists took part: Mulready, Maclise, Creswick, Horsley, Stanfield, on the one hand; Millais, Holman Hunt, and Rossetti on the other. The Pre-Raphaelites provided thirty of the drawings. Eighteen were by Millais, seven by Hunt, and five by Rossetti. Rossetti's designs are particularly memorable; his approach to the poems was very personal, and he preferred to allegorize in his own fashion rather than study the author's meaning. All the Pre-Raphaelites took infinite pains over their work, and Rossetti's constant re-drawing was a particular source of embarrassment and delay to the publisher. It was originally intended that Holman Hunt should illustrate the poem of *The Lady of Shalott*. He generously handed over the illustration of the latter part of the poem to Rossetti, however, when Rossetti made it clear that he had set his heart on illustrating that very subject. His drawing for *The Lady of Shalott*, shown here, was engraved by the Dalziel brothers, two of the foremost reproductive artists of the day.

Edward Moxon, the publisher of Lamb, Coleridge, Wordsworth, and Tennyson, was one of the few who demanded a high standard of printing, and his editions of poetry are among the best-looking of the period. His illustrated books were notable among the 'table-books' popular in the sixties. Bradbury and Evans were one of the most distinguished colour printers of the period, and pioneers of 'nature-printing'.

Edmund Evans, 1864

152 JAMES E. DOYLE, A Chronicle of England, 55 B.C.–A.D. 1485. Written and illustrated by James E. Doyle. *The designs engraved and printed in colours by Edmund Evans, London 1864*

Edmund Evans (1826–1906) was born in Southwark. After serving a period as 'reading boy' in the printing house of Samuel Bentley, he was apprenticed in 1840 to Ebenezer Landells, the wood-engraver. In 1847 Evans set up on his own. He is best known for his colour engravings. These were printed in oil-colour from a series of wood blocks. His first colour work of real importance in book-illustration was for *The Poems of Oliver Goldsmith*, 1858. The work shown here, *A Chronicle of England*, is described by Evans as 'the most carefully executed book I have ever printed'. In the introduction, he states that his intention here has been 'rather to express with clearness the action of the various scenes under description, than to give a series of attractive pictures'. It contained eighty illustrations printed on the text pages, many of the illustrations necessitating eight or ten printings, and was the last important colour work done by Evans on a hand-press.

Evans is famous for his production of children's books by Kate Greenaway, Walter Crane, and others, with their charming colour illustrations. The skill and accuracy with which he reproduced even the most delicate colours by the relatively unsympathetic process of wood-engraving has never been surpassed.

Richard Clay & Co., 1864

153 The New Testament. With engravings on wood from designs of Fra Angelico, Pietro Perugino and others. *Longmans, Green & Co., London 1864*

Longman's New Testament is a lavishly ornamented book in the style of the sixties. The typographical arrangement was planned by Whittingham. The drawings for the initial letters, and all the decorative portions, were designed or adapted and drawn on wood by Henry Shaw (1800–73). Shaw also supervised the drawing of the figure illustrations, and the whole of the engraving. The borders were engraved by Mary Byfield and others.

Henry Shaw was born in London. An architectural draughtsman, engraver, and antiquary, he was responsible for a series of splendid illuminated books, including his *Encyclopaedia of Ornament*, 1842. The copy of the New Testament shown here is one of 250 copies printed on large paper.

*The Chiswick Press, 1867

154 The Altar Service Book, according to the use of the United Church of England and Ireland. Edited by the Rev. Frederick George Lee. *[The Chiswick Press], London 1867*

This book, printed at the Chiswick Press by Charles Whittingham the Younger and his partner, John Wilkins, is a fine piece of liturgical printing of its period. An attempt has been made here to display the Prayer Book rite of Holy Communion as it would have been executed by a sixteenth-century London, Rouen, or Paris printer of books of the Latin rite. According to the editor, 'each of the books has been printed with an eye to the addition of... embellishment throughout, either by colouring the initial letters or by the introduction of suitable borders', if such be desired.

Jules Claye, 1873

155 François Rabelais, Œuvres. Illustrated by Gustave Doré, 2 volumes. *Jules Claye for Garnier Frères, Paris 1873*

Gustave Doré (1832–83) made his mark chiefly by his book-illustration. He opened up fresh avenues and poured forth a multitude of designs, many of them terrifying in their imaginative quality. He used professional engravers but knew how to make them get the utmost from the wood blocks on which his designs were usually drawn. In his later work he tended to treat the wood almost as if it were copper, and gave his engravers wash drawings to work from. He worked generally from black to white. Doré is universally admired for his earlier productions. The large folio volume shown here is, however, an effective piece of typographical layout of its period, in which the text and illustrations form a harmonious whole.

Alcan Lévy, 1875

156 Edgar Allan Poe, The Raven. Translated into French by Stéphane Mallarmé and illustrated by Édouard Manet. *Alcan Lévy for Richard Lesclide, Paris 1875*

Manet's illustrations to Poe's *The Raven* are a fascinating example of lithography in the hands of an Impressionist painter. Of all the Impressionists Édouard Manet (1832–83) was the best suited to adapt his style to the restriction of black and white. By means of transfer paper he was able to draw with the brush, thereby giving a painterly quality to his lithographs. It was significant that a publisher should commission work so early from an Impressionist painter, and Manet's illustrations foreshadow very strikingly the trend of subsequent French book-illustration.

Field and Tuer, 1885

157 Joseph Crawhall, Izaak Walton: his Wallet Booke. *Field and Tuer, London 1885*

Andrew White Tuer (1838–1900), a printer publisher with antiquarian tastes, was born in Sunderland. He came to London as a medical student, but never completed his studies, and by 1862 had established himself as a wholesale stationer in the Minories. In the following year he was joined by Robert Field, and the firm assumed the title of Field and Tuer. About 1868 they moved to Leadenhall St., where they printed and published *The Paper and Printing Trades Journal*. From the first this was printed in Old Style, a modernized old face type. In 1879 the firm began publishing books, including several of which Tuer himself was author or compiler. Many of the books were reprints of earlier works, illustrated by contemporary blocks. A few of the books were published in Caslon, but the great majority (as in the example shown here) were in Old Style. They were well printed, and often decorated in a manner daring for the period. During 1890 the imprint became the Leadenhall Press.

For the Northumbrian antiquary Joseph Crawhall Tuer produced some refreshing, boldly designed books; the cuts are generously spaced with a nice sense of balance.

The Chiswick Press, 1890

158 The Century Guild Hobby Horse. *The Chiswick Press, London 1890*

This periodical, edited by Herbert P. Horne and Selwyn Image from 1886–92, has often been quoted as a pioneer in the abandonment of modern face. It has already been shown (no. 157) that Old Style type was in use nearly twenty years earlier, and the real importance of *The Hobby Horse* lay in its contribution to the revival of interest in printing in the late 1880's, which was to culminate in the work of William Morris (no. 161) and his successors.

A trial number of *The Hobby Horse* was printed in Caslon in 1884, but the first regular issues in 1886 were set in a small size of Old Style. From 1888 a large size of this type was used, which displayed it to better advantage. The initials and tail-pieces shown are from designs by Horne.

The Ballantyne Press, 1894

159 Oscar Wilde, The Sphinx. With decorations by Charles Ricketts. *The Ballantyne Press for Elkin Mathews and John Lane, London 1894*

Charles de Sousy Ricketts (1866–1931) was a man of considerable versatility, combining the talents of artist, author, printer, and stage-designer. He was a lifelong friend of C. H. Shannon, with whom he owned and edited *The Dial* (1889–97). Like William Morris, Ricketts was caught up in the Arts and Crafts Movement of his time. He founded the Vale Press (1896–1904), and proceeded to design founts, bindings, and illustrations. Unlike Morris, however, Ricketts was much more of an individualist, and had no pretentions whatsoever to be democratic in his appeal. His productions are lighter and more graceful, the pages are not so congested, but the general effect is slighter than Morris's monumental typography.

The Sphinx (1894) was one of the immediate precursors of the Vale Press books, but was printed by Ballantyne & Hanson. It is a masterpiece of baroque poetry, entirely artificial in conception, and ideally suited to the decorative treatment it received from Ricketts.

W. Drugulin, 1895–6

160 PAN, Erster Jahrgang. 1895–6. *W. Drugulin for Verlag Pan, Berlin 1895–6*

A revived interest in printing first manifested itself in Germany in the publication in October 1892 of the first number of *Blätter für die Kunst* arranged by the poet Stefan George. This journal was succeeded by a second and more ambitious periodical, *Pan*, devoted to the arts and letters. It was issued by the Genossenschaft Pan, a group of young artists and writers led by Julius Meier-Graefe and Otto Julius Bierbaum, both of whom resigned after one year and were succeeded by an editorial board which included Baron Bodenhausen and Count Harry Kessler. It was printed by Drugulin and lavishly illustrated with lithographs, etchings, and decorations in the text. The editors were close followers of the Arts and Crafts Movement in England, and, in spite of their individuality, some of the artists were criticized as being 'too ready to cringe before the decayed remains of English Pre-Raphaelitism'. The 1896 volume included a number of Kelmscott facsimiles.

*The Kelmscott Press, 1896

161 GEOFFREY CHAUCER, Works. *Kelmscott Press, Hammersmith 1896*

Appalled by the mediocrity of contemporary book-production and by machine methods, William Morris (1834–96) reverted to the hand-press and determined to 'produce books which would be a pleasure to look upon as pieces of printing and arrangement of type'. He established the Kelmscott Press (1891–8) at Hammersmith; chose a handmade paper, modelled on a Bolognese paper of *c.* 1473, produced for him by Joseph Batchelor of Little Chart, Kent; and an ink manufactured by Janecké of Hanover. The punches for Morris's types were cut by E. P. Prince, and based on those of the early printers.

The Works of Geoffrey Chaucer was Morris's crowning achievement. It was printed in black and red, in double column, in his Chaucer type, with headings to the longer poems in Troy type; it contained eighty-seven woodcuts designed by Sir Edward Burne-Jones, and an abundance of borders, initials and ornaments, designed by Morris. Four hundred and twenty-five copies were printed on paper and thirteen on vellum. The copy shown here is on vellum. *Plate 15*

*The Chiswick Press, 1896

162 ALEXANDER POPE, The Rape of the Lock. Embroidered with nine drawings by Aubrey Beardsley. *The Chiswick Press for Leonard Smithers, London 1896*

The illustrations contained in this edition of *The Rape of the Lock*, printed by Charles Whittingham & Co., are masterpieces of line-engraving. Aubrey Beardsley was the first really original artist to understand and perfect the photo-engraved line-block method. By this method drawings need no longer be made the exact size in which they were to be cut out on the wood, but could be enlarged or reduced photographically. Beardsley shows here his consummate skill in the use of line to interpret various material surfaces, stone, velvet, or brocade. His employment of the dotted line to convey an impression of muslin and lighter fabrics is particularly successful. *Plate 13b*

Chamerot et Renouard, 1898

163 GEORGES CLEMENCEAU, Au pied du Sinaï. Illustrated by Henri de Toulouse Lautrec. *Henri Floury, Paris 1898*

Towards the close of the nineteenth century lithography came into its own again in France as a medium of book-illustration. It owed its revival very largely to the efforts of a professional lithographer, Jules Chéret, who made practical use of it for poster-work, and to E. Duchâtel, author of the *Manuel de lithographie artistique*, who was for years printer to Lemercier. The final impetus was given by an exhibition at the École des Beaux Arts in 1891. In the same year Henri de Toulouse Lautrec (1864–1901) made his sensational début as a lithographer with his startling poster of Louise Weber, commonly called La Goulue, dancing at the Moulin Rouge. He knew how to exploit, without abusing it, the freedom conferred by lithography. He worked almost entirely in outline, and in flat tints, deriving much of his inspiration from Japanese prints, then in vogue. The illustration, shown here, of the wealthy but decayed baron yawning at the opera over the shoulders of his fair companion, is a typical example of Lautrec's genius.

THE TWENTIETH CENTURY

BOOK typography in the twentieth century reaped the benefit of the Linotype and Monotype systems of mechanical composition. Although these were introduced at the end of the nineteenth century, both systems at first provided only slavish copies of types already made popular by typefounders. The English Private Press Movement encouraged a taste for revivals of the best types from past ages, especially for Jenson's roman. A spur was given by the American Type Founders Company who recut the types of Bodoni and Garamond between 1911 and 1917. During this period the Lanston Monotype Company recut Caslon's types and a Plantin design; but from 1922 it carried out an extensive programme which included many revivals and also several entirely new types by contemporary designers. This programme was supervised by Stanley Morison (b. 1889) whose writings exerted a considerable influence on book typography, and who was responsible for the design of Times New Roman (1931).

The proliferation of type-revivals encouraged the practice of 'allusive typography', but this style declined in popularity in the past three decades. To use archaic materials in printing went against the trend of taste in art and architecture. Ideas were propagated at the Bauhaus in Dessau for a 'new typography' (*see* no. 167) which eschewed ornaments and which favoured nineteenth-century sanserif types in asymmetrical arrangements. The reading public has not yet accepted sanserif types for general reading, although it accepts them in advertising and other forms of ephemeral printing. More extensive use of sanserif may depend upon the skill with which type-designers can reduce its monotony by introducing greater variety in weight between thick and thin strokes (*see* no. 191).

The use of photogravure and photolithography in book-production has made possible a much closer integration of text and illustration, and has given the typographer greater freedom in the disposition of his materials. As this freedom becomes better understood and more intelligently exploited, a distinctive twentieth-century style in book typography may gradually emerge.

The Doves Press, 1902

164 JOHN MILTON, Paradise Lost. *The Doves Press, Hammersmith 1902*

The Doves Press was founded in 1900 by T. J. Cobden-Sanderson (1840–1922) and Emery Walker (1851–1933). Both men had been associated in the Arts and Crafts Movement with William Morris, whose secretary Sydney Cockerell (1867–1962) stimulated them to make their own type by remarking how strange it was that in 1898 no one had yet had the good sense to reproduce the actual type of Nicholas Jenson. Their type was cut by Edward Prince (1847–1923) under Walker's supervision, and the result came far closer to Jenson's original than the Golden type used by the Kelmscott Press. The aim of the Doves Press was to solve typographical problems by the simplest arrangements, paying proper respect to the arrangement of the text, using calligraphical emphasis in its capital divisions, but avoiding applied ornament or decoration. The Doves Press had its own bindery which produced distinguished work. Many of the books had hand-painted initials by the calligraphers Edward Johnston (1872–1944) and Graily Hewitt (1864–1952); the present book, the fifth produced, is unusually ornate. The copy shown, one of twenty-five on vellum, belonged to Emery Walker.

The Ashendene Press, 1903

165 HORACE, Carmina Alcaica. *Ashendene Press, Chelsea 1903*

Like T. J. Cobden-Sanderson, C. H. St. John Hornby came under the influence of William Morris. For some time after the Ashendene Press's foundation in 1894, Hornby used either Caslon, or, more enterprisingly, Fell types borrowed from the Oxford University Press. In 1902 the first books appeared in the Subiaco type, based on the fount used by Sweynheym and Pannartz at Subiaco from 1465 (no. 7). Emery Walker and Sydney Cockerell designed the new type and it was cut by Edward Prince. Ashendene books were closer to incunabula than either Kelmscott or Doves books, an effect which was achieved by the bold type, wide margins, frequent use of vellum or japanese vellum, and the initials in gold, blue, and red. In the present book these were the work of Graily Hewitt. St. John Hornby (1867–1946) was a partner in the firm of W. H. Smith & Son and in this capacity was one of Eric Gill's first patrons. Initials by Gill appear in the Ashendene Press *Utopia*, 1906.

Rudolf Koch, 1918

166 RUDOLF KOCH, Die Schriftgiesserei im Schattenbild. *Gebr. Klingspor, Offenbach am Main 1918*

Rudolf Koch (1876–1934) enjoyed a reputation in Germany similar to that of Eric Gill in England. The son of a sculptor, he joined Klingspor in 1906; the book shown is a happy link between him and the Klingspor Foundry, illustrating its work. Karl (1868–1950) and Wilhelm Klingspor took over the Rudhard foundry in 1892 and sponsored the work of many of the leading German typographers of the earlier twentieth century. *Die Schriftgiesserei* is one of the private *Hausdrucke* issued by Klingspor. Both silhouettes and typography are by Koch. The type face is a bold-face Deutsche Schrift, characteristic of Koch's work in that it draws strength from traditional German calligraphy and makes no concession to the influence of roman. *Plate 16b*

El Lissitzky, 1923

167 VLADIMIR MAYAKOVSKY, Dlya golosa. *El Lissitzky for Lutze & Vogt, Berlin 1923*

This early example of 'the new typography' championed by the Bauhaus at Dessau was designed by Lazar (El) Lissitzky (1890–1941). Born in Smolensk Province, he studied engineering and architecture at Darmstadt. He returned to Moscow in 1914 and first met Malevich in 1919 when he was appointed Professor in the Vitebsk School of Art, which Malevich had just taken over from Chagall and renamed 'Unovis' (College of the New Art). In 1922 he accompanied the Russian Exhibition to Berlin where he arranged one room of the exhibition according to Constructivist principles. There, in the same year, with Ilya Ehrenburg, he published the international Constructivist magazine *Veshch/Gegenstand/Objet*. The Constructivists' Congress at Dusseldorf in 1922, led by Lissitzky and Ehrenburg, profoundly influenced the Bauhaus school.

Between 1919 and 1922 Bauhaus teaching had reflected the influence of Futurism and Dadaism, and especially of Dutch *Stijl*, through the teaching of Feininger and van Doesburg; but in 1922 the Hungarian Moholy-Nagy was appointed and, with Josef Albers, he developed Russian Constructivism as a powerful pedagogic method.

*The Bremer Press, 1924

168 ST AUGUSTINE, De civitate Dei. *Bremer Press, Munich 1924 [1925]*

The Bremer Press was founded at Munich in 1911 and ceased work in 1934. Its simple monumental typographical style was the result of a collaboration begun in 1913 by one of its founders, Wilhelm Wiegand (b. 1884), with the German calligrapher Anna Simons (1871–1951). Wiegand designed several types for the Bremer Press: a gothic, a greek, and two sizes of roman, for which punches were cut by Louis Holle of the Bauer typefoundry. The smaller size of roman used in this edition is shown to advantage in the large format chosen by Wiegand. The only decoration he allowed in Bremer Press books was the lettering for title-pages and initials. These were drawn by Anna Simons, a former pupil of Edward Johnston, two of whose works she translated into German. Her designs were cut on wood by Joseph Lehnacker, a craftsman attached to the printing office.

W. A. Dwiggins, 1926

169 ARCHIBALD MACLEISH, Streets in the Moon. *Houghton Mifflin Company, Boston and New York 1926*

Typography, binding-design, and decorations are by W. A. Dwiggins (1880–1956) whose work also extended to type-design and jacket-design. His work from 1926 to 1955 for the publishing firm of Alfred Knopf had a great influence upon other New York publishers, who were thus stirred into taking a more lively interest in the appearance of their own books. It was typical of Dwiggins to declare that he was keen on jacket-design if he could get some *invention and variety* into it. His interest in lettering and printing was first stimulated by his contact in 1899 with Frederic W. Goudy, the type-designer, then an instructor at Chicago where Dwiggins had gone for art training. Dwiggins's association with the Mergenthaler Linotype Company began in 1929 and was notable for his design of Electra (1935) and Caledonia (1939). In the book shown here, the asymmetrical title-page is composed of a number of small woodcut blocks, from which a photo-engraved line-block has been made. He also used stencils to build up both abstract and naturalistic designs.

The Halcyon Press, 1927

170 John Keats. Odes. *Enschedé en Zonen for A. A. M. Stols, Bussum 1927*

The Halcyon Press was founded at Maastricht by A. A. M. Stols (b. 1900), the son of a printer. Before he started his own publishing house in 1927 with the help of his younger brother, he had studied law. Stols had a great admiration for the work of Jan van Krimpen (no. 183), whose types were used in many of the books published by the Halcyon Press. This edition of Keats's *Odes* was composed in van Krimpen's first type, named Lutetia because its earliest use was in a book printed for the Paris Exhibition of 1925. Lutetia was later used in the *Catalogue of the Frick Collection*, designed by Porter Garnett who said of it: 'For the first time in one hundred and sixty years, a new (not merely novel) roman type-face has appeared.' Bruce Rogers commended it for having 'strength with delicacy, grace with dignity'.

The Cranach Press, 1928

171 William Shakespeare, Die tragische Geschichte von Hamlet Prinzen von Daenemark. *Cranach Press, Weimar 1928*

The Press was founded by Harry Graf von Kessler (1868–1937) at Weimar in 1913. The Cranach Press *Hamlet* is the most outstanding example of the influence in Germany of the English revival of fine printing. The woodcut decorations by Edward Gordon Craig (b. 1872) are clearly conceived in theatrical terms. The type was designed by Edward Johnston who modelled it upon that used by Fust and Schoeffer in the Psalter of 1457; some punches were cut by Edward Prince, and after his death the work was completed by G. T. Friend. Kessler first considered the production of this work in 1910, but the intervention of the war postponed its final appearance until 1927–9, when 255 copies in all were printed on Kessler's hand-press. Two hundred and thirty of these were on paper specially made by Kessler and Aristide Maillol.

Method Kaláb, 1928

172 František Táborský, Veliký sněm ptačí. *Průmyslová tiskárna, Prague 1928*

Czechoslovakia's attainment of independence and the subsequent foundation of the Státní tiskárna (Government Printing Works) under Karel Dyrynk in 1919 gave a powerful impetus to the graphic arts. The Státní tiskárna produced a number of new types, notably Malostranská Antikva and Preissig, a type of strong nationalistic appeal designed by the illustrator and typographer Vojtěch Preissig (1873–1944).

The book shown comes from the second centre of fine printing in Czechoslovakia, Průmyslová tiskárna (Industrial Printing Establishment) founded in 1922 and was designed by its director Method Kaláb. Kaláb was born in 1885 and was trained as a compositor by Šafránek. With Preissig and Dyrynk he laid the foundations of modern Czech typography.

The Průmyslová tiskárna produced Czech types, notably that designed by Slavoboj Tusar, but was also equipped with Monotype machines, and the present work is printed in Fournier italic. The woodcuts by Karel Svolinský (b. 1896) are coloured by hand.

The Merrymount Press, 1930

173 The Book of Common Prayer, according to the use of the Protestant Episcopal Church in the United States of America. *D. B. Updike, The Merrymount Press, Boston 1930*

The revised text of the Book of Common Prayer, authorized by the Protestant Episcopal Church of the United States, was prepared for printing at the expense of J. Pierpont Morgan. A commission examined specimen pages submitted by four well-known presses and justifiably decided that Updike's were the most practical. Daniel Berkeley Updike (1860–1941) learnt the art from experience with T. L. de Vinne of New York and at the Riverside Press of Houghton, Mifflin & Co. in Boston. He set up his own Merrymount Press in 1893 and made a deserved reputation as a scholar-printer who could be relied upon to use carefully chosen types and decorative material with taste and distinction. Among other specializations Updike possessed an enviable knowledge of liturgy and liturgical printing. The Book of Common Prayer was set in the so-called Janson types, which he first purchased in 1903. His *Printing Types, their History, Form and Use* (1922) remains the best general history of the subject.

*The Golden Cockerel Press, 1931

174 The Four Gospels. *Golden Cockerel Press, Waltham Saint Lawrence 1931*

Printed in the Golden Cockerel type, the book was designed by Robert Gibbings (1889–1958) and has decorations engraved on wood by Eric Gill (1882–1940). Apart from his work as a sculptor and illustrator, Gill designed a number of types, notably Gill Sans (1928), Perpetua (1929)—of which the Golden Cockerel type is a form—Solus (1929), and Bunyan (1936), recut by Linotype as Pilgrim (1953). The Golden Cockerel Press was founded by Harold Midgely Taylor in 1921 and was taken over by Robert Gibbings in 1924. The Press's long series of finely produced books is particularly memorable for its illustrators—Gill, Gibbings, John Nash, John Buckland-Wright, and David Jones—and Gibbings's great achievement as a printer was his successful disciplining of cuts and type into an evenly coloured page. *Plate 14*

*Léon Pichon, 1931

175 OVID, Métamorphoses, with etchings by Picasso. *Albert Skira, Lausanne 1931*

Although it bears the imprint of Skira at Lausanne, this book was printed in Paris by Léon Pichon. Pichon was the leading French publisher of illustrated books at the time, with an expressed preference for austere typography, here only relieved by the three-line red initials, and uncoloured etched or engraved illustrations. Picasso (b. 1881) made thirty engravings for this book, half of which are full-page. His treatment of the themes from Ovid is classical and traditional, and the clear flowing line of the illustrations is in perfect harmony with the typography.

The Albatross Library, 1932

176 JAMES JOYCE, Dubliners. *The Albatross, Hamburg, Paris, Milan, 1932*

The Albatross Library was conceived as a paper-back series of important contemporary English books in which a low cost was combined with a high standard of production. The original idea was that of John Holroyd-Reece, but the design of the cover and the typography came from Giovanni Mardersteig, whose work as the founder of the Officina Bodoni and the Stamperia Valdonega at Verona is shown elsewhere in this exhibition (no. 194). The Albatross Library exercised a strong influence on Allen Lane's Penguin books. The Albatross device was designed by Salzmann and the book was printed in Monotype Baskerville by Mondadori at Verona.

The Curwen Press, 1932

177 SIR THOMAS BROWNE, Urne Buriall and The Garden of Cyrus. *The Curwen Press for Cassell & Co., London 1932*

The Curwen Press became known, after it passed into the control of Harold Curwen (1885–1949), for jobbing printing of a very high quality. Oliver Simon (1895–1956) persuaded Curwen to undertake the printing of books. In Simon's opinion *Urne Buriall*, printed for Cassell's, was one of the finest illustrated books produced at the Press. The illustrations are by Paul Nash (1889–1946); thirty plates were printed in monochrome collotype and water-colours were then applied by stencilling. *Urne Buriall* was the last book to be illustrated by this process, one developed by Curwen from the French *pochoir* process (*see also* no. 182). The type of the text was Monotype Bembo, cut in 1929. The large letters are Bruce Rogers's Centaur, and the Greek notes are in New Hellenic designed by Victor Scholderer (b. 1880).

Bruce Rogers, 1933

178 STANLEY MORISON, Fra Luca de Pacioli. *University Press, Cambridge, for the Grolier Club, New York 1933*

Bruce Rogers (1870–1957) did his first important work as supervisor of the Riverside limited editions of the Houghton Mifflin Co. Leaving this firm in 1912 he became an independent advisor assisting among others, the presses of the universities of Cambridge, Harvard, and Oxford. He was specially noted for his skill in 'allusive typography'. In the present work the allusion is to the period of the Italian Renaissance. The interlacing pattern of the woodcut border and the *criblé* initials are re-drawn by Rogers from the Venetian edition of Pacioli published by Paganinus de Paganinis, and there is a further Venetian reference in the style of the Centaur type. Rogers's first type, inspired by Nicholas Jenson, was used in his celebrated Montaigne of 1902–4. He was dissatisfied with this and designed a second face, the Centaur, which first appeared in 1915, and is here used. A modified version was used in the Oxford Lectern Bible (no. 179).

This copy is one of an edition of 397 copies printed for the Grolier Club at the University Press, Cambridge. A special ink was prepared and the extra care given to the presswork ensured that brilliance of impression which makes the book a first-class achievement.

*Bruce Rogers, 1935

179 The Holy Bible. *University Press, Oxford 1935*

The plan for this Lectern Bible was discussed in 1929, when it was decided to use the Centaur type then being prepared by the Monotype Corporation from designs by Bruce Rogers (*see also* no. 178). Although he worked mainly as a freelance designer in the United States, Rogers spent several years in England. He worked in Oxford while this Bible was being composed and printed at the University Press, and he personally supervised its production. The type was in fact redrawn by Rogers for this particular book, where the 22-point Centaur is cast on a 19-point body. Special capitals and initial letters were also drawn. A few large-paper copies were worked. As a whole the Bruce Rogers Oxford edition ranks as the most monumental form given to the Bible since Baskerville printed his folio at Cambridge in 1763. The impression is admirably even. The calm splendour of the entire execution makes this Lectern Bible Rogers's lasting and finest memorial.

The Nonesuch Press, 1935

180 HERODOTUS, The History of Herodotus. . . . The translation of G. Rawlinson revised and annotated by A. W. Lawrence. *University Press, Cambridge, for Nonesuch Press, Bloomsbury 1935*

The Nonesuch Press was founded by Francis Meynell in 1923 with the intention of producing books which combined 'significance of subject, beauty of format, and moderation of price'. Nearly all the books were machine-set by various printers and were designed by Meynell himself. In his own words: 'One must intelligently exploit the best mechanical equipment and the highest technical skill available.' The variety of types in Nonesuch books increased with the expanding repertory of Monotype matrices, and many alternative matrices of special design were made for this Press. Thus the text of the Herodotus was set in Monotype Plantin, but with lengthened lower-case ascending and descending letters (e.g. *d, f, j, p*). The italics used for the notes are set in Eric Gill's Felicity design, made to accompany his Perpetua roman.

Philippe Gonin, 1937

181 LONGUS, Daphnis and Chloe. Illustrated by Aristide Maillol. *Philippe Gonin, Paris 1937*

The sculptor Aristide Maillol (1861–1944) had a natural aptitude for the woodcut and his most successful book illustrations were carried out in this medium. His *Daphnis and Chloe* is particularly remarkable for the harmony between the illustrations and the story as well as for its purely typographic virtues. The woodcuts are reminiscent of the work of the Italian Renaissance, but Maillol has also managed to suggest the rather naive eroticism of the text, which in the English edition is heightened by the use of the mid-seventeenth century translation of George Thornley. The paper for this book, like that for the Cranach Press *Hamlet* (no. 171) was specially made by Maillol.

The book was printed in Paris on the hand-press of Philippe Gonin. *Plate 16a*

The Limited Editions Club, 1938

182 OSCAR WILDE, Salomé. Illustrated by André Derain. *Dehon et Cie, Paris, for the Limited Editions Club, New York 1938*

The aim of George Macy (1900–56) in founding the Limited Editions Club of New York in 1929 was to provide its 1500 members with their favourite books in editions designed by leading typographers, with illustrations made by 'the greatest of artists'.

This book was the first to be set in the Peignot type, designed by A. M. Cassandre, who claimed to have realized that 'the principle of evolution implicit in the history of letter-formation could be logically pursued in this twentieth century; and, if the logic were consistently distributed throughout the fount, the resulting design would possess artistic as well as scientific merit'. Although the type was a failure, its spirited use in this book by René Ben Sussan added considerably to the interest of a book which is already remarkable for its illustrations by André Derain (1880–1954). His gouache drawings on black paper were reproduced by Jean Saudé's *pochoir* process, a form of stencilling in which the colours are applied with a stiff brush through thin metal stencils.

Jan van Krimpen, 1947

183 The Book of Psalms. *Printed by Enschedé en Zonen, Haarlem for the Stichting de Roos, Utrecht 1948*

This edition was designed for a society of Dutch bibliophiles by Jan van Krimpen (1892–

1958), a self-taught type-designer and typographer whose early interest in lettering was much influenced by the writings of Edward Johnston. His association with the ancient printing house of Enschedé en Zonen at Haarlem began in 1923 and lasted until his death. The text of the Psalms was composed by hand in his Romanée type, which he had designed in 1928 to accompany an original seventeenth-century italic in the Enschedé collection. Although he frequently used types from this collection, he preferred to design books composed in his own types, which also included Lutetia (*see* no. 170), Romulus, and Spectrum. This bibliophile edition was printed on English hand-made paper, but van Krimpen devoted much of his time to the design of ordinary trade editions, and to liturgical printing. He frequently applied his skill as a calligrapher to the embellishment of title-pages and bindings.

Penguin Books, 1949

184 William Shakespeare, The Sonnets and A Lover's Complaint. *Penguin Books, 1949*

The first ten Penguin books appeared in 1935. The novelty of Sir Allen Lane's venture into publishing lay in the fact that these titles were copyright titles licensed from their original publishers and therefore competing with the hard-cover original. Albatross books, to which the Penguin series owed much, were licensed copyright books but were excluded from Britain and the U.S.A. The Penguin achievement was the greater, therefore, as high quality of production was maintained under more difficult economic conditions.

Jan Tschichold (b. 1902) was appointed to advise Penguin Books on design in 1945. A radical reorganization of the typography of the series resulted, and his principles were codified as the Penguin Composition Rules, which helped to ensure a uniform level of excellence from the several printers responsible for the manufacture of Penguin books. Shakespeare's *Sonnets*, one of the first fruits of Tschichold's presence, is printed in Monotype Bembo. The engraved portrait on the title-page is by Reynolds Stone (b. 1909).

Imprimerie Nationale, 1951

185 J. W. von Goethe, Prometheus. Translated by André Gide, with lithographs by Henry Moore. *Imprimerie Nationale for Henri Jonquières, Paris 1950 [1951]*

At the turn of the century the Imprimerie Nationale was under the administration of one of the most vigorous and influential directors in its history, Arthur Christian (1838–1906). Under Christian's influence the Imprimerie Nationale undertook the printing of magnificently illustrated *éditions de luxe*, many of them, like the present, executed for commercial publishers. Gide's translation of Goethe's *Prometheus* is one of the most recent and distinguished examples of a series which began in 1900 with Verlaine's *Parallèlement*. The face employed is Grandjean's celebrated 'Romain du Roi' of about 1700. The type for the characters' names was cut by Robert Blanchet. The lithographs represent one of the rare excursions into book-illustration by Henry Moore (b. 1898). They were printed by the Parisian firm of Mourlot.

Karl-Erik Forsberg, 1954

186 Bibeln, eller den heliga skrift med bilder av Rembrandt. *P. A. Norstedt & Söners Förlag, Stockholm 1954*

This edition, illustrated with gravure reproductions of Rembrandt's drawings, etchings, and paintings, was printed by Esselte AB for the publishing-house of P. A. Norstedt & Sons. The typographical reputation of Norstedt's was established by Akke Kumlien, who was their art director from 1916 until his death in 1949. Kumlien's successor was Karl-Erik Forsberg, who planned the typography of this Bible; he also designed the Berling type-face used for the text, and drew the lettering for chapter-headings and initials. Forsberg designed the Carolus type (1954), and has designed many books and calligraphical jackets for Norstedt. He had previously worked with Almqvist and Wiksell, printers to the University of Uppsala.

*Fequet et Baudier, 1955

187 Hesiod, Theogony. Etchings by Georges Braque. *Maeght, Paris 1955*

The conception of a magnificent edition of Hesiod's *Theogony* illustrated by Georges Braque was originally that of Ambroise Vollard (1867–1939), unquestionably the greatest patron of French book-art of the twentieth century. Originally an art dealer, from about 1900 onwards Vollard published books illustrated by artists such as Bonnard, Chagall, Dufy, Picasso, and Rouault. The illustrations for the *Theogony* were commissioned in 1933, but Vollard, a perfectionist, kept them in his shop until his death. Braque completed the work by designing the covers, frontispiece, and head- and tail-pieces in 1953. The type with which the illustrations have been matched is a Greek alphabet of upper-case 'Europe', the name given in France to the popular German sanserif Futura, designed by Paul Renner. Braque (b. 1882) has illustrated few books, but the etchings for the present work are a tremendously vigorous interpretation of some of the most primitive Greek myths.

C. Volmer Nordlunde, 1958

188 H. C. ANDERSEN, Skyggen. *C. V. Nordlunde, Copenhagen 1958*

C. Volmer Nordlunde (b. 1888) has established his reputation as a book-designer by the work produced at his printing house in Copenhagen in accordance with his own typographical designs and under his own supervision. His types are carefully chosen from the range available to the trade at large, but his standards are those of the English Private Press Movement. He has had a considerable influence upon book design and production in Denmark, both by his work and by his writings. Each year he issues an illustrated edition of a tale by Hans Christian Andersen. The book shown here is *The Shadows* composed in Linotype Janson and illustrated by Spang Olsen (b. 1921) who studied at the Royal Academy of Art in Copenhagen.

Magyar Helikon, 1959

189 OMAR KHAYYAM, Robáiyát. *Magyar Helikon, Budapest 1959*

This Hungarian translation of the *Rubaiyat* of Omar Khayyam is presented in an unusual typographical arrangement. Each quatrain (printed in Bembo italic) is accompanied by an engraving by Endre Szász (b. 1926). To overcome the difficulty of printing on the reverse side of a sheet containing engravings made direct from the artist's plates, the sheets have been printed on one side only. They have been folded on the fore-edge in Japanese fashion and have been 'perfect' bound without stitching.

György Haiman (b. 1914), who was responsible for the typography now lectures in that subject at Budapest. The text was printed by Kossuth Nyomda and the engravings by Pénzjegy Nyomda.

Raymond Gid, 1959

190 Livre d'Heures, *SPES, Paris 1959*

Raymond Gid (b. 1905) began his career as an architect at the École des Beaux Arts in Paris, but he has since made his reputation as a painter, lithographer, poster-designer, and typographer. Gid belongs to a group of French designers who cannot agree that typography should always be invisible, nor that it should be denied (in Cobden-Sanderson's words) 'a beauty or interest of its own'. Gid maintains that an honourable place can be found for visible typography provided that it helps the reader's comprehension of the text. He extends the traditional resources of typography by introducing *graphismes*, a recently coined French word which embraces designs such as those shown in the pages at which this book is opened. The text was composed in Vendôme, a type designed in 1952 by François Ganeau, who sought to distill from Garamond's types a stronger design better suited for present-day methods of printing. Gid drew special lettering for the headings in this book, and he also drew its many decorations and *graphismes*.

Hermann Zapf, 1961

191 RAÚL M. ROSARIVO, Divina proportio typographica. *Scherpe Verlag, Krefeld 1961*

The type, diagrams, and typographical arrangement of this book were all designed by Herman Zapf (b. 1918), who has drawn more than fifty type faces since 1939. The text of this work was composed in his Optima types (designed 1952–5) which have no serifs, but which show far more contrast between thick and thin lines than is usually seen in sanserif types. Zapf has observed that 'Numerous historical examples from past centuries, indeed even early Greek inscriptions, show serifless letters made with alternating stroke-weights, but this principle has hitherto scarcely been applied to text types'. Zapf was a member of the advisory board of the Stempel typefoundry 1947–56 and has been design consultant to the Mergenthaler Linotype Co. since 1957. He is also very active as a book-designer and calligrapher.

Trajanus Press, 1961

192 ARISTOPHANES, Die Frösche. *Trajanus-Presse, Frankfurt 1961*

Gotthard de Beauclair (b. 1907) established his own private press in 1951 on the premises of the Stempel typefoundry, which he had joined in the previous year as typographic and design consultant. De Beauclair had worked from 1928 to 1945 as book-designer with the Insel Verlag. The Trajanus-Presse provided greater scope for his literary and artistic tastes. He gave several little-known artists their first major opportunity as illustrators, but for this edition of *The Frogs*, wood-engravings were made by a recognized master, Imre Reiner (b. 1900), also known as a painter and as the designer of several types. De Beauclair has been responsible for the typographical arrangement of all books issued by the Trajanus-Presse, and for this edition the text was composed by hand in the so-called Janson types of the Stempel typefoundry.

Alvin Eisenman, 1962

193 Eero Saarinen on his work. *Yale University Press, New Haven 1962*

The form and content of this book have been admirably matched by the skill of the typographer, Alvin Eisenman (b. 1921), who worked in close collaboration with the architect's widow. In this large format, excellent photographs of Saarinen's buildings have been faithfully reproduced in offset by photolithography, using an exceptionally fine (300-line) screen, which retains detail even in the dark shadows of buildings. Line-drawings supplement a symposium of the architect's own words, which are filmset in Monophoto Bodoni.

This book was printed in the plant of Yale University Press, which Eisenman joined as typographer in 1950. He is also lecturer in Graphic Arts at Yale, and was elected President of the American Institute of Graphic Arts in 1960.

*Officina Bodoni, 1962

194 The Holy Gospel according to Matthew, Mark, Luke and John. *Officina Bodoni, Verona 1962*

The Officina Bodoni is so named because of its exclusive privilege, granted by the Italian government, to use types cast from the original matrices of Giovanni Battista Bodoni (no. 128). Since its foundation in 1922 by Giovanni Mardersteig (b. 1892), the imprint has come to be recognized as a mark of scrupulously edited texts printed with exceptional precision, elegance, and clarity. Mardersteig published his first hand-printed books in Switzerland at Montagnola, but transferred his press to its present location at Verona in 1927, after receiving a commission to produce the official Italian edition of d'Annunzio's works. Other types besides Bodoni's are now used by Mardersteig, who has himself designed three types for which punches were cut by Charles Malin (1883–1956). This recently published edition of the Four Gospels was composed by hand in his Zeno type.

The illustrations are recut by Bruno Bramanti after the original woodcuts in *Epistole e Evangelii*, printed for Piero Pacini by Lorenzo Morgiani and Johannes Petri at Florence, 27 July 1495. Berenson's attribution of these cuts on stylistic grounds to Bartolommeo di Giovanni has yet to be confirmed, but they form, as Hind has said, 'the most considerable achievement of fifteenth-century Florentine book-illustration'.

INDEX

MEMBERS OF THE BOOK TRADES, ILLUSTRATORS, DESIGNERS, AND PATRONS

Printed in Great Britain at The University Press, Oxford, by Vivian Ridler, Printer to the University

THE PLATES

PLATE 1

sup humerali· et racionali quod con-
stringes baltheo: et pones thyaram
in capite eius· & laminā sanctam sup
thyaram· et oleum unctionis fundes
sup caput eius: atqȝ hoc ritu consecra-
bitur. Filios quoqȝ illius applicabis
et indues tunicis lineis: cingesqȝ bal-
theo· aaron scilicet & liberos eius· & im-
pones eis mitras: eruntqȝ sacerdotes mi-
chi religione ꝑpetua. Postqȝ̄ iniciaue-
ris manꝰ eoꝝ: applicabis et vitulū co-
ram tabernaclo testimonij. Imponēt-
qȝ aaron et filij eius manꝰ sup caput
illius· & mactabis eū in conspectu dn̄i:
iuxta ostiū tabernacli testimonij: sum-
ptumqȝ de sanguine vituli· pones sup
cornua altaris digito tuo: reliquum
autē sanguinē fundes iuxta basim eiꝰ.
Sumes et adipē totū q̄ operit intesti-
na· & reticlm iecoris· ac duos renes· et
adipē q̄ sup eos ē et offeres incensum
sup altare: carnes vero vituli et coriū
et fimū combures foris extra castra: eo
qd̄ pro pctō sit. Unū quoqȝ arietē sumes·
sup cuius caput ponent aaron & filij
eius manus: quē cū mactaueris: tolles de sanguine eiꝰ et fundes circa altare: ipm̄ autem arietē secabis in frusta:
lotaqȝ intestina eiꝰ & pedes pones sup
cōcisas carnes· et sup caput illius: et
offeres totū arietē ī incensū super altare. Oblatio est dn̄o: odor suauissimus
victime dn̄i. Tolles quoqȝ arietē alte-
rum: sup cuius caput aaron & filij eiꝰ
ponent manus. Quē cum immolaue-
ris· sumes de sanguine eius· & pones
sup extremū auricle dextre aaron et filioꝝ eius· et super pollices manus eoꝝ
ac pedis dextri: fundesqȝ sanguinē sup
altare ꝑ circuitū. Cūqȝ tuleris de sanguine q̄ est sup altare· et de oleo unctionis: asperges aaron et vestes eius·

filios & vestimēta eorū. Consecratisqȝ
ipis et vestibꝫ· tolles adipē de ariete·
& caudam & aruinā que opit vitalia·
ac reticulū iecoris· et duos renes atqȝ
adipem q̄ sup eos ē· armūqȝ dextrū eo
quod sit aries cōsecrationis: tortāqȝ
panis unius· crustulam conspersam
oleo· laganū de canistro azimorum
quod positū est ī cōspectu dn̄i: ponesqȝ
oīa super manus aaron et filiorū
eius· & sanctificabis eos· eleuans corā
domino. Suscipiesqȝ uniūsa de mani-
bus eoꝝ et incendes sup altare in olo-
caustū: odorem suauissimū in cōspectu
dn̄i: quia oblatio eiꝰ est· Sumes quoqȝ
pectusculū de ariete quo iniciatꝰ est aaron: sanctificabisqȝ illud eleuatū corā
dn̄o: et cedet in partē tuā. Sanctificabisqȝ et pectusculū cōsecratū et armum
quē de ariete separasti· quo iniciatꝰ est
aaron et filij eius: cedentqȝ in partem
aaron & filioꝝ eius iure ꝑpetuo a filijs
israhel: quia primicia sūt et inicia de
victimis eoꝝ pacificis que offerūt dn̄o.
Vestem autē sanctam qua utetur aa-
ron· habebūt filij eius post eum· ut un-
gantꝰ in ea: et cōsecrentur manus eoꝝ.
Septē diebꝫ utetur illa qui pontifex ꝓ
eo fuerit constitutus de filijs eius: et q̄
ingredietꝰ tabernaculum testimonij ut
ministret in sanctuario. Arietem autē
consecrationis tolles: et coques carnes eius ī loco sancto: quibꝫ vescetur
aaron et filij eius. Panes quoqȝ qui
sunt ī canistro· in vestibulo tabernacli
testimonij comedent· ut sit placabile
sacrificiū: et sanctificent offerentiū ma-
nus· alienigena non vescetur ex eis:
quia sancti sunt. Quod si remanserit
de carnibus cōsecratis siue de panibꝫ
usqȝ mane: combures reliquias igni
nō comedentur: quia sanctificata sūt.

PLATE 2

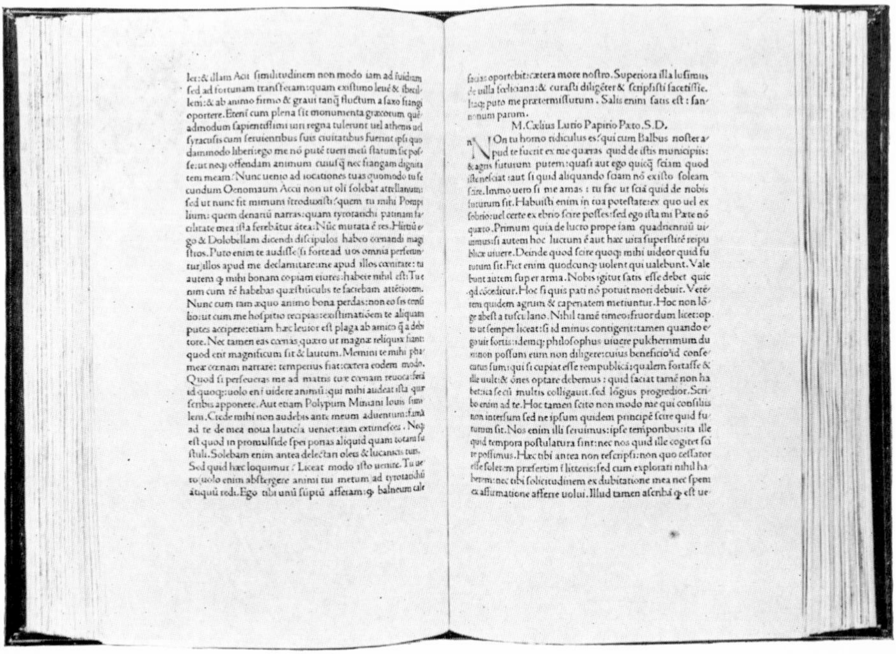

ler:& illam Acci similitudinem non modo iam ad suidiam
sed ad fortunam transferam: quam existimo leué & imbecil-
lem: & ab animo firmo & graui tanq̃ fluctum a saxo frangi
oportere. Etení cum plena sit monumenta græcorum quē-
admodum sapientissimi uiri regna tulerunt uel athenis uel
syracusis cum seruientibus suis ciuitatibus fuerint ipsi quo
dammodo liberi: ego me nó puté tueri meū statum sic pos-
se: ut neq; offendam animum cuiusq̃ nec frangam dignita
tem meam? Nunc uenio ad iocationes tuas quomodo tu se
cundum Oenomaum Accii non ut olí solebat attellanum:
sed ut nunc fit mimum ítroduxisti? quem tu mihi Pomp
lium: quem denariū narras: quam tyrotarichi patinam fa-
cilitate mea ista ferebātur ātea: Nūc mutata é res. Hirtiū e-
go & Dolobellam dicendi discipulos habeo cœnandi magi
stros. Puto enim te audisse (si forte ad uos omnia perferun-
tur) illos apud me declamitare: me apud illos cœnitare: tu
autem q̄ mihi bonam copiam eiures: habere nihil est: Tu e-
nim cum ré habebas quæstiūculis te faciebam attētiorem.
Nunc cum tam æquo animo bona perdas: non eo sis consi
lio: ut cum me hospitio recipias: existimatiōem te aliquam
putes accipere: etiam hæc leuior est plaga ab amico q̃ a debi
tore. Nec tamen eas cœnas quæro ut magnæ reliquiæ fiant:
quod erit magnificum sit & lautum. Memini te mihi pha-
meæ cœnam narrare: temperius fiat: cætera eodem modo.
Quod si perseueras me ad matris tuæ cœnam reuoca: ferā
id quoq;: uolo ení uidere animū: qui mihi audeat ista quæ
scribis apponere. Aut etiam Polypum Miniani Iouis simi-
lem. Crede mihi non audebis ante meum aduentum: famā
ad te de mea noua lauticia ueniet: eam extimesces. Neq;
est quod in promulside spei ponas aliquid quam totam su
stuli. Solebam enim antea delectari oleis & lucanicis tuis.
Sed quid hæc loquimur? Liceat modo isto uenire. Tu ue
ro (uolo enim abstergere animi tui metum) ad tyrotarichū
ātiquū redi. Ego tibi unū sūptū afferam: q̄ balneum cale

facias oportebit: cætera more nostro. Superiora illa lusimus
de uilla sodiciana: & curasti diligēter & scripsisti facetissie.
Itaq; puto me prætermissurum. Salis enim satis est: san-
nonum parum.

M. Cælius Lucio Papirio Pæto. S. D.

N[a] On tu homo ridiculus es? qui cum Balbus noster a-
pud te fuerit ex me quæras quid de istis municipiis:
& agris futurum putem: quasi aut ego quicq̃ sciam quod
iste nesciat: aut si quid aliquando sciam nó ex isto soleam
scire. Immo uero si me amas: tu fac ut sciá quid de nobis
futurum sit. Habuisti enim in tua potestate: ex quo uel ex
sobrio: uel certe ex ebrio scire posses: sed ego ista mi Pæte nó
quæro. Primum quia de lucro prope iam quadrienniū ui-
uimus: si autem hoc lucrum é aut hæc uita superstité reipu
blicæ uiuere. Deinde quod scire quoq; mihi uideor quid fu
turum sit. Fiet enim quodcunq; uolent qui ualebunt. Vale
bunt autem super arma. Nobis igitur satis esse debet quic
qd cōceditur. Hoc si quis pati nó potuit mori debuit. Veie-
tem quidem agrum & capenatem metiuntur. Hoc non lō-
ge abest a tusculano. Nihil tamé timeo: fruor dum licet: op
to ut semper liceat: si id minus contigerit: tamen quando e-
go uir fortis: idemq; philosophus uiuere pulcherrimum du
xi: non possum eum non diligere: cuius beneficio id conse-
cutus sum: qui si cupiat esse rempublicā: qualem fortasse &
ille uult: & ōnes optare debemus: quid faciat tamé non ha
bet: ita se cū multis colligauit. sed lōgius progredior. Scri-
bo enim ad te. Hoc tamen scito non modo me qui consiliis
non intersum sed ne ipsum quidem principé scire quid futurum sit. Nos enim illi seruimus: ipse temporibus: ita ille
quid tempora postulatura sint: nec nos quid ille cogitet sci
re possimus. Hæc tibi antea non rescripsi: non quo cessator
esse solerem præsertim í litteris: sed cum explorati nihil ha
berem: nec tibi solicitudinem ex dubitatione mea nec spem
ex affirmatione afferre uolui. Illud tamen ascribā q̄ est ue-

17

Liber ·xiiii·

des and foules &c. as culuours & turtyls
whan they drede ẏ egle & the hawke to
[illegible] in the ayre / Also [illegible] hilpi-
les and haares fle to holowe stones whan
they here houndes and knowe that hun
ters come ¶ Also in holowe holes & den
nes of the erthe & of trees ben made ho
ny. and some maner of foules make the
re there nestes. and [illegible] / Also in
holowe dennes ben adders that hurte &
stynge wyth venemous byttynge man &
beste that come nyghe to suche dennes /
And ofte whan the erthe is holowe and
full of dennes · it shakyth & meuith by
wyndes that come therin · that fyllyth ẏ
dennes and gendrith erthe shakynge as
Arystotle sayth /

Of partyes of the erthe & dy-

Liber ·xv·

se prouynce by the whiche the
worlde is generally departyd
somwhat shal be shortly sette
to this werke by helpe of oure
lorde. but not of al. but oonly
of suche as holy wrytte ma-
kyth remembraunce.

Incipit liber ·xv· de prouinci-
is. Capitulū Primum

Prologus

The worlde wide is depar
ted in thre as Ysider sa-
yth li° xv° / For one part
hight Asia. a nother Eu
ropa. the thrydde Affrica /
Thise thre partes of the
worlde were assygned [illegible] in ol
de tyme by men / For Asia stretchyth oute
of ẏ south by ẏ est unto the northe / And
Europa oute of the northe unto ẏ west /
But Affrica stretchyth out of ẏ weste &
passeth by ẏ southe / But Asia conteyn-
neth oonly on parte. ẏ is ẏ halfe parte of
the londe ẏ men dwelle in / And ẏ other
two countrees conteyne the other halfe /
The grete see comyth out of ẏ Occean
& stretchyth bytwene thyse partyes / & de
partyth theym asonder: therfore yf ẏ dy
uidest ẏ worlde in two partes of ẏ est
& of the weste. In on parte is Asia. & in ẏ
other is bothe Affrica & Europa / And so
Noes sones departed & dyuyded ẏ worl
de after the flood amonge theym / Sem
w^t his ofspringe had Asiam. & Japhet
Europam. Cam Affricam. as ẏ glose sa
yth sup Gen[illegible] x° & sup li° pale ·i° / Ori[illegible]
sayth ẏ same & Plinius also /

¶ De Asia / Capitu[illegible]

Asia is take for halfe parte of ẏ
worlde. & had ẏ name Asia of a
woman ẏ helde ẏ kyngdome of
the eest in olde tyme as Ysider sayth li°
xv° / This Asia dispolyth & hath ẏ thyr
de part of ẏ worlde. he hath by ẏ eest the
spryngе of ẏ sonne & by southe Occean
& stretchyth unto our see. and endyth by
northe at lake & marys. ẏ hyghte Meo
[illegible] & at flode Tanay. And hath ma
ny prouynces & regyons & dyuers naci
ons · & wondfull in lyuynge. maners &
fygures & shape of body. & ben wonderly
dyuers in wyll. herte & thought / There
names & places we shall shortly sette fo
lowynge ẏ ordre of. a. b. c.

¶ De Assiria / Capitu[illegible]

Assiria is a countree & prouince
of Asia. & hath ẏ name of Assur
ẏ sone of Sem ẏ fyrste dwellyd
there after the flode This prouynce hath
Inde in ẏ eest syde. & stretchyth to ẏ southe of Media in ẏ south syde. & hath
in the weste ẏ ryuer Tigris. & in ẏ north
the hylle ẏ is callyd mount Caucasus /
There ben ẏ yates of Caspia as Ysider
sayth li° xv° / ¶ Also out of ẏ countree
came fyrst the use of purpur. ẏ ornemen
tes bothe of heere & of bodyes. also odou
res & smelles. & therof sprange ẏ lechery
of romaynes & of Grekes as Ysider sa
yth / And is a londe moost separate in se-
perate countrees / But in many places in
ẏ [illegible] endes for dyuers places
ẏ londe is unpassyble in beis & serpent[illegible]
& also in maners of men as Plini^s lib[illegible]
in? there [illegible] of [illegible] / ẏ
Assiriens dwellyd in this prouynce. & ha
ue the name of Assur moost myghty per

f iiii

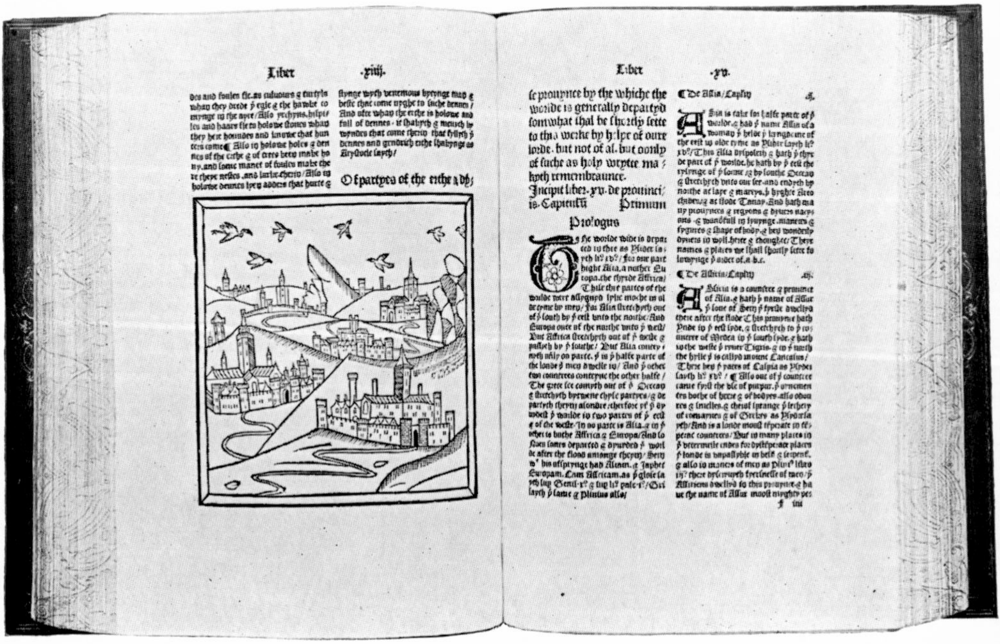

37

PLATE 3

tus ampliores sunt; q̃ iis in locis, quae uel mari uicina sunt, uel a mari prótenus alluuntur: nam cum éxedit sẽper mare, consumítq; suoptecontactu, suáq; natura omnia; tum autem, si partem est nactum aliquam debiliorem, membráq; non adeo robusta telluris; eródit illa multo facillime; pergitq; in uiscera ipsa, q̃ potest: itaq; cum in aliena regna sibi uiã faciat; uentis etiam facit: ex quo fit; ut loca quaeq; maritima maxime terraemotibus subiecta sint, parum mediterranea. ꝙ si etiã in sulfuris uenas uenti furentes inciderint; tum incendia suscitantur sanè non difficulter; quoniam et in sulfure cócipiendi permagna ignis uis inest, et uenti etiam aliena succendunt ui sua: haec autem tu ut in Aetna accidant omnia, uide, quippe (ut modo tute dixisti), quae mare in radicibus habeat, quae sulfurea sit, quae cauernosa; seu ꝙ natura ita fuerit semper ipsa; seu ꝙ

salo aliquando subexesa uentos admiserit aestuantes, per quos idonea flammae materies incenderetur. Habes, unde incendia oriantur Aetnae tuae: habe nunc quómodo etiam orta perdurent: in quo quidem nolo ego te illud admirari, quod uulgus solet: magnũ esse scilicet tantas flammas, tam immensos ignes post hominum memoriam semper habuisse, quo alerétur: quid est enim magnum ipsi magistrae rerum omniũ, et parenti naturae? quid arduum; quid illa tandem non potest? qui stellas; qui solem; qui coeli conuexa; qui terras omnes, ac maria; qui mundum deniq; ipsum, quo nihil est admirabilius, uel potius extra quem nihil est, quod admireris; saepe sine admiratione intuemur; iisdem nobis esse Aetna miraculum potest: caue sis tam imprudens fili; ut tu id putes: nam si naturam respicimus; nihil in Aetna est, quod mirum uoces: si rem

39

POLIPHILO QVIVI NARRA, CHE GLI PARVE ANCORA DI DORMIRE, ET ALTRONDE IN SOMNO RITROVARSE IN VNA CONVALLE, LAQVALE NEL FINE ERA SERATA DE VNA MIRABILE CLAVSVRA CVM VNA PORTENTOSA PYRAMIDE, DE ADMIRATIONE DIGNA, ET VNO EXCELSO OBELISCO DE SOPRA. LAQVALE CVM DILIGENTIA ET PIACERE SVBTILMENTE LA CONSIDEROE.

LA SPAVENTEVOLE SILVA, ET CONSTIPATO Nemore euaso, & gli primi altri lochi per el dolce somno che se haueа per le fesse & prosternate mébre diffuso relicti, me ritrouai di nouo in uno piu delectabile sito assai piu che el præcedente. El quale non era de monti horridi, & crepidinose rupe intorniato, ne falcato di strumosi iugi. Ma compositamente de grate montagniole di non tropo altecia. Siluose di giouani quercioli, di roburi, fraxini & Carpini, & di frondosi Esculi, & Ilice, & di teneri Coryli, & di Alni, & di Tilie, & di Opio, & de infructuosi Oleastri, dispositi secondo laspecto de gli arboriferi Colli. Et giu al piano erano grate siluule di altri siluatici

arboscelli, & di floride Geniste, & di multiplice herbe uerdissime, quiui uidi il Cythiso, La Carice, la commune Cerinthe. La muscariata Panachia el fiorito ranunculo, & ceruicello, o uero Elaphio, & la seratula, & di uarie assai nobile, & de molti altri proficui simplici, & ignote herbe & fiori per gli prati dispensate. Tutta questa læta regione de uiridura copiosamente adornata se offeriua. Poscia poco piu ultra del mediano suo, io ritrouai uno sabuleto, o uero glareosa plagia, ma in alcuno loco dispersamente, cum alcuni cespugli de herbatura. Quiui al gliochii mei uno iocundissimo Palmeto se appræsento, cum le foglie di cultrato mucrone ad tanta utilitate ad gli ægyptii, del suo dolcissimo fructo fæcũde & abundante. Tra lequale racemose palme, & picole alcune, & molte mediocre, & laltre drite erano & excelse, Electo Signo de uictoria per el resistere suo ad lurgente pondo. Ancora & in questo loco non trouai incola, ne altro animale alcuno. Ma peregrinando solitario tra le non densate, ma interuallate palme spectatissime, cogitando delle Rachelaide, Phaselide, & Libyade, non essere forsa a queste comparabile. Ecco che uno affermato & carniuoro lupo alla parte dextra, cum la bucca piena mi apparue.

45

56

Nicht lanng darnach auf einen tag
Vnfalo die morgen rót sah
Gedacht gewiß wirdt hewt enntstan
Ein windt/mocht Jch den Tewren man
Bringen an das gembsen geiaid
So hoffet Jch Er kem in laid
Bald Er darzu dem Tewrdannck gieng
Mit Jm Er zureden anfieng

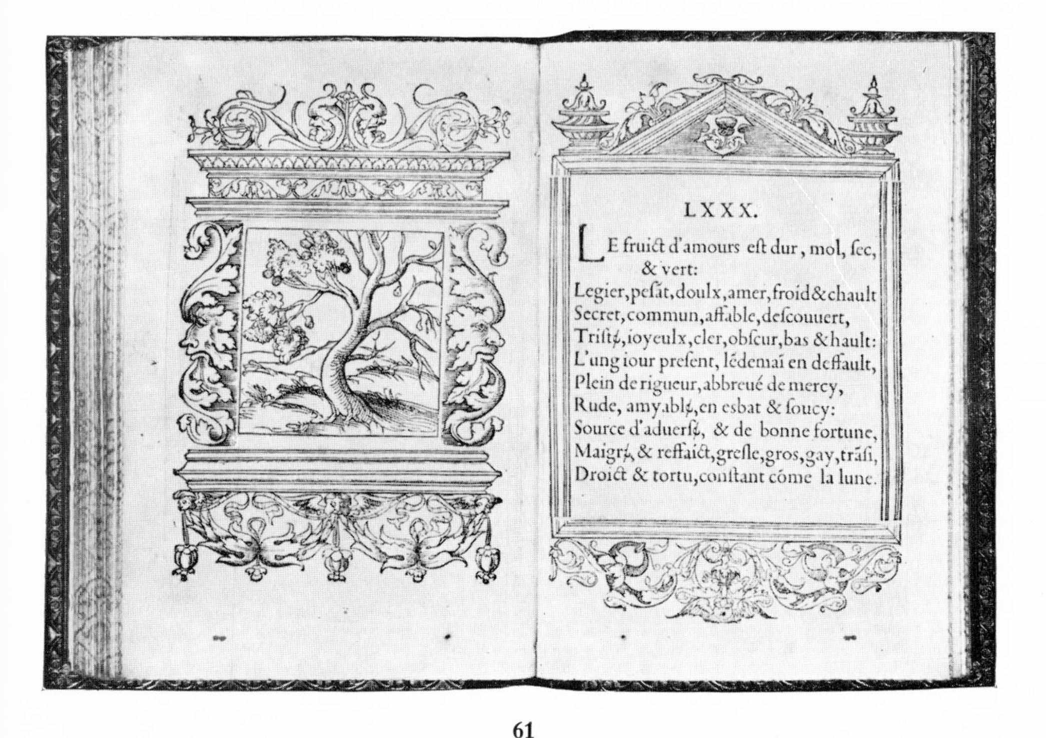

LXXX.

LE fruict d'amours est dur, mol, sec,
& vert:
Legier, pesãt, doulx, amer, froid & chault
Secret, commun, affable, descouuert,
Tristé, ioyeulx, cler, obscur, bas & hault:
L'ung iour present, lẽdemaĩ en deffault,
Plein de rigueur, abbreué de mercy,
Rude, amyablé, en esbat & soucy:
Source d'aduersité, & de bonne fortune,
Maigré, & reffaict, gresle, gros, gay, trãsi,
Droict & tortu, constant cõme la lune.

61

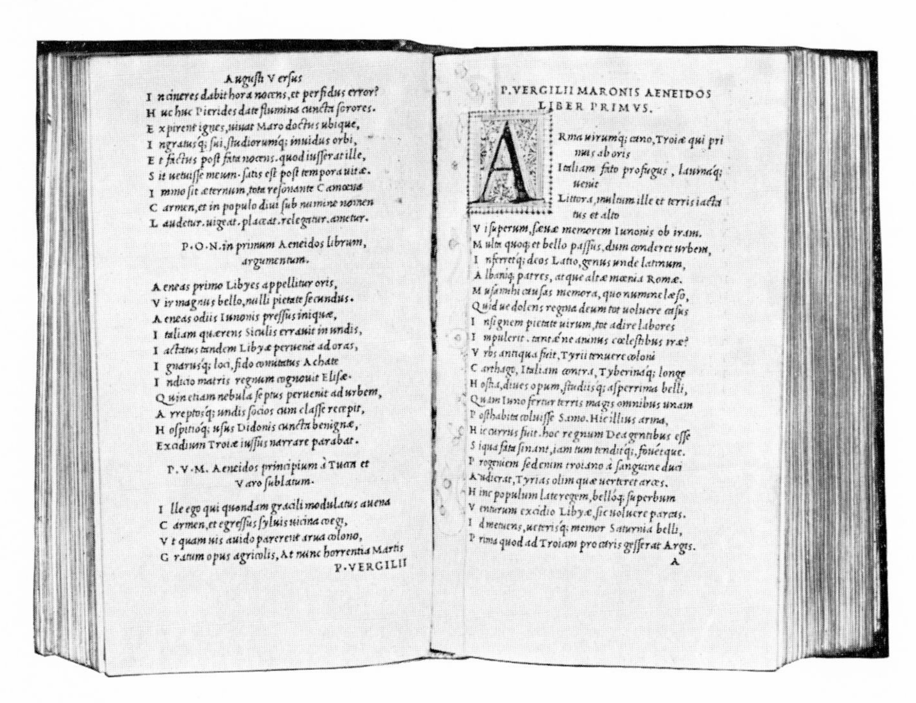

Augusti Versus

Incineres dabit hora nocens, et perfidus error?
Huc huc Pierides date flumina cuncta sorores.
Expirent ignes, uiuat Maro doctus ubique,
Ingratusq; sui, studiorumq; inuidus orbi,
Et factus post fata nocens. quod iusserat ille,
Sit uetuisse meum. satis est post tempora uitæ.
Immo sit æternum, tota resonante Camœna
Carmen, et in populo diui sub numine nomen
Laudetur. uigeat. placeat. relegatur. ametur.

P. O. N. in primum Aeneidos librum,
argumentum.

Aeneas primo Libyes appellitur oris,
Vir magnus bello, nulli pietate secundus.
Aeneas odiis Iunonis pressus iniquæ,
Italiam quærens Siculis errauit in undis,
Iactatus tandem Libyæ peruenit ad oras,
Ignarusq; loci, fido comitatus Achate
Indicio matris regnum cognouit Elisæ.
Quin etiam nebula septus peruenit ad urbem,
Arreptosq; undis socios cum classe recepit,
Hospitioq; usus Didonis cuncta benignæ,
Excidium Troiæ iussus narrare parabat.

P. V. M. Aeneidos principium à Tucca et
Varo sublatum.

Ille ego qui quondam gracili modulatus auena
Carmen, et egressus syluis uicina coegi,
Vt quamuis auido parerent arua colono,
Gratum opus agricolis, At nunc horrentia Martis
P. VERGILII

P. VERGILII MARONIS AENEIDOS
LIBER PRIMVS.

ARma uirumq; cano, Troiæ qui pri
mus ab oris
Italiam fato profugus, lauinaq;
uenit
Littora, multum ille et terris iacta
tus et alto
Vi superum, sæuæ memorem Iunonis ob iram.
Multa quoq; et bello passus, dum conderet urbem,
Inferretq; deos Latio, genus unde latinum,
Albaniq; patres, atque altæ mœnia Romæ.
Musa mihi causas memora, quo numine læso,
Quid ue dolens regina deum tot uoluere casus
Insignem pietate uirum, tot adire labores
Impulerit. tantæne animis cœlestibus iræ?
Vrbs antiqua fuit, Tyrii tenuere coloni
Carthago, Italiam contra, Tyberinaq; longe
Hostia, diues opum, studiisq; asperrima belli,
Quam Iuno fertur terris magis omnibus unam
Posthabita coluisse Samo. Hic illius arma,
Hic currus fuit. hoc regnum Dea gentibus esse
Si qua fata sinant, iam tum tenditq;, fouetque.
Progeniem sed enim troiano à sanguine duci
Audierat, Tyrias olim quæ uerteret arces.
Hinc populum late regem, belloq; superbum
Venturum excidio Libyæ, sic uoluere parcas.
Id metuens, ueterisq; memor Saturnia belli,
Prima quod ad Troiam pro caris gesserat Argis.
A

47

E in quanto a Gioue, o che costui mentiua
Che quei, come dicea, gli fosse padre;
O s'era pur suo padre, egli scopriua
Il fallo, e l'adulterio de la madre;

Ch'era bastardo a dimostrar ueniua,
E procacciaua insegne oscure & adre
E biasimo, onde hauesse ad abbassarsi,
Credendosi lodare & inalzarsi.

Con toruo aspetto, come irato suole,
Mi guarda; e meco (dice) hora combatti,
Che se ben uinci me ne le parole,
Poco mi cal, pur ch'io ti uinca in fatti.
Ceder la lingua a la mia destra uuole,
Ch'è assai di lei migliore; e i nostri patti
Saranno, che qual resti uincitore,
De la bella fanciulla habbia l'honore.

Stimai uergogna a rifiutar l'impresa,
Poscia che detto hauea parole tali.
Spoglio la uesta, e uengo a la contesa,
Ma con forze al nimico disuguali:
Le braccia oppongo intento a mia difesa,
Stanci a ueder la turba e i principali:
Hercole quà e là fiero si uolue,
Indi se stesso e me sparge di polue.

Mi da l'assalto, e quando esso annodarmi
Cerca le gambe, e un folgore mi pare,
Quando al collo l'altier ueggo accennarmi
Con atto, che potea farmi tremare.

Io sto saldo a lo schermo, e al ripararmi,
E sembro un scoglio a l'impeto del mare;
Che non lo moue, ne piegar lo puote,
Se ben la minacciosa onda il percuote.

Ci discostammo un poco; e poi di nouo
Tornammo insieme a la crudel tenzone,
Ei superarmi, io di non ceder prouo,
E l'uno e l'altro ingegno e forza pone:
Ma si auinto da lui mi sento e trouo,
Ch'è forza di ualor far paragone:
Giungemmo petto a petto, e piede a piede,
E mano a mano, e un fronte l'altro fiede.

Non altrimenti due feroci Tori
Vidi accozzar di molta rabbia ardenti,
Tratti a la zuffa da comuni amori,
Onde si parton poi fiacchi e dolenti:
I cui mortali assalti, i cui furori
Timidi da lontan guardan gli armenti.
Tre uolte affaticossi da que nodi
Sbrigarsi Alcide, e cercò tutti i modi.

PROPHETIA
SOPHONIÆ.
Capvt Primvm.

[1]Verbvm Domini, quod factum eſt ad Sophoniam filium Chuſi, filii Godoliæ, filii Amariæ, filii Ezeciæ, in diebus Ioſiæ filii Amon regis Iudæ. [2]Congregans congregabo omnia a facie terræ, dicit Dominus: [3]congregans hominem, & pecus, congregans volatilia cæli, & piſces maris: & ruinæ impiorum erunt: & diſperdam homines a facie

Q

42 LABYRINTE DE VERSAILLES. 43

FABLE XXI.

LE LOUP ET LA GRUË.

LA Gruë ayant tiré de la gorge du Loup
Un os de son long bec qui le pressoit beaucoup:
Il n'a tenu qu'à moy de vous manger, Commere,
Luy dit le Loup ingrat, & c'est vostre salaire.

96

726 Des saintes Metamorphoses. 727

des Saints. Long-temps aprés, à sçauoir l'an 1356. on s'aduisa d'ouurir son tombeau, où se firent de nouueaux Miracles; & l'année d'aprés, le 25. jour de Juin, son corps fut transporté solennellement en la principale Eglise de Cremone, & mis dans vn tombeau magnifique. La deuotion y est fort grande aujourd'huy, & ceux de ce pays-là, dont ce grand Saint se peut nommer l'Ange tutelaire, reçoiuent par son intercession vne continüelle assistance de la Misericorde diuine.

Aduis

Aux Marchands.

Quand je considere la vie de S. Homebon, j'y trouue diuerses instructions qui sont données à toute sorte de personnes, & particulierement aux gens de commerce. Car outre la bonne foy qu'ils sont obligez de garder inuiolablement en tous leurs traittez, ils se doiuent proposer encore à l'exemple de ce grand Saint, d'estre toûjours

90

LES DELICES DE L'ESPRIT, DIALOGVES.

TROISIESME PARTIE.

QVATORZIESME IOVRNE'E.

Instruction pour apprendre le langage des choses de l'Interieur dans les saintes Escritures.

PHILEDON. EVSEBE.

PHILEDON.

Mon cher Eusebe, que j'ay d'impatience de sçauoir si tu as obtenu de Dieu la permission de me découurir les rares merueilles, & le grand tresor que tu m'as fait esperer.

EVSEBE. Ouy, Philedon, il m'en a enuoyé ce matin la permission; car lors que i'ay ouuert la grande fenestre du balcon de ma chambre, i'ay veu vn grand Aigle qui fondoit du plus haut des nuës, & qui a laissé tomber dans le balcon vne clef d'or, qui est la clef de ce rare tresor; & ainsi il m'a donné le moyen de satisfaire en mesme temps à toutes les choses ausquelles ie me suis engagé enuers toy.

Le grand Aigle, c'est S. Iean l'Euangeliste.

PHIL. Dieu soit loüé à iamais pour vne si grande bonté. Commence donc à satisfaire aux choses que tu m'as promises.

A

THE

Hiſtory of the Rebellion, &c.

BOOK VI.

Iſa. XVIII. 2.

Go, ye ſwiſt Meſſengers, to a Nation ſcattered and peeled, to a People terrible from their beginning hitherto; a Nation meted out and troden down, whoſe Land the Rivers have ſpoiled.

Iſa. XIX. 13, 14.

The Princes of Zoan are become fools.
The Lord hath mingled a perverſe Spirit in the midſt thereof.

The King's condition at Nottingham.

HEN the King ſet up his Standard at *Nottingham,* which was on the 25th of *Auguſt*, as is before remember'd, he found the place much emptier than he thought the fame of his Standard would have ſuffer'd it to be; and receiv'd Intelligence the next day, that the Rebel's Army, for ſuch now he had declared them, was Horſe, Foot, and Cannon, at *Northampton*; beſides that Party which, in the end of the Fifth Book, we left at *Coventry*: whereas His few Cannon and Ammunition were ſtill at *York*, being neither yet in an equipage to march, though Sr *John Heydon*, his Majeſties faithful Lieutenant of the Ordnance, uſed all poſſible diligence to form and prepare it; neither were there Foot enough levied to guard it: and at *Nottingham,* beſides ſome few of the Train'd-bands, which Sr *John Digby*, the active Sheriff of that County, drew into the old ruinous Caſtle there, there were not of Foot levied for the Service Yet three hundred Men. So that they who were not over much given to fear, finding very many places in that great River, which was looked upon as the only ſtrength and ſecurity of the Town, to be eaſily fordable, and nothing towards an Army for defence but the Standard ſet up, begun ſadly to apprehend the danger of the Kings own Perſon. Inſomuch that Sr *Jacob Aſhley*, his Serjeant-Major-General of his intended Army, told him, "that he could not give any aſſurance againſt his Ma-

LA GUERRA
DE JUGURTA
POR
CAYO SALUSTIO CRISPO.

SIN causa alguna se quexan los hombres de que su naturaleza es flaca y de corta duracion; y que se govierna mas por la suerte, que por su virtud. Porque si bien se mira, se hallarà por el contrario, que no hai en el mundo cosa mayor, ni mas excelente; y que no la falta vigor ni tiempo, si solo aplicacion e industria. Es pues la guia y el governo entero de nuestra vida el animo; el qual, si se encamina a la gloria por el sendero de la virtud, harto

C. SALLUSTII CRISPI
IUGURTHA.

FALSO queritur de natura sua genus humanum, quod imbecille, atque ævi brevis, sorte potius, quam virtute, regatur. Nam contra reputando, neque majus aliud, neque præstabilius invenias; magisque naturæ industriam hominum, quam vim, aut tempus deesse. Sed dux, atque imperator vitæ mortalium, animus est: qui ubi ad gloriam virtutis via grassa-

N

ON NE S'AVISE JAMAIS
DE TOUT.

CONTE TIRÉ DES CENT NOUVELLES NOUVELLES.

CERTAIN jaloux, ne dormant que d'un œil,
Interdisoit tout commerce à sa femme.
Dans le dessein de prévenir la dame,
Il avoit fait un fort ample recueil
De tous les tours que le sexe sait faire.
Pauvre ignorant! comme si cette affaire
N'étoit une hydre, à parler franchement!
Il captivoit sa femme cependant,
De ses cheveux vouloit savoir le nombre,
La faisoit suivre, à toute heure, en tous lieux,
Par une vieille au corps tout rempli d'yeux,
Qui la quittoit aussi peu que son ombre.
Ce fou tenoit son recueil fort entier:
Il le portoit en guise de psautier,
Croyant par-là cocuage hors de gamme.
Un jour de fête, arrive que la dame,
En revenant de l'église, passa
Près d'un logis, d'où quelqu'un lui jeta

131

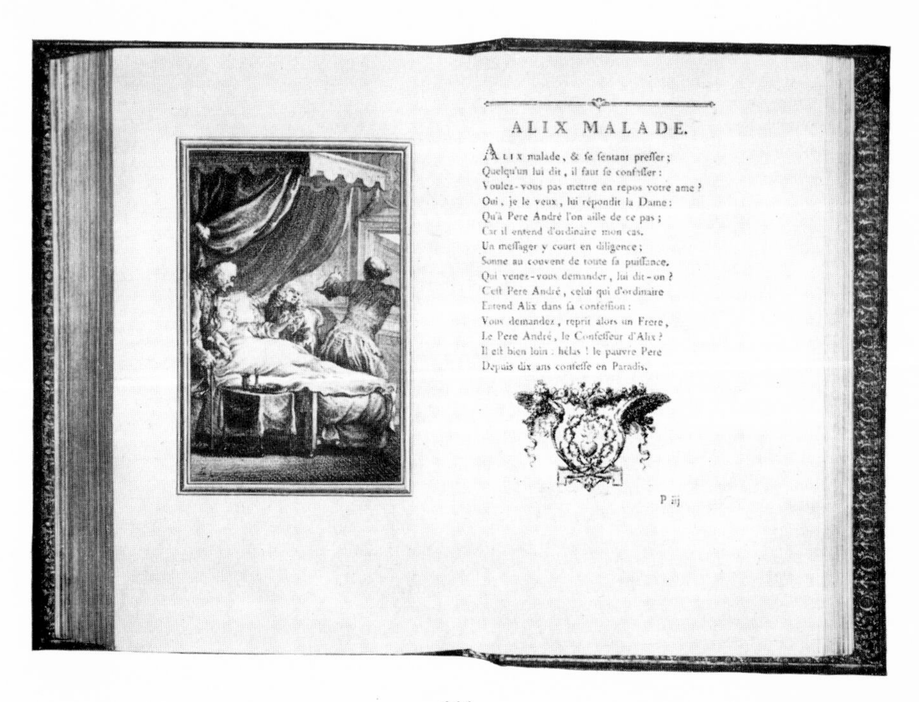

ALIX MALADE.

ALIX malade, & se sentant presser;
Quelqu'un lui dit, il faut se confesser:
Voulez-vous pas mettre en repos votre ame?
Oui, je le veux, lui répondit la Dame:
Qu'à Pere André l'on aille de ce pas;
Car il entend d'ordinaire mon cas.
Un messager y court en diligence;
Sonne au couvent de toute sa puissance.
Qui venez-vous demander, lui dit-on?
C'est Pere André, celui qui d'ordinaire
Entend Alix dans sa confession:
Vous demandez, reprit alors un Frere,
Le Pere André, le Confesseur d'Alix?
Il est bien loin: hélas! le pauvre Pere
Depuis dix ans confesse en Paradis.

P iij

111

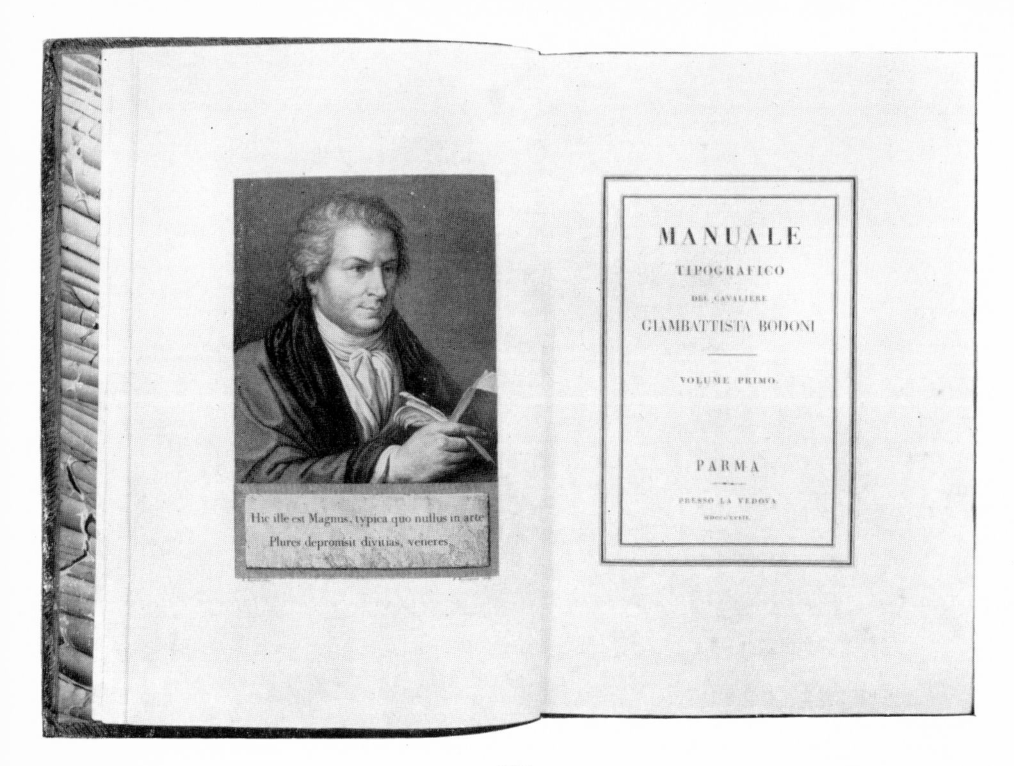

Hic ille est Magnus, typica quo nullus in arte
Plures depromsit divitias, veneres.

MANUALE
TIPOGRAFICO
DEL CAVALIERE
GIAMBATTISTA BODONI

VOLUME PRIMO.

PARMA

PRESSO LA VEDOVA
MDCCCXVIII.

139

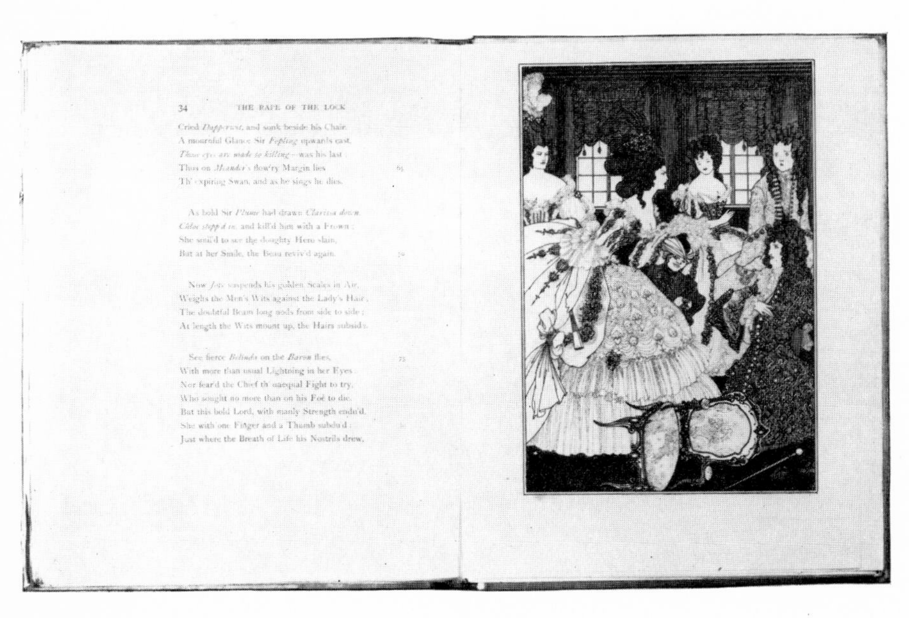

34 THE RAPE OF THE LOCK

Cried *Dapperwit*, and sunk beside his Chair.
A mournful Glance Sir *Fopling* upwards cast,
Those eyes are made so killing—was his last:
Thus on *Mæander*'s flow'ry Margin lies
Th' expiring Swan, and as he sings he dies. 65

As bold Sir *Plume* had drawn *Clarissa down*,
Chloe stepp'd in, and kill'd him with a Frown;
She smil'd to see the doughty Hero slain,
But at her Smile, the Beau reviv'd again. 70

Now *Jove* suspends his golden Scales in Air,
Weighs the Men's Wits against the Lady's Hair;
The doubtful Beam long nods from side to side;
At length the Wits mount up, the Hairs subside.

See fierce *Belinda* on the *Baron* flies, 75
With more than usual Lightning in her Eyes.
Nor fear'd the Chief th' unequal Fight to try,
Who sought no more than on his Foe to die.
But this bold Lord, with manly Strength endu'd,
She with one Finger and a Thumb subdu'd: 80
Just where the Breath of Life his Nostrils drew,

162

of Jesus, which said unto him, Before the cock crow, thou shalt deny me thrice. And he went out, and wept bitterly.

THE MORNING WAS COME, ALL THE CHIEF PRIESTS and elders of the people took counsel against Jesus to put him to death: And when they had bound him, they led him away, and delivered him to Pontius Pilate the governor. ❦ Then Judas, which had betrayed him, when he saw that he was condemned, repented himself, and brought again the thirty pieces of silver to the chief priests and elders, Saying, I have sinned in that I have betrayed the innocent blood. And they said, What is that to us? see thou to that. And he cast down the pieces of silver in the temple, and departed, and went and hanged himself. And the chief priests took the silver pieces, and said, It is not lawful for to put them into the treasury, because it is the price of blood. And they took counsel, and bought with them the potter's field, to bury strangers in. Wherefore that field was called, The field of blood, unto this day. Then was fulfilled that which was spoken by Jeremy the prophet, saying, And they took the thirty pieces of silver, the price of him that was valued, whom they of the children of Israel did value; And gave them for the potter's field, as the Lord appointed me.

72

HEREBEGINNETH THE TALES OF CANTERBURY AND FIRST THE PROLOGUE THEREOF

WHAN THAT Aprille with his shoures soote
The droghte of March hath perced to the roote,
And bathed every veyne in swich licour,
Of which vertu engendred is the flour;
Whan Zephirus eek with his swete breeth
Inspired hath in every holt and heeth
The tendre croppes, and the yonge sonne
Hath in the Ram his halfe cours yronne,
And smale foweles maken melodye,
That slepen al the nyght with open eye,
So priketh hem nature in hir corages;
Thanne longen folk to goon on pilgrimages,
And palmeres for to seken straunge strondes,
To ferne halwes, kowthe in sondry londes;
And specially, from every shires ende
Of Engelond, to Caunterbury they wende,
The hooly blisful martir for to seke,
That hem hath holpen whan that they were seeke.

BIFIL that in that seson on a day,
In Southwerk at the Tabard as I lay,
Redy to wenden on my pilgrymage
To Caunterbury with ful devout corage,
At nyght were come into that hostelrye
Wel nyne and twenty in a compaignye,
Of sondry folk, by aventure yfalle
In felaweshipe, and pilgrimes were they alle,
That toward Caunterbury wolden ryde.

his best skill to have his Goats as fat as might be; for their Lord would be sure to see them too, who now would come into the Countrey after he had bin so long away. And Daphnis had a good mind to it, because he thought he should be lookt upon, and praised for them. For he had doubled the number he had received of Lamo, nor had the Wolf raven'd away so much as one, and they were all more twadding fat then the very sheep. And because he would win the Lord to be more forward to approve and confirm the match, he did his businesse with great diligence, and great alacrity; he drove out his Goats betimes in the mornings; and late in the evening brought them home; twice a day he water'd them, and culled out for them the best pasture ground; he took care too to have the dairy-vessels new, good store of milking pales and piggins, and fairer Crates, or presses for the Cheese. He was so far from being negligent in any thing, that he tryed to make their horns to shine with vernich, and comb'd their very shag to make them sleek. Insomuch, as, if you had seen

166

this, you had said it was Pan's own sacred flock. Chloe her self too would take her share in this labour about the Goats; and Daphnis thought 'twas Chloe's hand, and Chloe's eyes that made his flocks appear so fair. While both of them are thus busied, there came another Messenger from the City, and brought a command, that the grapes should be gather'd with all speed: and told them withall, he was to tarry with

167

181

Sind die Stempel geschnitten, so macht der hurtige Setzer
mit der Gußprobe hier den allerersten Versuch.
Oftmals erkennt man erst dann des Entwurfs unvollkommene Fassung,
und es macht sich, schwer seufzend, der Zeichner wieder ans Werk. –
Aber auch von den fertigen Schriften druckt er hier Proben,
daß man am Beispiel erkenne die Schönheit des neuen Produkts.

166